About IFPRI

The International Food Policy Research Institute (IFPRI), established in 1975, provides research-based policy solutions to sustainably reduce poverty and end hunger and malnutrition. The Institute conducts research, communicates results, optimizes partnerships, and builds capacity to ensure sustainable food production, promote healthy food systems, improve markets and trade, transform agriculture, build resilience, and strengthen institutions and governance. Gender is considered in all of the Institute's work. IFPRI collaborates with partners around the world, including development implementers, public institutions, the private sector, and farmers' organizations. IFPRI is a member of the CGIAR Consortium.

About IFPRI's Peer Review Process

IFPRI books are policy-relevant publications based on original and innovative research conducted at IFPRI. All manuscripts submitted for publication as IFPRI books undergo an extensive review procedure that is managed by IFPRI's Publications Review Committee (PRC). Upon submission to the PRC, the manuscript is reviewed by a PRC member. Once the manuscript is considered ready for external review, the PRC submits it to at least two external reviewers who are chosen for their familiarity with the subject matter and the country setting. Upon receipt of these blind external peer reviews, the PRC provides the author with an editorial decision and, when necessary, instructions for revision based on the external reviews. The PRC reassesses the revised manuscript and makes a recommendation regarding publication to the director general of IFPRI. With the director general's approval, the manuscript enters the editorial and production phase to become an IFPRI book.

West African Agriculture and Climate Change

A Comprehensive Analysis

Edited by Abdulai Jalloh, Gerald C. Nelson, Timothy S. Thomas,
Robert Zougmoré, and Harold Roy-Macauley

A peer-reviewed publication

International Food Policy Research Institute
Washington, DC

International Food Policy Research Institute
2033 K Street, NW
Washington, DC 20006-1002, USA
Telephone: +1-202-862-5600
www.ifpri.org

DOI: http://dx.doi.org/10.2499/9780896292048

Library of Congress Cataloging-in-Publication Data

West African agriculture and climate change : a comprehensive analysis /
    edited by Abdulai Jalloh ... [et al.].—1st ed.
        p.   cm.
    Includes bibliographical references and index.
    ISBN 978-0-89629-204-8 (alk. paper)
    1. Crops and climate—Africa, West.   2. Agriculture—Africa, West.
I.   Jalloh, Abdulai.
    S600.64.A358W47   2013
    338.10966—dc23   2012041429

Cover design: Carolyn Hallowell
Book layout: Princeton Editorial Associates Inc., Scottsdale, Arizona.

Contents

Figures

Tables

Foreword

As the world's population grows from around 7 billion in 2012 to around 9 billion by 2050, the population in countries south of the Sahara is likely to surge from around 850 million today to around 1.7 billion in 2050. West Africa alone will make up more than 35 percent of Africa south of the Sahara and almost 7 percent of the world's population in 2050. Most of the people making up this population increase are expected to live in urban areas and to have higher incomes than currently is the case, which will result in increased demand for food. In the best of circumstances, the challenge of meeting this demand in a sustainable manner will be enormous. When one takes into account the effects of climate change (higher temperatures, shifting seasons, more frequent and extreme weather events, flooding, and drought) on food production, that challenge grows even more daunting. The global food price spikes of 2008, 2010, and 2012 are harbingers of a troubled future for global food security.

At the end of 2010, IFPRI published *Food Security, Farming, and Climate Change to 2050: Scenarios, Results, Policy Options,* a research monograph by Gerald Nelson and a team of IFPRI researchers that assessed quantitatively the additional challenges to sustainable food security that climate change would bring, focusing on global outcomes but also including national and subnational results. Two years later, Nelson and a group of leading agriculturists and climate change researchers have written a monograph that draws out those national results based on a detailed global model and enhances them with country-specific analysis and insights for most of the countries making up West Africa.

This first of three publications (covering West, East, and Southern Africa) provides the most comprehensive analysis to date of the scope of climate change as it relates to food security, including who will be most affected and what policymakers can do to facilitate adaptation. Augmenting the text are dozens of detailed maps that provide graphical representations of the range of food security challenges and the special threats from climate change.

Using comprehensive empirical analysis, the authors put climate change in the forefront of national development issues and suggest that policymakers should take into account (1) the value of broad-based sustainable development, (2) the power of investments in relevant economic sectors as well as agricultural research to enhance agricultural productivity, (3) the importance of the ongoing economic integration initiatives in the West Africa region under the auspices of the Economic Community of West African States within the framework of an open world trade system, and (4) the need for early action on both adaptation and mitigation. It is becoming increasingly clear to policymakers in the developing world that neither food security nor climate change can be viewed in isolation. This monograph will be indispensable to a wide range of readers, including policymakers, development workers, and researchers who tackle these inextricably linked issues.

Shenggen Fan
Director General, International Food Policy Research Institute

Acknowledgments

The editors of this monograph and the authors of the individual chapters thank the following organizations for their financial support: the EU through its support for CCAFS (Climate Change, Agriculture, and Food Security) of the CGIAR (Consultative Group on International Agricultural Research), the GIZ (Gesellschaft für Internationale Zusammenarbeit), and the Bill and Melinda Gates Foundation and their respective home institutions—CORAF (Conseil Ouest et Centre Africain pour la Recherche et le Developpement Agricoles), IFPRI, and CCAFS—for encouraging them to undertake this work. We also give special recognition to Abdulai Jalloh of WECARD (the West and Central African Council for Agricultural Research and Development). He identified counterpart national scientists to undertake the national reports and provided invaluable intellectual leadership in managing the challenging process of coordinating and supporting many different authors while leading the development of the regional overview chapter. Any errors or omissions remain the responsibility of the authors. As this monograph was being finalized we learned of the passing of Dr. Mamadou Khouma, who led the study and writing of the Senegal chapter but unfortunately could not see its final publication. We wish him God's grace.

Abbreviations and Acronyms

A1B   greenhouse gas emissions scenario that assumes fast economic growth, a population that peaks midcentury, and the development of new and efficient technologies, along with a balanced use of energy sources (Nakicenovic, N., et al. 2000. *Special Report on Emissions Scenarios: A Special Report of Working Group III of the Intergovernmental Panel on Climate Change.* Cambridge: Cambridge University Press. http://www.grida.no/climate/ipcc/emission/index .htm)

A2   greenhouse gas emissions scenario that assumes "a very heterogeneous world with continuously increasing global population and regionally oriented economic growth that is more fragmented and slower than in other storylines"

AGRHYMET   Regional Centre for Agriculture, Hydrology, and Meteorology (Centre Regional de Formation et d'Application en Agrométéorologie et Hydrologie Opérationnelle)

AR4   Fourth Assessment Report of the Intergovernmental Panel on Climate Change

B1   greenhouse gas emissions scenario that assumes a population that peaks midcentury (like the A1B), but with rapid changes toward a service and information economy, and the introduction of clean and resource-efficient technologies

CCAFS	the Climate Change, Agriculture, and Food Security Research Program of the CGIAR
CGIAR	Consultative Group on International Agricultural Research
CNR	National Meteorological Research Center, France
CNRM-CM3	National Meteorological Research Center–Climate Model 3
CORAF/ WECARD	Conseil Ouest et Centre Africain pour la Recherche et le Developpement Agricoles/Western and Central African Council for Agricultural Research and Development
CSIRO	Commonwealth Scientific and Industrial Research Organisation, Australia
CSIRO MARK 3	climate model developed at the Australia Commonwealth Scientific and Industrial Research Organization
DSSAT	Decision Support Software for Agrotechnology Transfer
ECHAM 5	fifth-generation climate model developed at the Max Planck Institute for Meteorology (Hamburg)
ECOWAP	regional agricultural policy for West Africa
ECOWAS	Economic Community of West African States
FPU	food production unit
GCM	general circulation model
GDP	gross domestic product
GIZ	Gesellschaft für Internationale Zusammenarbeit
IAR4D	Integrated Agricultural Research for Development
IFPRI	International Food and Policy Research Institute
IMPACT	International Model for Policy Analysis of Agricultural Commodities and Trade
IUCN	International Union for the Conservation of Nature
MIROC	Model for Interdisciplinary Research on Climate, developed at the University of Tokyo Center for Climate System Research

NAIP	National Agricultural Investment Programme
NAPA	National Adaptation Programmes of Action
PRC	Publications Review Committee (IFPRI)
RAIP	Regional Agricultural Investment Programme
SPAM	Spatial Production Allocation Model
SRES	Special Report on Emissions Scenarios (IPCC)
UN	United Nations
UNPOP	United Nations Department of Economic and Social Affairs–Population Division
WASCAL	West African Science Service Center on Climate Change and Adapted Land Use
w.r.t.	with respect to
WWF	World Wildlife Fund

Chapter 1

OVERVIEW

Abdulai Jalloh, Mbène Dièye Faye, Harold Roy-Macauley, Paco Sérémé,
Robert Zougmoré, Timothy S. Thomas, and Gerald C. Nelson

The part of Africa designated as West Africa is made up of 16 countries—Benin, Burkina Faso, Cape Verde, Côte d'Ivoire, Gambia, Ghana, Guinea, Guinea-Bissau, Liberia, Mali, Mauritania, Niger, Nigeria, Senegal, Sierra Leone, and Togo. Its land area is about 5 million square kilometers, and its population in 2010 was about 290 million. With the exception of Mauritania, these countries are members of the Economic Community of West African States (ECOWAS). The subregion comprises a diversified agricultural base spread over a wide range of agroecological zones with significant potential for improved agricultural productivity.

Agriculture is the major source of livelihood for the majority of West Africans. The agricultural sector employs 60 percent of the active labor force but contributes only 35 percent of gross domestic product (GDP). The disparity between contribution to GDP and share of population means that many West African farmers are very poor, producing close to subsistence levels and facing numerous constraints such as droughts, soil acidity, and nutrient-depleted and degraded soils that impinge on agricultural development. The most important foodcrops grown and consumed in West Africa are cereals—sorghum, millet, maize, and rice; roots and tubers—cassava, sweet potatoes, and yams; and legumes—cowpeas and groundnuts. Major cash crops are cocoa, coffee, and cotton.

Climate change, in terms of both climate means and variability, poses a great threat to farmers in the region. Possible impacts include reduced yields, lower farm incomes, and reduced welfare. There is increasing awareness of these threats among national governments and the regional economic community. Along with other African countries, the West African states have identified medium- and long-term adaptive measures in their national communications to the United Nations Framework Convention on Climate Change. Several of these countries have identified emergency priority measures for adaptation in their National Adaptation Programmes of Action (NAPAs), which center on agriculture, food security, and water resources management.

The purpose of this monograph is to help policymakers and researchers better understand and anticipate the likely impacts of climate change on agriculture and on vulnerable households. This is done by reviewing current data on agriculture and economic development, modeling plausible changes in climate between now and 2050, using crop models to assess the impact of climate changes on agricultural production, and globally modeling supply and demand for food in order to assess plausible food price trends. For each country, national authors worked with modeling results provided by the International Food Policy Research Institute (IFPRI) and then augmented them with other analysis as necessary. This is a unique initiative that capitalizes on the synergies among the respective countries covered in this study, the Conseil Ouest et Centre Africain pour la Recherche et le Developpement Agricoles (CORAF), and IFPRI to contribute to a climate-resilient agricultural system in West Africa.

This chapter provides an overview of the region, its current economic situation, and its vulnerability to climate change. It is designed to provide useful input into the efforts of ECOWAS in developing appropriate policies related to climate for the region. This chapter is followed by one that describes the common methodologies used by the authors of all country chapters and then by the individual country chapters. The monograph ends with a chapter that draws lessons for the region from the individual country studies.

The Intergovernmental Panel on Climate Change (IPCC), Climate Change and Agriculture, and Food Security

In the Fourth Assessment Report of the IPCC, Working Group 1 reports that "climate is often defined as 'average weather.' Climate is usually described in terms of the mean and variability of temperature, precipitation, and wind over a period of time, ranging from months to millions of years (the classical period is 30 years)" (Le Treut et al. 2007, 496).

The growth of greenhouse gas emissions is raising average temperatures. The consequences include changes in precipitation patterns, more and more extreme weather events, and shifting seasons. The accelerating pace of climate change, combined with global population and income growth, threatens food security everywhere.

Agriculture is vulnerable to climate change in a number of dimensions. Higher temperatures eventually reduce yields of desirable crops and tend to encourage weed and pest proliferation. Greater variations in precipitation patterns increase the likelihood of short-run crop failures and long-run production declines. Although there might be gains in some crops in certain regions of the world, the overall impacts of climate change on agriculture are expected to be negative, particularly in the Sahelian countries, threatening regional food security. The impacts are

- direct, on crops and livestock productivity domestically,
- indirect, on the availability or prices of food domestically and in international markets, and
- indirect, on income from agricultural production at both the farm and country levels.

Roudier et al. (2011) review 16 studies on the impact of climate change on West African agriculture. Müller (2011) uses the results of Roudier et al. together with the results of Neumann et al. (2010) to point out that in addition to climate change, there are existing inefficiencies in agriculture. The main points to take away from these studies, which have a lot of uncertainty built into them, are that it appears that climate change will unequivocally hurt agriculture and that right now there is room for improvements in yield with the proper investments.

More generally, Hertel and Rosch (2010) provide an insightful review of various approaches to analyzing the impacts of climate change on agriculture, as do Tubiello and Rosenzweig (2008).

Review of Current Regional Trends

This section provides an overview of the starting point for an assessment of the potential vulnerability of West African agriculture to climate change. It looks at recent population and income developments to provide a backdrop to potential futures. Two key indicators of well-being are reviewed—under-five mortality and life expectancy at birth. The current climate situation is discussed along with the role of regional programs in supporting food security.

Economic and Demographic Indicators

Population

The population of West Africa was estimated at 291.3 million in 2008 with Nigeria accounting for half of the total (Table 1.1). West Africa's population

TABLE 1.1   Population of West Africa, annualized growth rate, and percent urban, 1988 and 2009

Country	Total population			Percent urban	
	Number (millions)				
	1988	2008	Annualized growth rate (%)	1988	2008
Benin	4.5	8.66	4.62	33	41
Burkina Faso	8.37	15.21	4.09	13	20
Cape Verde	0.34	0.50	2.35	39	60
Côte d'Ivoire	11.73	20.59	3.78	39	49
Gambia	0.83	1.66	5.00	36	56
Ghana	14.17	23.35	3.24	35	50
Guinea	5.74	9.83	3.56	27	34
Guinea-Bissau	0.98	1.58	3.06	26	30
Liberia	2.24	3.79	3.46	43	60
Mali	7.30	12.71	3.71	22	32
Mauritania	1.85	3.20	3.65	38	41
Niger	7.34	14.67	4.99	15	17
Nigeria	89.05	151.32	3.50	34	48
Senegal	7.11	12.21	3.59	38	42
Sierra Leone	3.95	5.56	2.04	32	38
Togo	3.70	6.46	3.73	29	42
Totals	169.20	291.30	3.61	32	43

Source: World Development Indicators (World Bank 2009a).

increased by about 60 percent between 1988 and 2008, and the populations in many of the countries almost doubled. In general, there is growing urbanization resulting in higher population densities in capital cities and major towns (Figure 1.1). Rapid urbanization in the region is posing a great challenge to governments in providing basic amenities for the inhabitants. Increasing unemployment, particularly of youth, is a growing concern with serious sociopolitical implications.

Settlement areas in West Africa are linked to the current climate. Three-quarters of the population lives in the humid and subhumid zones, 20 percent in the semiarid zone (the Sahel), and 5 percent in the arid zone (ECOWAS–SWAC/OECD 2007). In all the countries, there is a general pattern of high population densities in and around urban areas. There is also a generally higher

FIGURE 1.1 Population distribution in West Africa, 2000 (persons per square kilometer)

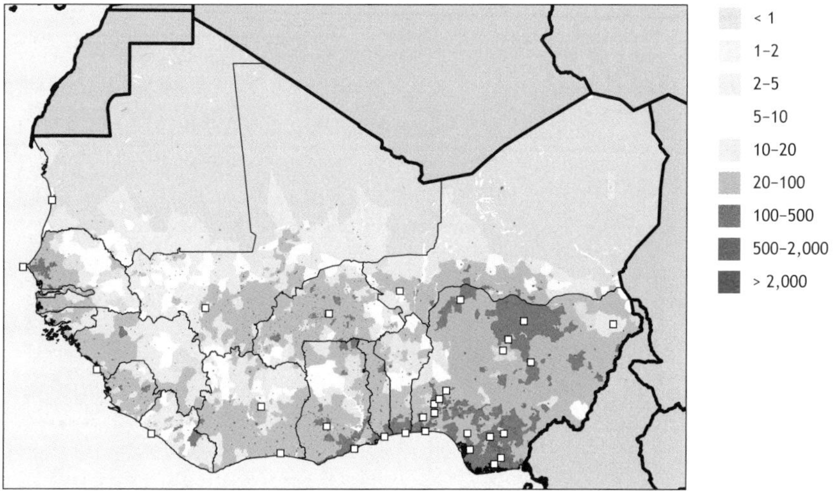

Legend: < 1, 1–2, 2–5, 5–10, 10–20, 20–100, 100–500, 500–2,000, > 2,000

Source: CIESIN et al. (2004).

population density along the coast. Nigeria also has a high population density in the states of Katsina, Kano, and Jigawa in the north (see Figure 1.1).

Income

Per capita GDP in West African states has been growing at diverse rates but invariably remains low across the region. In countries like Côte d'Ivoire, Guinea-Bissau, Liberia, Niger, and Togo, per capita GDP declined between 1988 and 2008 (Table 1.2). In most of these countries, the decline is attributed to civil wars and political unrest. Niger has suffered from adverse climatic conditions. In 2008, per capita GDP ranged from about 128 US dollars (US$128) in Guinea-Bissau to more than US$1,500 in Cape Verde, with all other countries having less than US$500 except Côte d'Ivoire (US$530) and Senegal (US$530).

Across the region, there has been a slow decline in the share of agriculture in overall GDP (see Table 1.2). This pattern occurs in all countries as economic development progresses. Specific causes include relatively slow increase in crop productivity and production and more rapid growth in the service sector, including tourism.

TABLE 1.2   Income of West Africans (GDP per capita and share of GDP from agriculture), 1988 and 2008

	GDP per capita (constant 2000 US$)		Share of GDP from agriculture (%)	
Country	1988	2008	1988	2008
Benin	313	359	34	n.a.
Burkina Faso	183	263	30	n.a.
Cape Verde	839	1,632	18	8
Côte d'Ivoire	695	530	32	24
Gambia	336	374	31	29
Ghana	212	327	50	32
Guinea	335	417	23	8
Guinea-Bissau	169	128	58	55
Liberia	539	148	38	n.a.
Mali	204	295	45	n.a.
Mauritania	429	n.a.	33	n.a.
Niger	206	180	35	n.a.
Nigeria	339	487	n.a.	31
Senegal	471	530	21	15
Sierra Leone	247	262	46	43
Togo	278	245	34	n.a.

Source: World Development Indicators (World Bank 2009a).
Notes: GDP = gross domestic product; n.a. = not available; US$ = US dollars.

Well-being indicators (regional)

Under-five mortality still remains relatively high in West Africa despite a decline in the figures between 1988 and 2008 (Table 1.3). Cape Verde has the lowest (32/1,000) under-five mortality in the region, while Sierra Leone has the highest (262/1,000). A majority of the countries have an under-five mortality ranging between 100 and 200. Life expectancy at birth is also generally improving across the region, with Cape Verde having the most favorable life expectancy at birth (71 years), while Guinea-Bissau, Nigeria, and Sierra Leone show an average life expectancy of only 47 years. The majority of the countries have a life expectancy of between 50 and 60 years. The general decrease in under-five mortality and increase in life expectancy are due to increasing campaigns for and implementation of vaccinations against major diseases and gradual improvement in health facilities.

TABLE 1.3 Under-five mortality and life expectancy at birth in West Africa, 1988 and 2008

Country	Under-five mortality (deaths per 1,000)		Life expectancy at birth (years)	
	1988	2008	1988	2008
Benin	184	123	54	61
Burkina Faso	206	191	50	52
Cape Verde	60	32	66	71
Côte d'Ivoire	151	127	57	57
Gambia	153	109	51	56
Ghana	120	115	58	56
Guinea	231	150	49	58
Guinea-Bissau	240	198	44	48
Liberia	205	133	49	58
Mali	250	196	48	54
Mauritania	130	119	58	64
Niger	304	176	47	57
Nigeria	230	189	47	47
Senegal	149	114	52	55
Sierra Leone	290	262	40	47
Togo	150	100	58	62

Source: World Development Indicators (World Bank 2009a).

Widespread poverty remains a challenge. Except for Côte d'Ivoire and Mauritania, where only 40–50 percent of the population lives on less than US$2 per day, an average of about 70–80 percent of the population lives on less than US$2 per day in all the other countries in the subregion (Figure 1.2). However, the coastal areas of Ghana and several states in Nigeria, including Lagos state and the federal capital state, have 20 percent to less than 10 percent of the population living on less than US$2 per day.

Climate, Land Use, and Agriculture

In West Africa today, rainfall generally decreases northward from the coast (Figure 1.3). The coasts of Guinea, Sierra Leone, Liberia, and Nigeria receive the highest amount of rainfall per year (ranging from 2,500 millimeters to more than 4,000 millimeters). In the Sahelian belt, extending from Senegal through Mali, Burkina Faso, Niger, and northern Nigeria, rainfall ranges from 800 to 1,100 millimeters, while Mauritania and most parts of Mali and Niger are largely

FIGURE 1.2   Poverty in West Africa, circa 2005 (percentage of population below US$2 per day)

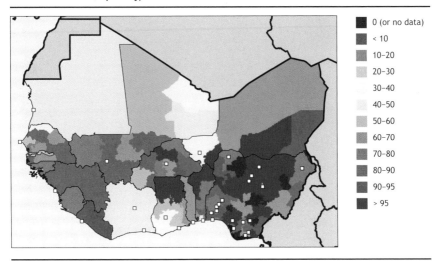

Source: Wood et al. (2010).
Note: Based on 2005 US$ (US dollars) and on purchasing power parity value.

FIGURE 1.3   Annual average precipitation in West Africa, 2000s (millimeters per year)

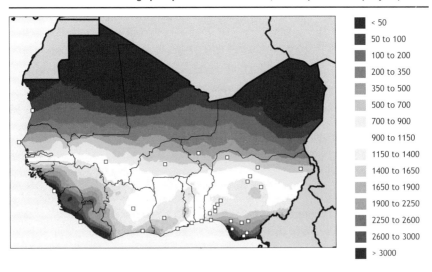

Source: WorldClim version 1.4 (Hijmans et al. 2005).

FIGURE 1.4   Annual maximum temperature in West Africa, 2000s (°C)

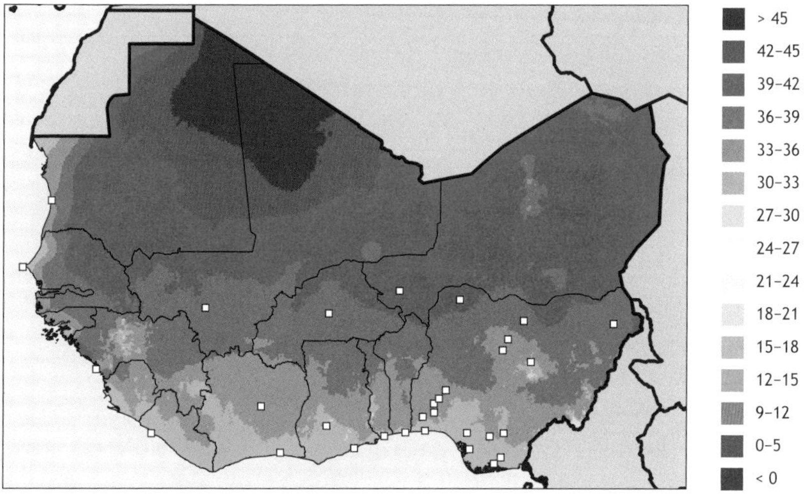

Legend:
- \> 45
- 42–45
- 39–42
- 36–39
- 33–36
- 30–33
- 27–30
- 24–27
- 21–24
- 18–21
- 15–18
- 12–15
- 9–12
- 0–5
- \< 0

Source: WorldClim version 1.4 (Hijmans et al. 2005).

desert. As rainfall decreases, from south to north, temperature increases northward from the southern coast (Figure 1.4). Maximum temperatures range from 30°–33°C along the coast to 36°–39°C in the Sahel and 42°–45°C on the fringe of the desert.

As precipitation declines, the agroecology of West Africa shifts from humid forest along the coast to the Guinea savanna and the Sudan savanna northward (Figure 1.5). As a result of shifting cultivation and indiscriminate logging, only patches of the Guinea forest that once stretched from Guinea through Nigeria now remain. The belt of savanna (mostly the Sudan savanna) that stretches from northern Senegal across Mali, Burkina Faso, Niger, and northern Nigeria is referred to as the Sahel. The Sudan savanna of the Sahel merges into the Sahara Desert in the north. In general, plantation tree crops as well as root crops dominate the humid coastal areas, while cereals become predominant northward. The Sahelian region is dominated by a crop/livestock production system.

The existing farming systems, including the crops and livestock, have largely adapted to the respective agroecosystems in the region. Major imbalances in these agroecosystems could be caused by changes in climate, thereby affecting livelihoods in the region. Dwindling forests and consequently increasing

FIGURE 1.5   Regional land use distribution in West Africa, 2000

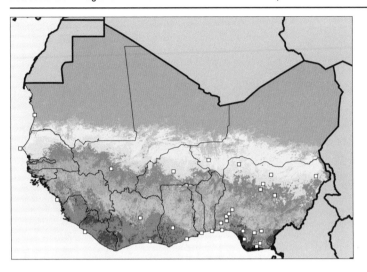

- Tree cover, broadleaved, evergreen
- Tree cover, broadleaved, deciduous, closed
- Tree cover, broadleaved, deciduous, open
- Tree cover, broadleaved, needle-leaved, evergreen
- Tree cover, broadleaved, needle-leaved, deciduous
- Tree cover, broadleaved, mixed leaf type
- Tree cover, broadleaved, regularly flooded, fresh water
- Tree cover, broadleaved, regularly flooded, saline water
- Mosaic of tree cover/other natural vegetation
- Tree cover, burnt
- Shrub cover, closed-open, evergreen
- Shrub cover, closed-open, deciduous
- Herbacious cover, closed-open
- Sparse herbacious or sparse shrub cover
- Regularly flooded shrub or herbacious cover
- Cultivated and managed areas
- Mosaic of cropland/tree cover/other natural vegetation
- Mosaic of cropland/shrub/grass cover
- Bare areas
- Water bodies
- Snow and ice
- Artificial surfaces and associated areas
- No data

Source: GLC2000 (Global Land Cover 2000) (Bartholome and Belward 2005).

savannahs could provide unfavorable conditions for farming systems suited to forest conditions, while such a situation could be good for systems that require relatively drier conditions. This could require adjustments to living conditions, including land tenure. There is, however, growing awareness of the adverse effects of deforestation in the region. Many governments are increasingly supporting initiatives aimed at conserving and protecting key natural resources, including forests (Figure 1.6).

In general, major cities are linked within each country (Figure 1.7), a major highway runs along the coast from Côte d'Ivoire to Nigeria, and a major linkage in the north connects Senegal, Guinea, Mali, and Burkina Faso. Coastal countries like Côte d'Ivoire, Ghana, Togo, Benin, and Nigeria are also linked with

FIGURE 1.6 Protected areas in West Africa, 2009

- Ia: Strict Nature Reserve
- Ib: Wilderness Area
- II: National Park
- III: National Monument
- IV: Habitat / Species Management Area
- V: Protected Landscape / Seascape
- VI: Managed Resource Protected Area
- Not applicable
- Not known

Sources: Protected areas are from the World Database on Protected Areas (UNEP and IUCN 2009). Water bodies are from the World Wildlife Fund's Global Lakes and Wetlands Database (Lehner and Döll 2004).

FIGURE 1.7   Travel time in West Africa, circa 2000

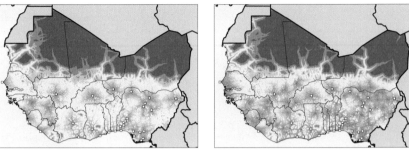

To cities of 500,000 or more people

To cities of 100,000 or more people

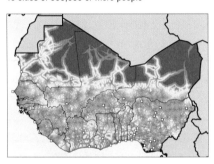

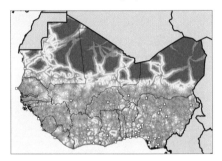

To towns and cities of 25,000 or more people

To towns and cities of 10,000 or more people

Urban location

< 1 hour

1–3 hours

3–5 hours

5–8 hours

8–11 hours

11–16 hours

16–26 hours

> 26 hours

Source: Authors' calculations.

their adjacent landlocked countries. There is a need to upgrade these international highways to facilitate regional trade.

Tables 1.4–1.7 provide information on the major crops grown in West Africa. The major cereals are maize, millet, rice, and sorghum (see Table 1.4). Millet occupies the largest area among the cereal crops, followed by sorghum. Both crops are mainly produced in the Sahelian countries (Burkina Faso, Mali,

TABLE 1.4   Average harvest area of leading agricultural commodities in West Africa, grains, 2005–07 (thousands of hectares)

Country	Maize	Millet	Rice (paddy)	Sorghum	Total
Benin	679	42	30	149	900
Burkina Faso	509	1,328	51	1,613	3,501
Cape Verde	31	0	0	0	31
Côte d'Ivoire	292	61	375	67	795
Gambia	37	127	23	24	211
Ghana	764	190	122	333	1,409
Guinea	403	377	781	48	1,608
Guinea-Bissau	16	29	73	20	137
Liberia	0	0	160	0	160
Mali	382	1,566	429	998	3,380
Mauritania	25	10	18	182	235
Niger	9	6,410	20	2,859	9,303
Nigeria	3,898	4,977	2,519	7,579	19,014
Senegal	167	793	93	175	1,229
Sierra Leone	60	25	1,000	22	1,107
Togo	475	69	32	221	797
Total	7,747	16,002	5,726	14,289	43,815

Source: FAOSTAT (FAO 2010).

TABLE 1.5   Average harvest area of leading agricultural commodities in West Africa, pulses and nuts, 2005–07 (thousands of hectares)

Country	Beans, dry	Cashew nuts	Cowpeas	Groundnuts	Soybeans	Total
Benin	145	212	0	116	19	492
Burkina Faso	0	9	702	385	5	1,101
Cape Verde	0	0	0	0	0	0
Côte d'Ivoire	32	657	0	68	1	758
Gambia	0	0	0	120	0	120
Ghana	0	61	0	470	0	531
Guinea	0	3	0	210	0	212
Guinea-Bissau	0	212	2	24	0	239
Liberia	0	0	0	9	8	17
Mali	0	0	245	332	3	581
Mauritania	10	0	23	1	0	34
Niger	18	0	4,743	460	0	5,221
Nigeria	0	327	4,395	2,251	626	7,599
Senegal	0	16	187	624	0	827
Sierra Leone	0	0	0	150	0	150
Togo	188	0	0	57	0	246
Total	394	1,496	10,298	5,277	661	18,127

Source: FAOSTAT (FAO 2010).

TABLE 1.6   Average harvest area of leading agricultural commodities in West Africa, root crops, bananas, and plantains, 2005–07 (thousands of hectares)

Country	Bananas	Cassava	Plantains	Potatoes	Sweet potatoes	Yams	Total
Benin	3	175	0	0	26	185	389
Burkina Faso	0	2	0	1	7	3	12
Cape Verde	0	0	0	0	1	0	2
Côte d'Ivoire	8	339	382	0	25	723	1,476
Gambia	0	3	0	0	0	0	3
Ghana	7	797	301	0	65	299	1,469
Guinea	41	139	84	2	63	2	330
Guinea-Bissau	1	4	14	0	0	0	19
Liberia	11	85	19	0	2	2	120
Mali	4	6	0	5	13	3	31
Mauritania	0	0	0	0	2	0	3
Niger	0	5	0	2	3	0	10
Nigeria	0	3,821	464	266	1,086	3,068	8,705
Senegal	1	67	0	1	1	0	70
Sierra Leone	0	73	7	0	12	0	91
Togo	2	130	0	0	0	60	193
Total	77	5,645	1,271	277	1,307	4,346	12,922

Source: FAOSTAT (FAO 2010).

TABLE 1.7   Average harvest area of leading agricultural commodities in West Africa, other crops, 2005–07 (thousands of hectares)

Country	Cocoa beans	Coffee grain	Seed cotton	Sesame seeds	Sugar cane	Total
Benin	0	0	225	11	1	238
Burkina Faso	0	0	483	51	5	538
Cape Verde	0	0	0	0	1	1
Côte d'Ivoire	2,151	585	247	6	25	3,015
Gambia	0	0	1	7	0	8
Ghana	1,678	10	25	0	6	1,718
Guinea	17	48	36	2	5	108
Guinea-Bissau	0	0	4	0	0	4
Liberia	17	17	0	0	26	60
Mali	0	0	320	14	5	339
Mauritania	0	0	5	73	4	82
Niger	1,110	4	513	201	57	1,884
Nigeria	0	0	44	27	7	78
Senegal	38	11	0	4	1	54
Sierra Leone	104	34	67	5	0	210
Togo	5,115	709	1,970	401	143	8,339
Total	394	1,496	10,298	5,277	661	18,127

Source: FAOSTAT (FAO 2010).

and Niger) and northern Nigeria. Cowpeas and groundnuts are the major legumes cultivated in the region (see Table 1.5). Niger and Nigeria dominate cowpea production, while Nigeria leads the region in groundnut production, followed by Senegal, Ghana, and Niger. Cassava is the major root crop grown and consumed in West Africa (see Table 1.6). The major cash crops in the region are cocoa, coffee, and cotton (see Table 1.7). Cocoa and coffee production are confined to the humid forest areas along the coast, while cotton is produced mainly in savannah regions, particularly in Nigeria, Burkina Faso, Mali, Côte d'Ivoire, and Benin.

Figures 1.8–1.11 show the distribution and yield of major cereal crops grown in West Africa. Rainfed maize is produced across the region, with major producing countries being Côte d'Ivoire, Ghana, Togo, Benin, and Nigeria (see Figure 1.8). Millet (see Figure 1.9) and sorghum (see Figure 1.10) are produced mainly in the Sahel and the northernmost parts of the coastal countries.

FIGURE 1.8 Yield (metric tons per hectare) and harvest area density (hectares) for rainfed maize in West Africa, 2000

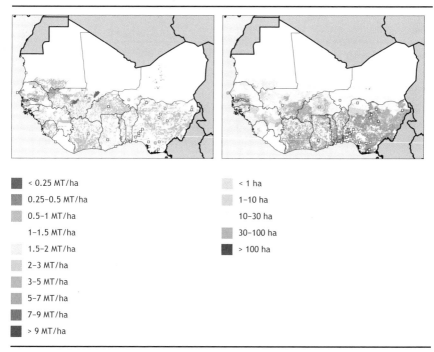

< 0.25 MT/ha	< 1 ha
0.25–0.5 MT/ha	1–10 ha
0.5–1 MT/ha	10–30 ha
1–1.5 MT/ha	30–100 ha
1.5–2 MT/ha	> 100 ha
2–3 MT/ha	
3–5 MT/ha	
5–7 MT/ha	
7–9 MT/ha	
> 9 MT/ha	

Sources: SPAM (Spatial Production Allocation Model) (You and Wood 2006; You, Wood, and Wood-Sichra 2006, 2009).
Notes: ha = hectare; MT/ha = metric tons per hectare.

FIGURE 1.9   Yield (metric tons per hectare) and harvest area density (hectares) for millet in West Africa, 2000

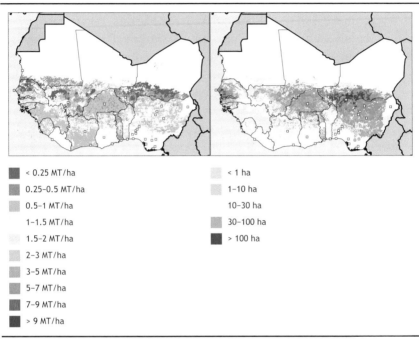

■ < 0.25 MT/ha		▫ < 1 ha	
■ 0.25–0.5 MT/ha		▫ 1–10 ha	
0.5–1 MT/ha		10–30 ha	
1–1.5 MT/ha		■ 30–100 ha	
1.5–2 MT/ha		■ > 100 ha	
2–3 MT/ha			
3–5 MT/ha			
5–7 MT/ha			
■ 7–9 MT/ha			
■ > 9 MT/ha			

Sources: SPAM (Spatial Production Allocation Model) (You and Wood 2006; You, Wood, and Wood-Sichra 2006, 2009).
Notes: ha = hectare; MT/ha = metric tons per hectare.

Similar to maize production, rice production is concentrated in the coastal countries (see Figure 1.11). Rainfed cereal yields are still very low in West Africa compared to the world average and even other regions in Africa. Rice and maize yield an average of 1 metric ton per hectare, while sorghum and millet yield about 0.5 ton per hectare.[1] Against the background of limited inputs, the predominantly resource-poor farmers are faced with such biophysical constraints as pests and diseases, droughts, soil acidity, and nutrient-depleted and degraded soils. The threats of climate change could prove most challenging to an already overstretched production system.

Regional Program on Food Security
West Africa is unique in Africa in terms of the degree of regional economic integration efforts. The premier institution in this regard is ECOWAS, a regional

---

1 All tons are metric tons.

FIGURE 1.10   Yield (metric tons per hectare) and harvest area density (hectares) for sorghum in West Africa, 2000

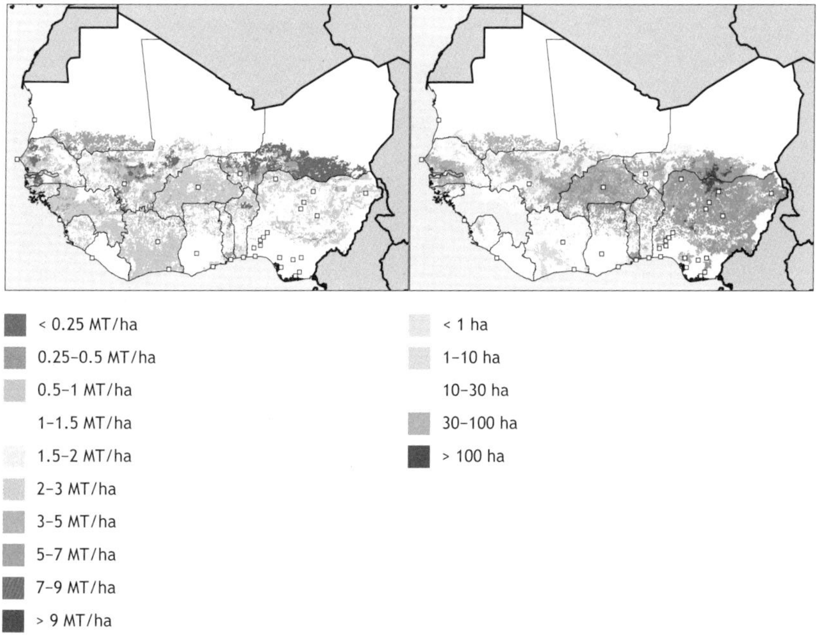

< 0.25 MT/ha	< 1 ha
0.25–0.5 MT/ha	1–10 ha
0.5–1 MT/ha	10–30 ha
1–1.5 MT/ha	30–100 ha
1.5–2 MT/ha	> 100 ha
2–3 MT/ha	
3–5 MT/ha	
5–7 MT/ha	
7–9 MT/ha	
> 9 MT/ha	

Sources: SPAM (Spatial Production Allocation Model) (You and Wood 2006; You, Wood, and Wood-Sichra 2006, 2009).
Notes: ha = hectare; MT/ha = metric tons per hectare.

group of 15 countries founded in 1975. Its mission is to promote economic integration in "all fields of economic activity, particularly industry, transport, telecommunications, energy, agriculture, natural resources, commerce, monetary and financial questions, social and cultural matters" (ECOWAS 2012).

The framework for the ECOWAS Agricultural Policy (ECOWAP) was adopted by member heads of state and government in January 2005. The three major themes of the ECOWAP policy framework are

1. increasing the productivity and competitiveness of West African agriculture,

2. implementing a trade regime in West Africa, and

3. adapting the trade regime vis-à-vis countries outside the region (ECOWAS 2008).

FIGURE 1.11 Yield (metric tons per hectare) and harvest area density (hectares) for rice in West Africa, 2000

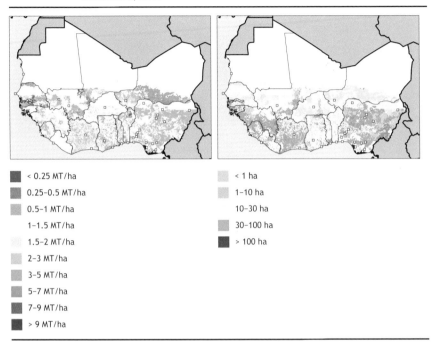

■ < 0.25 MT/ha	< 1 ha
0.25–0.5 MT/ha	1–10 ha
0.5–1 MT/ha	10–30 ha
1–1.5 MT/ha	30–100 ha
1.5–2 MT/ha	■ > 100 ha
2–3 MT/ha	
3–5 MT/ha	
5–7 MT/ha	
7–9 MT/ha	
■ > 9 MT/ha	

Sources: SPAM (Spatial Production Allocation Model) (You and Wood 2006; You, Wood, and Wood-Sichra 2006, 2009).
Notes: ha = hectare; MT/ha = metric tons per hectare.

In July 2005, ECOWAS drew up a regional action plan for the implementation of ECOWAP and the Comprehensive Africa Agriculture Development Programme of the New Partnership for Africa's Development in the period 2006–10 based on six priorities for joint implementation of National Agricultural Investment Programmes (NAIPs) and long-term Regional Agricultural Investment Programmes (RAIPs):

1. improved water management by promoting irrigation and integrated water resource management;

2. improved management of other natural resources through organized transhumance and rangeland development, sustainable forest resources management, and sustainable fishery resources management;

3. sustainable agricultural development at the farm level through integrated soil fertility management, better support services for producers, and dissemination of improved technologies;

4. development of agricultural supply chains and promotion of markets by developing the different supply chains (foodcrops, periurban agriculture, export crops, short-cycle livestock rearing, agroforestry food products, and artisanal fishing and fish farming), developing processing operations, strengthening support services for operators, and promoting national, international, and regional trade;

5. prevention and management of food crises and other natural disasters by promoting early warning systems, developing crisis management systems, assisting the recovery of crisis-hit areas, and formulating mechanisms for disaster-related insurance and compensation; and

6. institution building through gender-sensitive approaches, support for capacity building in the formulation of agricultural and rural policies and strategies, long-term funding for agriculture, communication, and capacity building in steering and coordination and in monitoring and evaluation.

ECOWAS recognizes the intricate relationship between agriculture and climate and therefore the potential impact of climate change on agricultural production. This is reflected in the list of priorities for NAIPs and long-term RAIPs. What is needed now is the explicit mainstreaming of climate change in these programs. It is expected that a well-integrated regional market will not only provide a much-needed pull for agricultural produce, thereby encouraging further increase in production, but will also provide an opportunity to respond to regional imbalances in production as a result of climate. Therefore, since the international conference on the mitigation of vulnerability to climate change in natural, economic, and social systems in West Africa, held in Burkina Faso in January 2007, ECOWAS has elaborated a subregional program of action to mitigate vulnerability to climate change in West Africa. The program of action emphasizes efforts to stem soil degradation on the one hand and, on the other, to foster technical and institutional synergies for climate adaptation in the region.

TABLE 1.8 Summary statistics for assumptions on West Africa's population and per capita GDP used in the IMPACT model, 2010 and 2050

Category/country	2010	2050 Optimistic	2050 Baseline	2050 Pessimistic
Population (millions)				
Benin	9,212	19,402	21,982	24,744
Burkina Faso	16,287	36,189	40,830	45,757
Cape Verde	513	595	703	822
Côte d'Ivoire	21,571	37,845	43,373	49,350
Gambia	1,751	3,292	3,763	4,270
Ghana	24,333	39,660	45,213	51,163
Guinea	10,324	21,131	23,975	27,025
Guinea-Bissau	1,647	3,147	3,555	3,990
Liberia	4,102	7,730	8,841	10,040
Mali	13,323	24,941	28,260	31,792
Mauritania	3,366	5,304	6,061	6,873
Niger	15,891	52,568	58,216	64,156
Nigeria	158,259	254,129	289,083	326,395
Senegal	12,861	22,814	26,102	29,620
Sierra Leone	5,836	10,904	12,446	14,100
Togo	6,780	11,481	13,196	15,054
Income per capita (2000 US$)				
Benin	373	2,539	1,397	149
Burkina Faso	340	2,579	1,428	791
Côte d'Ivoire	710	6,265	3,401	1,536
Gambia	412	3,162	1,724	750
Ghana	543	4,975	2,724	988
Guinea	162	2,140	835	683
Guinea-Bissau	697	5,234	2,876	1,456
Liberia	85	1,594	394	347
Mali	417	3,818	2,108	1,122
Niger	221	1,671	637	559
Nigeria	344	2,491	1,364	684
Senegal	678	5,602	3,055	1,362
Sierra Leone	337	2,566	1,410	378
Togo	309	2,653	1,438	660

Sources: Computed from GDP data from the World Bank Economic Adaptation to Climate Change project (World Bank 2010), from the Millennium Ecosystem Assessment (2005) reports, and from population data from the United Nations (UNPOP 2009).
Notes: 2010 income per capita is for the baseline scenario. GDP = gross domestic product; IMPACT = International Model for Policy Analysis of Agricultural Commodities and Trade (International Food Policy Research Institute); US$ = US dollars.

Scenarios for the Future

Population and Income Scenarios

All scenarios for the future, described further in Chapter 2, include a significant increase in the population of West African countries except for Cape Verde by 2050 (Table 1.8). In the pessimistic scenario, populations of all countries in the region with the exception of Cape Verde will more than double. A similar outcome occurs in the baseline scenario for all countries except Cape Verde and Nigeria. In the optimistic scenario, the population doubles only in Benin, Burkina Faso, and Niger. Income per capita does not improve significantly in the pessimistic scenario and could even decline in the case of Benin (see Table 1.8). However, in the optimistic scenario income per capita in 2050 could range from US$1,594 for Liberia to US$6,265 for Côte d'Ivoire.

Climate Change Scenarios and Their Effects on Agriculture

The rainfall scenarios used in this monograph are generally dissimilar (Figures 1.12 and 1.13).[2] There is similarity in the predictions for reduction in rainfall in the southern parts of Ghana, Togo, Benin, and Nigeria, but the CSIRO A1B scenario has a greater reduction in precipitation than the MIROC A1B scenario.[3] The CSIRO A1B scenario predicts no change to as much as 100 millimeters per year decline in the Sahelian region and an increase in precipitation along the coast of Sierra Leone and most parts of Liberia, while the MIROC A1B scenario predicts an increase in precipitation in the Sahelian region (50–100 to 100–200 millimeters per year) and severe drought in Liberia (a decline of 200–400 millimeters per year). As indicated earlier, a substantial change in climate could require adjustments for which resource-poor farmers lack the essential means. Heavy and persistent rainfall in hitherto dry areas of the Sahel could cause an increase in diseases and pests that livestock in those areas are not adapted to. On the other hand, a marked decrease in rainfall in hitherto wet regions like Liberia could cause significant changes in the growing conditions that may require changes in the farming system with

---

2   See Chapter 2 for details on how these scenarios were produced.

3   CSIRO and MIROC are acronyms for two of the general circulation models (GCMs) discussed in this book. CSIRO is a climate model developed at the Australia Commonwealth Scientific and Industrial Research Organisation. MIROC is the Model for Interdisciplinary Research on Climate, developed at the University of Tokyo Center for Climate System Research. The A1B scenario is a greenhouse gas emissions scenario that assumes fast economic growth, a population that peaks midcentury, and the development of new and efficient technologies, along with a balanced use of energy sources.

FIGURE 1.12   Change in average annual precipitation in West Africa, 2000–2050, CSIRO A1B (millimeters)

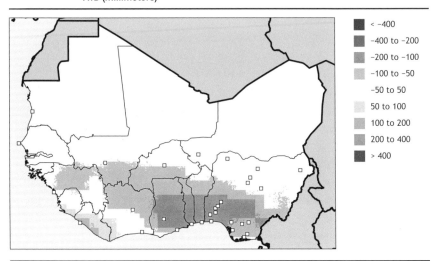

Source: Authors' calculations based on Jones, Thornton, and Heinke (2009).

Notes: A1B = greenhouse gas emissions scenario that assumes fast economic growth, a population that peaks midcentury, and the development of new and efficient technologies, along with a balanced use of energy sources; CSIRO = climate model developed at the Australia Commonwealth Scientific and Industrial Research Organization.

FIGURE 1.13   Change in average annual precipitation in West Africa, 2000–2050, MIROC A1B (millimeters)

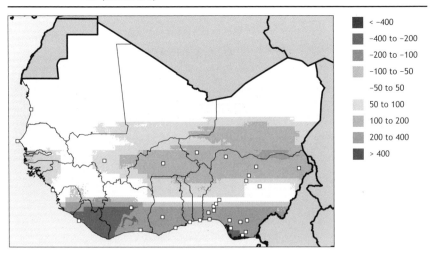

Source: Authors' calculations based on Jones, Thornton, and Heinke (2009).

Notes: A1B = greenhouse gas emissions scenario that assumes fast economic growth, a population that peaks midcentury, and the development of new and efficient technologies, along with a balanced use of energy sources; MIROC = Model for Interdisciplinary Research on Climate, developed at the University of Tokyo Center for Climate System Research.

FIGURE 1.14 Changes in yields (percent), 2000–2050, from the DSSAT crop model, maize (rainfed), CSIRO A1B

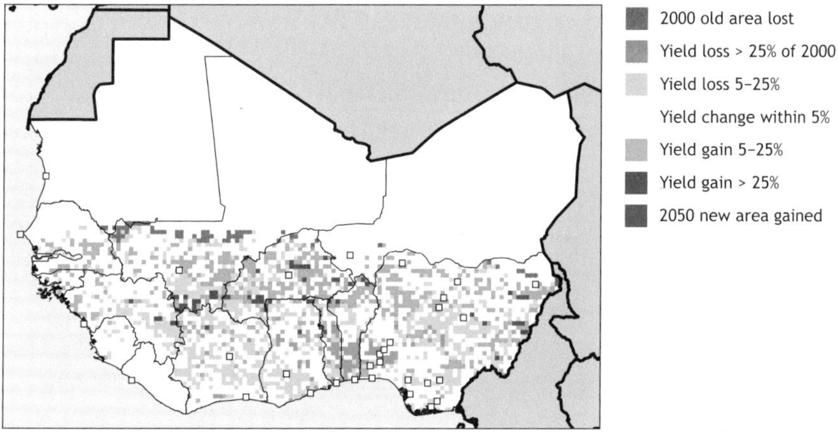

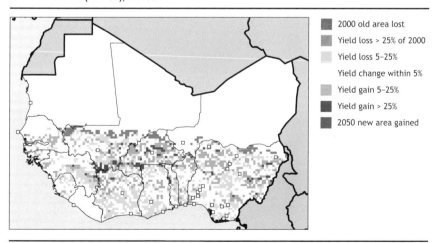

Source: Authors' estimates.
Notes: A1B = greenhouse gas emissions scenario that assumes fast economic growth, a population that peaks midcentury, and the development of new and efficient technologies, along with a balanced use of energy source; CSIRO = climate model developed at the Australia Commonwealth Scientific and Industrial Research Organisation; DSSAT = Decision Support Software for Agrotechnology Transfer.

FIGURE 1.15 Changes in yields (percent), 2000–2050, from the DSSAT crop model, maize (rainfed), MIROC A1B

Source: Authors' estimates.
Notes: A1B = greenhouse gas emissions scenario that assumes fast economic growth, a population that peaks midcentury, and the development of new and efficient technologies, along with a balanced use of energy sources; MIROC = Model for Interdisciplinary Research on Climate, developed at the University of Tokyo Center for Climate System Research.

regard to crops and livestock composition and management. The real issue is the inability of resource-poor farmers to react appropriately and fast enough.

Crop models using the CSIRO and the MIROC general circulation models' climate outputs predict a general decrease in maize yields of 5–25 percent of baseline in most parts of the countries along the southern coast of West Africa and a yield gain of 5–25 percent in the Sahel (Figures 1.14 and 1.15). Both models also have a loss in baseline area in the northernmost parts of Mali, Burkina Faso, and Nigeria.

Based on both the CSIRO and the MIROC climate outcomes in the A1B SRES (Special Report on Emissions Scenarios) scenario, sorghum yields will decline by 5–25 percent across West Africa, with greater reductions in parts of Togo, Benin, and adjacent areas of Ghana and Nigeria (Figures 1.16 and 1.17). Both climate scenarios also have a loss in baseline area in the Sudan savanna from Senegal to Nigeria. However, the MIROC scenario has a greater reduction than the CSIRO scenario.

Rainfed rice yields are predicted to decrease by 5–25 percent in most parts of Côte d'Ivoire, Ghana, and Togo based on both the CSIRO and the MIROC models (Figures 1.18 and 1.19) and in Nigeria as well based on the

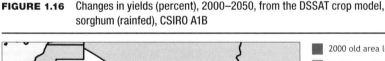

FIGURE 1.16   Changes in yields (percent), 2000–2050, from the DSSAT crop model, sorghum (rainfed), CSIRO A1B

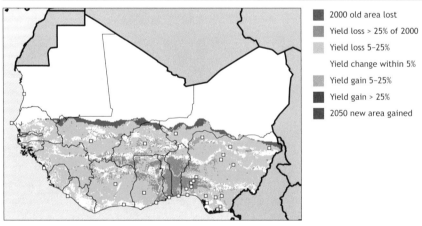

2000 old area lost
Yield loss > 25% of 2000
Yield loss 5–25%
Yield change within 5%
Yield gain 5–25%
Yield gain > 25%
2050 new area gained

Source: Authors' estimates.

Notes: A1B = greenhouse gas emissions scenario that assumes fast economic growth, a population that peaks midcentury, and the development of new and efficient technologies, along with a balanced use of energy sources; CSIRO = climate model developed at the Australia Commonwealth Scientific and Industrial Research Organisation; DSSAT = Decision Support Software for Agrotechnology Transfer.

FIGURE 1.17 Changes in yields (percent), 2000–2050, from the DSSAT crop model, sorghum (rainfed), MIROC A1B

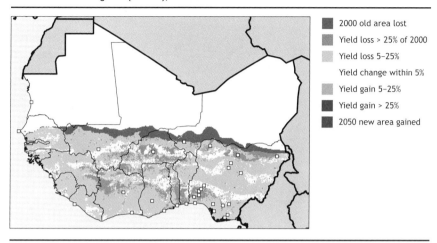

2000 old area lost

Yield loss > 25% of 2000

Yield loss 5–25%

Yield change within 5%

Yield gain 5–25%

Yield gain > 25%

2050 new area gained

Source: Authors' estimates.

Notes: A1B = greenhouse gas emissions scenario that assumes fast economic growth, a population that peaks midcentury, and the development of new and efficient technologies, along with a balanced use of energy sources; DSSAT = Decision Support Software for Agrotechnology Transfer; MIROC = the Model for Interdisciplinary Research on Climate, developed at the University of Tokyo Center for Climate System Research.

FIGURE 1.18 Changes in yields (percent), 2000–2050, from the DSSAT crop model, rice (rainfed), CSIRO A1B

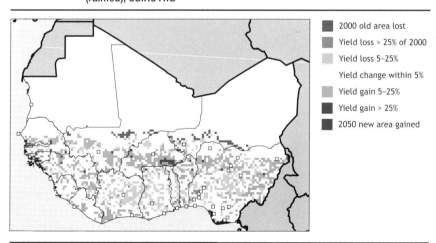

2000 old area lost

Yield loss > 25% of 2000

Yield loss 5–25%

Yield change within 5%

Yield gain 5–25%

Yield gain > 25%

2050 new area gained

Source: Authors' estimates.

Notes: A1B = greenhouse gas emissions scenario that assumes fast economic growth, a population that peaks midcentury, and the development of new and efficient technologies, along with a balanced use of energy sources; CSIRO = climate model developed at the Australia Commonwealth Scientific and Industrial Research Organisation; DSSAT = Decision Support Software for Agrotechnology Transfer.

FIGURE 1.19   Changes in yields (percent), 2000–2050, from the DSSAT crop model, rice
(rainfed), MIROC A1B

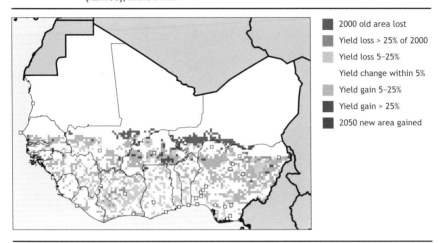

Source: Authors' estimates.

Notes: A1B = greenhouse gas emissions scenario that assumes fast economic growth, a population that peaks midcentury, and the development of new and efficient technologies, along with a balanced use of energy sources; DSSAT = Decision Support Software for Agrotechnology Transfer; MIROC = Model for Interdisciplinary Research on Climate, developed at the University of Tokyo Center for Climate System Research.

FIGURE 1.20   Changes in yields, 2000–2050, from the DSSAT crop model, groundnuts
(rainfed), CSIRO A1B

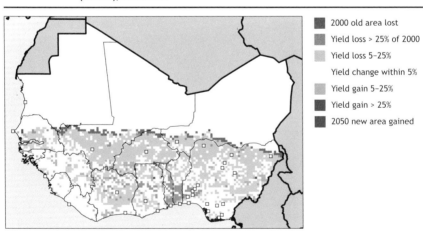

Source: Authors' estimates.

Notes: A1B = greenhouse gas emissions scenario that assumes fast economic growth, a population that peaks midcentury, and the development of new and efficient technologies, along with a balanced use of energy sources; CSIRO = climate model developed at the Australia Commonwealth Scientific and Industrial Research Organisation; DSSAT = Decision Support Software for Agrotechnology Transfer.

FIGURE 1.21 Changes in yields, 2000–2050, from the DSSAT crop model, groundnuts (rainfed), MIROC A1B

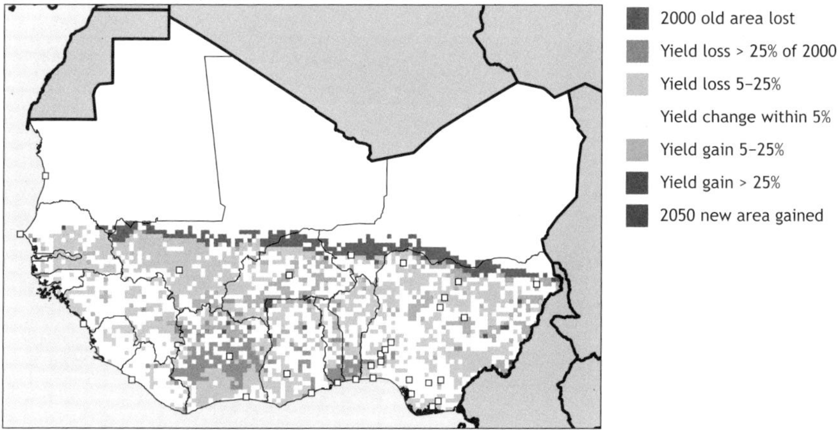

2000 old area lost
Yield loss > 25% of 2000
Yield loss 5–25%
Yield change within 5%
Yield gain 5–25%
Yield gain > 25%
2050 new area gained

Source: Authors' estimates.
Notes: A1B = greenhouse gas emissions scenario that assumes fast economic growth, a population that peaks midcentury, and the development of new and efficient technologies, along with a balanced use of energy sources; DSSAT = Decision Support Software for Agrotechnology Transfer; MIROC = Model for Interdisciplinary Research on Climate, developed at the University of Tokyo Center for Climate System Research.

CSIRO model (Figure 1.20). Both models also have an increase in rice yield in the Sahelian belt, while baseline area will be lost in Mali and Niger.

Both the CSIRO A1B and the MIROC A1B results show a decline in rainfed groundnut yield across West Africa, but the impact will be relatively less in the Mano River Union countries of Guinea, Liberia, and Sierra Leone (see Figures 1.20 and 1.21). However, both models show certain areas of the northern parts of Côte d'Ivoire, Ghana, Burkina Faso, and Nigeria with an increase in yield of 5–25 percent. In this regard, the MIROC model is more positive than the CSIRO, though more area is lost in the MIROC model, so in that sense it is less positive.

In general, both climate models (CSIRO and MIROC) indicate declining rains along the coasts of Nigeria, Togo, Benin, Ghana, and Côte d'Ivoire, while there is either increased rainfall (MIROC) or slight dryness or wetness in the Sahel (CSIRO). This outcome seems to be related to the relatively higher prevalence of yield gain for both rice and maize in the Sahel compared to the more pronounced yield loss in the coastal areas. The increase in wetness in the Sahel may suggest an unfavorable condition for drought-tolerant and -adapted sorghum, with yield loss under increasingly wet conditions. This scenario suggests that farmers could face various predicaments and the need to adapt to conditions they are not used to.

TABLE 1.9 Global commodity prices, 2010 and 2050 (2000 US$ per metric ton)

		2050					
		Pessimistic		Baseline		Optimistic	
Crop	Model price, 2010	Min	Max	Min	Max	Min	Max
Maize	111	209	265	216	272	200	253
Millet	341	305	327	291	307	267	283
Rice	239	433	441	378	388	323	328
Sorghum	145	184	193	184	193	175	184
Wheat	146	218	252	222	254	206	236

Source: Based on analysis conducted for Nelson et al. (2010).

Notes: The minimum (min) and maximum (max) price increases arise from the differences in the climate model effects on yields. US$ = US dollars.

TABLE 1.10 Maize changes in West Africa under the baseline scenario, 2010 and 2050

				2050					
		2010		Yield (MT/ha)		Area (thousands of ha)		Production (MT)	
Country	Yield (MT/ha)	Area (thousands of ha)	Production (MT)	Min	Max	Min	Max	Min	Max
Benin	1.08	748	810	1.87	2.08	886	929	1,660	1,911
Burkina Faso	1.41	458	646	2.20	2.61	408	424	900	1,105
Côte d'Ivoire	1.11	745	824	1.98	2.09	787	825	1,601	1,661
Gambia	1.93	16	31	2.55	2.73	17	18	43	48
Ghana	1.52	825	1,255	2.44	2.59	945	990	2,311	2,538
Guinea	1.15	138	159	2.14	2.29	161	168	344	386
Guinea-Bissau	1.90	16	31	2.03	2.15	18	19	37	41
Mali	1.39	381	531	2.31	2.61	304	313	703	803
Niger	0.78	4	3	1.57	1.69	1	2	2	3
Nigeria	1.29	4,696	6,070	1.74	1.90	4,405	4,829	7,664	9,181
Senegal	1.98	132	263	2.76	2.90	144	151	398	439
Sierra Leone	1.92	10	20	2.98	3.10	10	11	30	33
Togo	1.11	477	531	1.78	2.01	318	334	567	661

Source: Based on analysis conducted for Nelson et al. (2010).

Notes: The minimum (min) and maximum (max) price increases arise from the differences in the climate model effects on yields. ha = hectares; MT = metric tons.

Regional Agricultural Outcomes

Scenarios reflecting the prices of major foodcrops are presented in Table 1.9. World market prices for maize, rice, sorghum, and wheat are predicted to increase in all scenarios, while the price of millet will be less in 2050 than in 2010. In 2050, prices for millet, rice, sorghum, and wheat will be higher in the pessimistic scenario than in the optimistic scenario as the higher populations of the pessimistic scenario combine with lower income to increase demand for these crops.

The production of maize (Table 1.10), millet (Table 1.11), and sorghum (Table 1.12) is predicted to increase in West Africa by 2050. The area under cultivation of both millet and sorghum will increase, while the area under cultivation of maize will decrease. The productivity of all three crops is assumed to increase due to increased use of inputs under improved management practices and assuming the availability of improved varieties. It is, however,

TABLE 1.11   Millet changes in West Africa under the baseline scenario, 2010 and 2050

				2050					
	2010			Yield (MT/ha)		Area (thousands of ha)		Production (MT)	
Country	Yield (MT/ha)	Area (thousands of ha)	Production (MT)	Min	Max	Min	Max	Min	Max
Benin	0.75	48	36	2.21	2.35	80	85	180	198
Burkina Faso	0.83	1,369	1,142	2.34	2.62	1,669	1,760	3,992	4,539
Côte d'Ivoire	0.55	95	52	1.65	1.75	143	152	237	267
Gambia	1.29	102	132	2.85	2.92	156	166	447	485
Ghana	0.78	211	166	1.68	1.74	333	354	562	616
Guinea	0.77	19	14	2.45	2.54	16	17	40	44
Guinea-Bissau	1.49	31	46	2.77	2.93	48	52	134	151
Mali	0.67	1,726	1,149	2.17	2.54	2,067	2,204	4,641	5,408
Niger	0.46	5,964	2,737	1.23	1.51	6,190	7,915	9,188	10,570
Nigeria	1.31	5,555	7,299	3.12	3.23	5,580	5,895	17,727	19,010
Senegal	0.51	831	425	1.39	1.42	1,267	1,358	1,758	1,922
Sierra Leone	1.14	8	9	2.52	2.61	8	8	20	22
Togo	0.81	62	51	1.82	1.93	78	83	145	160

Source: Based on analysis conducted for Nelson et al. (2010).

Notes: The minimum (min) and maximum (max) price increases arise from the differences in the climate model effects on yields. ha = hectares; MT = metric tons.

TABLE 1.12   Sorghum changes in West Africa under the baseline scenario, 2010 and 2050

Country	2010 Yield (MT/ha)	2010 Area (thousands of ha)	2010 Production (MT)	2050 Yield (MT/ha) Min	2050 Yield (MT/ha) Max	2050 Area (thousands of ha) Min	2050 Area (thousands of ha) Max	2050 Production (MT) Min	2050 Production (MT) Max
Benin	0.90	211	190	1.96	2.06	375	385	739	787
Burkina Faso	1.02	1,594	1,632	1.86	2.08	1,952	1,981	3,638	4,109
Côte d'Ivoire	0.62	107	67	1.25	1.29	167	171	210	219
Gambia	1.64	25	41	3.51	3.59	41	42	144	151
Ghana	0.95	369	352	2.04	2.09	631	647	1,290	1,342
Guinea	0.63	10	6	1.40	1.43	8	8	11	12
Guinea-Bissau	0.99	27	27	1.97	2.05	45	46	89	93
Mali	0.86	983	846	2.70	3.03	1,142	1,176	3,142	3,517
Niger	0.46	2,329	1,075	1.19	1.42	2,724	3,360	3,847	4,241
Nigeria	1.15	8,412	9,675	2.04	2.13	9,947	10,145	20,336	21,617
Senegal	0.79	188	149	1.74	1.77	315	323	550	571
Sierra Leone	1.91	10	20	2.83	2.88	14	14	39	41
Togo	1.16	236	274	2.32	2.45	321	329	747	803

Source: Based on analysis conducted for Nelson et al. (2010).

Notes: The minimum (min) and maximum (max) price increases arise from the differences in the climate model effects on yields. ha = hectares; MT = metric tons.

important to note that despite the projected increases in yields of these crops, the maximum yields are far lower than the potential for these crops and even lower than the yields currently obtained in developed countries. For example, although developed countries now typically get over 5 tons per hectare, the highest projected yield for maize is only 3.10 tons per hectare (in Sierra Leone), whereas the highest yields for millet (Nigeria) and for sorghum (Gambia) are below 4 tons per hectare. Against the possible limitations of climate, the low use of fertilizers could partly account for the low productivity of these crops. Compared with a current total world consumption of fertilizers of approximately 150 million tons and an application rate of 100 kilograms per hectare of arable land, Africa south of the Sahara (SSA) is stranded at 6 kilograms per hectare. The projected annual growth rate in SSA before 2030 is a dismal 1.9 percent per year (FAO 2003). This situation calls for a holistic strategy including the development of appropriate production technologies as

TABLE 1.13 Number of malnourished children in West Africa, 2010 and 2050 (thousands)

Country	2010	Pessimistic		Baseline		Optimistic	
		Min	Max	Min	Max	Min	Max
Benin	423	741	794	520	554	375	404
Burkina Faso	1,047	1,439	1,462	1,159	1,180	866	887
Côte d'Ivoire	740	851	904	500	541	222	254
Gambia	48	59	60	28	29	6	7
Ghana	836	977	1,057	620	683	365	417
Guinea	420	526	555	312	334	127	145
Guinea-Bissau	102	92	96	65	68	0	2
Liberia	312	365	384	295	310	61	72
Mali	7,817	8,410	8,720	6,325	6,596	4,338	4,587
Nigeria	884	915	946	605	631	313	337
Niger	1,398	2,821	2,846	2,485	2,506	1,757	1,776
Senegal	449	388	400	169	178	13	21
Sierra Leone	242	450	462	227	236	108	116
Togo	254	274	296	168	185	80	94

Source: Based on analysis conducted for Nelson et al. (2010).

Notes: Min (minimum) represents the smallest projected number from the simulations based on the CSIRO A1B, CSIRO B1, MIROC A1B, and MIROC B1 climate model/scenario combinations. Max (maximum) represents the largest of the four simulated values. A1B = greenhouse gas emissions scenario that assumes fast economic growth, a population that peaks midcentury, and the development of new and efficient technologies, along with a balanced use of energy sources; B1 = greenhouse gas emissions scenario that assumes a population that peaks midcentury (like the A1B), but with rapid changes toward a service and information economy and the introduction of clean and resource-efficient technologies; CSIRO = climate model developed at the Australia Commonwealth Scientific and Industrial Research Organisation; MIROC = Model for Interdisciplinary Research on Climate, developed at the University of Tokyo Center for Climate System Research.

well as enabling farmers to access vital inputs required for improved productivity and production under climate change conditions.

Vulnerability Outcomes

In the optimistic scenario, the number of malnourished children decreases for all the countries in West Africa except Niger (Table 1.13). In the pessimistic scenario, the number increases in all countries except Guinea-Bissau and Senegal. The results are mixed in the baseline scenario. It is important to keep in mind that although in some cases the absolute number of malnourished children increases, in most cases this still represents a drop in the proportion of children who are malnourished because the populations will increase significantly between now and 2050.

Adaptation and Means of Implementation

The challenges to the agricultural sector and its stakeholders from a changing climate are growing and pose a serious threat to the welfare of people in the region, particularly farmers. Although higher temperatures are likely, the magnitude of the increase is uncertain, and the effects will differ across the region depending on which climate scenario eventually occurs. Precipitation outcomes are even more uncertain. The general consequences of drought and excess availability of water on the physiology and productivity of crops are largely known. However, the effects of changes in climate on the limits of tolerance of existing varieties as well as the possible emergence of diseases and pests will be a real challenge.

Consequently, possible avenues for adaptation must include dealing with drought, floods, high temperatures, waterlogging, new and increasing incidence of plant pests and diseases, a shorter growing season, and associated human health concerns, such as malaria and sleeping sickness in the Sahel due to wetter conditions favorable to mosquitoes and tsetse flies. Selection and breeding of appropriate varieties will be crucial in any adaptation venture. Developing appropriate management practices of such varieties is imperative.

Against the background of the debate on the relative emphasis on adaptation and mitigation, it is worth noting that in many instances the best bets for improved agricultural production and sustainable management of natural resources also have considerable mitigation potential (see Nin-Pratt et al. 2011 for an analysis of the best opportunities for productivity research). The existing traditional farming practices in West Africa, notably shifting cultivation, burning as a means of clearing, inefficient use of paddies, indiscriminate plowing of lands, and so on, offer significant avenues for improvement that will also reduce the production of greenhouse gasses and conserve the natural resource base needed by farmers in the region. The World Bank (2009b) reported that although Africa accounts for only 4 percent of global carbon dioxide emissions, more than 60 percent of its emissions are due to deforestation and land degradation. Therefore, crop intensification, minimum tillage, and agroforestry coupled with designation and maintenance of protected forests will go a long way toward carbon sequestration as well as conserving and improving the natural resource base.

Finance, Technology, and Capacity Building

The majority of farmers in West Africa are resource poor. In addition to biophysical constraints to their farming pursuits, lack of access to funds as well as markets severely limits their ability to break out of the vicious circle of poverty. In view of their scale of production, targeted subsidies coupled with microcredit with practical and reasonable collateral requirements will go a long way toward enabling small-scale farmers to acquire vital inputs required for boosting production. In addition, access to payments for carbon credits will encourage farmers to join hands in the global effort to meet the challenges of climate change.

It is critical that appropriate technologies be available for farmers to effectively undertake adaptation and mitigation measures. There is also a need for appropriate awareness raising to inform mostly illiterate farmers about how to efficiently use technologies as well as to ensure that they are aware of their rights and are able to negotiate for benefits. In this regard, CORAF, with a mandate to coordinate agricultural research in West and Central Africa, has developed a strategic framework to guide climate change research in its mandate region, including West Africa. The strategy identifies priority research areas for climate change adaptation and mitigation and provides for capacity building, knowledge management, and partnerships in the context of an IAR4D (Integrated Agricultural Research for Development) approach. This monograph supports that mandate of CORAF in researching the impact of climate change on agriculture, not only providing important data and analysis but also helping to identify future research issues. It also assists planners and policymakers in the region to identify areas that need to be strengthened and potential positive changes that they might capitalize.

References

Bartholome, E., and A. S. Belward. 2005. "GLC2000: A New Approach to Global Land Cover Mapping from Earth Observation Data." *International Journal of Remote Sensing* 26 (9): 1959–1977.

CIESIN (Center for International Earth Science Information Network, Columbia University), Columbia University, IFPRI (International Food Policy Research Institute), World Bank, and CIAT (Centro Internacional de Agricultura Tropical). 2004. *Global Rural–Urban Mapping Project, Version 1 (GRUMPv1)*. Palisades, NY, US: Socioeconomic Data and Applications Center (SEDAC), Columbia University. http://sedac.ciesin.columbia.edu/gpw.

ECOWAS (Economic Community of West African States). 2008. "Regional Agricultural Policy for West Africa: ECOWAP; Make Agriculture the Lever for Regional Integration." Document produced for the conference Regional Agricultural Policy for West Africa, December 9, in Paris. Abuja, Nigeria. 12 pp.

————. 2012. "ECOWAS in Brief." ECOWAS website. Accessed March 1. www.comm.ecowas.int/sec/index.php?id=about_a&lang=en.

ECOWAS–SWAC/OECD (Economic Community of West African States–Sahel and West Africa Club/Organisation for Economic Co-operation and Development). 2007. *Rural Areas and Agricultural Changes: Atlas on Regional Integration in West Africa.* Land Series. Abuja, Nigeria.

FAO (Food and Agriculture Organization of the United Nations). 2003. *World Agriculture: Towards 2015/2030: An FAO Perspective.* London: Earthscan.

————. 2010. *FAOSTAT Database on Agriculture.* Rome.

Hertel, T. W., and S. D. Rosch. 2010. "Climate Change, Agriculture, and Poverty." *Applied Economic Perspectives and Policy* 32 (3): 355–385. doi:10.1093/aepp/ppq016.

Hijmans, R. J., S. E. Cameron, J. L. Parra, P. G. Jones, and A. Jarvis. 2005. "Very High Resolution Interpolated Climate Surfaces for Global Land Areas." *International Journal of Climatology* 25: 1965–1978. www.worldclim.org/worldclim_IJC.pdf.

Jones, P. G., P. K. Thornton, and J. Heinke. 2009. "Generating Characteristic Daily Weather Data Using Downscaled Climate Model Data from the IPCC's Fourth Assessment." Project report for the International Institute for Land Reclamation and Improvement, Wageningen, the Netherlands. Accessed May 7, 2010. www.ccafs-climate.org/pattern_scaling/.

Lehner, B., and P. Döll. 2004. "Development and Validation of a Global Database of Lakes, Reservoirs, and Wetlands." *Journal of Hydrology* 296 (1–4): 1–22.

Le Treut, H., R. Somerville, U. Cubasch, Y. Ding, C. Mauritzen, A. Mokssit, T. Peterson, and M. Prather. 2007. "Historical Overview of Climate Change." In *Climate Change 2007: The Physical Science Basis; Contribution of Working Group I to the Fourth Assessment Report of the Intergovernmental Panel on Climate Change,* edited by S. Solomon, D. Qin, M. Manning, Z. Chen, M. Marquis, K. B. Averyt, M. Tignor, and H. L. Miller. New York: Cambridge University Press.

Millennium Ecosystem Assessment. 2005. *Ecosystems and Human Well-being: Synthesis.* Washington, DC: Island Press. http://www.maweb.org/en/Global.aspx.

Müller, C. 2011. "Agriculture: Harvesting from Uncertainties." *Nature Climate Change* 1 (5): 253–254. doi:10.1038/nclimate1179.

Nelson, G. C., M. W. Rosegrant, A. Palazzo, I. Gray, C. Ingersoll, R. Robertson, S. Tokgoz, et al. 2010. *Food Security, Farming, and Climate Change to 2050: Scenarios, Results, Policy Options.* Washington, DC: International Food Policy Research Institute.

Neumann, K., P. H. Verburg, E. Stehfest, and C. Müller. 2010. "The Yield Gap of Global Grain Production: A Spatial Analysis." *Agricultural Systems* 103 (5): 316–326. doi:10.1016/j.agsy.2010.02.004.

Nin-Pratt, A., M. Johnson, E. Magalhaes, L. You, X. Diao, and J. Chamberlin. 2011. *Yield Gaps and Potential Agricultural Growth in West and Central Africa.* Washington, DC: International Food Policy Research Institute. doi:10.2499/9780896291829.

Roudier, P., B. Sultan, P. Quirion, and A. Berg. 2011. "The Impact of Future Climate Change on West African Crop Yields: What Does the Recent Literature Say?" *Global Environmental Change* 21 (3): 1073–1083. doi:10.1016/j.gloenvcha.2011.04.007.

Tubiello, F., and C. Rosenzweig. 2008. "Developing Climate Change Impact Metrics for Agriculture." *Integrated Assessment Journal* 8 (1): 165–184.

UNEP and IUCN (United Nations Environment Programme and International Union for the Conservation of Nature). 2009. *World Database on Protected Areas (WDPA): Annual Release.* Accessed 2009. www.wdpa.org/protectedplanet.aspx.

UNPOP (United Nations Department of Economic and Social Affairs–Population Division). 2009. *World Population Prospects: The 2008 Revision.* New York. http://esa.un.org/unpd/wpp/.

Wood, S., G. Hyman, U. Deichmann, E. Barona, R. Tenorio, Z. Guo, et al. 2010. *Sub-national Poverty Maps for the Developing World Using International Poverty Lines: Preliminary Data Release.* Washington, DC: Harvest Choice and International Food Policy Research Institute. http://labs.harvestchoice.org/2010/08/poverty-maps/.

World Bank. 2009a. *World Development Indicators.* Accessed May 2011. http://data.worldbank.org/data-catalog/world-development-indicators.

———. 2009b. *Africa's Development in a Changing Climate.* Washington, DC: International Bank for Reconstruction and Development/World Bank.

———. 2010. *Economics of Adaptation to Climate Change: Synthesis Report.* Washington, DC. http://climatechange.worldbank.org/content/economics-adaptation-climate-change-study-homepage.

You, L., and S. Wood. 2006. "An Entropy Approach to Spatial Disaggregation of Agricultural Production." *Agricultural Systems* 90(1–3): 329–347.

You, L., S. Wood, and U. Wood-Sichra. 2006. "Generating Global Crop Distribution Maps: From Census to Grid." Paper presented at the International Association of Agricultural Economists Conference, Brisbane, Australia, August 11–18.

———. 2009. "Generating Plausible Crop Distribution and Performance Maps for Sub-Saharan Africa Using a Spatially Disaggregated Data Fusion and Optimization Approach." *Agricultural Systems* 99 (2–3): 126–140.

Chapter 2

METHODOLOGY

Gerald C. Nelson, Amanda Palazzo, Daniel Mason-d'Croz, Richard Robertson, and Timothy S. Thomas

M odeling the impacts of climate change on agriculture presents a com-
plex challenge arising from the wide-ranging processes underlying
the working of markets, ecosystems, and human behavior. The ana-
lytical framework used in this monograph integrates modeling components
that range from the macro to the micro to model a range of processes, from
those driven by economics to those that are essentially biological in nature.
This chapter brings together in one place the technical details associated with
models used in this monograph along with other technical information that
is common to most or all of the chapters. Figure 2.1 provides a diagram of the
links among the three models used: the International Food Policy Research
Institute's (IFPRI's) International Model for Policy Analysis of Agricultural
Commodities and Trade (IMPACT) (Rosegrant et al. 2008), a partial equilibrium agriculture model that emphasizes policy simulations; a hydrology
model incorporated into IMPACT; and the Decision Support Software for
Agrotechnology Transfer (DSSAT) crop model suite (Jones et al. 2003),
which is used to estimate yields of crops under varying management systems
and climate change scenarios.

General Circulation Models (GCMs) and Climate Scenarios

GCMs model the physics and chemistry of the atmosphere and its interactions with oceans and the land surface. Several GCMs have been developed
independently around the world. For the Fourth Assessment Report (AR4)
of the Intergovernmental Panel on Climate Change, 23 GCMs made some
model results publicly available. Results from four are used in this monograph.

The GCMs create estimates of precipitation and temperature values
around the globe, often at something close to 2-degree intervals (about

---

This chapter draws heavily on Nelson et al. (2010).

FIGURE 2.1   The International Model for Policy Analysis of Agricultural Commodities and Trade (IMPACT) modeling framework

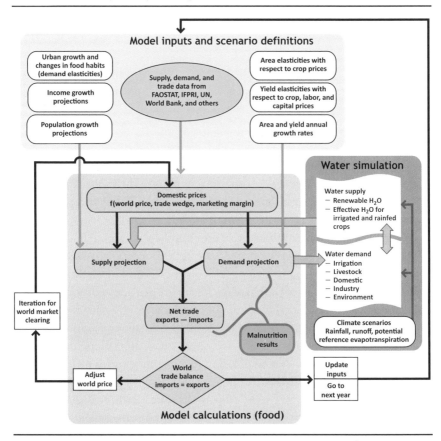

Source: Nelson et al. (2010).

Notes: FAOSTAT = *FAOSTAT Database on Agriculture* (FAO 2010); IFPRI = International Food Policy Research Institute; UN = United Nations.

200 kilometers at the equator) for most models. This is very coarse and may hide important differences on a more local scale. To have finer resolution, it is common to "downscale" the data. Data downscaled by Jones, Thornton, and Heinke (2009) provide precipitation and temperature data at a 5 arc-minute resolution (around 9 kilometers at the equator, less away from it, which is called 10-kilometer resolution in this monograph).

Greenhouse gas emissions alter atmospheric chemistry, ultimately increasing temperatures and altering precipitation patterns. AR4 had three main scenarios of greenhouse gas emissions pathways: B1, A1B, and A2.[1] Scenario B1 was a low-emissions scenario, which by 2011 does not appear realistic. Scenarios A2 and A1B are higher-emission scenarios, with similar trajectories through 2050 but different ones after 2050. Because this monograph is primarily concerned with changes between now and 2050, we elected to focus on scenario A1B when presenting the biophysical effects on crop yields, but we used both B1 and A1B in IMPACT to present a wider range of scenario outcomes.

To illustrate the range of potential effects on crops, we used results from four GCMs, CNRM-CM3, CSIRO Mark 3, ECHAM 5, and MIROC 3.2 medium resolution.[2] For inputs into the IMPACT model, results from only two GCMs were used, the CSIRO Mark 3 and the MIROC 3.2 medium-resolution models. The rationale for doing that can be seen more clearly in Table 2.1, in which we see that the lowest levels of precipitation change and lowest levels of temperature change are given by the CSIRO GCM and the highest levels of precipitation and temperature change are given by the MIROC GCM.

In the country analyses in the other chapters of this monograph, we display two kinds of maps that show spatially differentiated predictions of the GCMs. One shows changes in annual rainfall, and the other shows changes in the mean daily maximum temperature for the warmest month. The changes in the latter are determined by finding the month in 2000 with the highest mean daily maximum temperature and subtracting that mean value from the mean value for the month in 2050 with the highest mean daily maximum temperature.

The Spatial Production Allocation Model (SPAM)

SPAM is a set of raster datasets showing harvest area, production, and yield for 20 crops or aggregates of crops and for three management systems (irrigated, high-input rainfed, and low-input rainfed, with the latter two combined

---

1 B1 is a greenhouse gas emissions scenario that assumes a population that peaks midcentury (like A1B), but with rapid changes toward a service and information economy, and the introduction of clean and resource-efficient technologies. A1B is a greenhouse gas emissions scenario that assumes fast economic growth, a population that peaks midcentury, and the development of new and efficient technologies, along with a balanced use of energy sources. A2 is a greenhouse gas emissions scenario that assumes a very heterogeneous world with continuously increasing global population and regionally oriented economic growth that is more fragmented and slower than in other storylines (Nakicenovic et al. 2000).

2 CNRM-CM3 is National Meteorological Research Center–Climate Model 3. CSIRO Mark 3 is a climate model developed at the Australia Commonwealth Scientific and Industrial Research Organisation. ECHAM 5 is a fifth-generation climate model developed at the Max Planck Institute for Meteorology in Hamburg. MIROC 3.2 is the Model for Interdisciplinary Research on Climate, developed at the University of Tokyo Center for Climate System Research.

TABLE 2.1   GCM and SRES scenario global average changes, 2000–2050

GCM	SRES scenario	Change between 2000 and 2050 in the annual averages			
		Precipitation (percent)	Precipitation (millimeters)	Minimum temperature (°C)	Maximum temperature (°C)
CSIRO	**B1**	**0.0**	**0.1**	**1.2**	**1.0**
CSIRO	**A1B**	**0.7**	**4.8**	**1.6**	**1.4**
CSIRO	A2	0.9	6.5	1.9	1.8
ECHAM 5	B1	1.6	11.6	2.1	1.9
CNRM-CM3	B1	1.9	14.0	1.9	1.7
ECH	A2	2.1	15.0	2.4	2.2
CNR	A2	2.7	19.5	2.5	2.2
ECH	A1B	3.2	23.4	2.7	2.5
MIROC	A2	3.2	23.4	2.8	2.6
CNRM-CM3	A1B	3.3	23.8	2.6	2.3
MIROC	**B1**	**3.6**	**25.7**	**2.4**	**2.3**
MIROC	**A1B**	**4.7**	**33.8**	**3.0**	**2.8**

Source: Nelson et al. (2010).

Note: In this table and elsewhere in the text, a reference to a particular year for a climate realization, such as 2000 or 2050, in fact refers to mean values around that year. For example, the data described as 2000 in this table are representative of the period 1950–2000. The data described as 2050 are representative of the period 2041–2060. GCM scenario combinations in boldface type are the ones used in the climate scenario analysis. A1B = greenhouse gas emissions scenario that assumes fast economic growth, a population that peaks midcentury, and the development of new and efficient technologies, along with a balanced use of energy sources; B1 = greenhouse gas emissions scenario that assumes a population that peaks midcentury (like A1B), but with rapid changes toward a service and information economy, and the introduction of clean and resource-efficient technologies; CNR = climate model developed by the National Meteorological Research Center; CSIRO = climate model developed at the Australia Commonwealth Scientific and Industrial Research Organisation; ECHAM 5 = climate model developed at the Max Planck Institute for Meteorology (Hamburg); GCM = general circulation model; MIROC = Model for Interdisciplinary Research on Climate, developed by the University of Tokyo Center for Climate System Research; SRES = Special Report on Emissions Scenarios, a report by the Intergovernmental Panel on Climate Change that was published in 2000.

in this monograph to produce a rainfed total). The model employs a cross-entropy approach to manage inputs with different levels of likelihood in indicating the specific locations of agricultural production (You and Wood 2006; You, Wood, and Wood-Sichra 2006, 2009).

SPAM spatially allocates crop production from large reporting units (administrative units such as those at the province or district level) to a raster grid at a spatial resolution of 5 arc-minutes. The allocation model works by inferring likely production locations from multiple indicators that, in addition to subnational crop production statistics, also include satellite data on land cover, maps of irrigated areas, biophysical crop suitability assessments, data on population density, and secondary data on irrigation and rainfed production.

In some of the maps presented in this monograph, SPAM areas are reported in units of hectares per raster cell. A 5-arc-minute grid cell is just over

8,500 hectares at the equator, which is a reasonable value to use when gauging how great a proportion of the cell might be used by the crop shown in the map.

SPAM areas are used to provide weights for calculating provincial and national yield changes due to climate change in the regional overview chapter. Cells with greater current levels of that crop are weighted higher when aggregating the crop model results. This was also the approach used for aggregating crop model results to the national level for use in the IMPACT model.

DSSAT

DSSAT is a software package used for modeling crop production (Jones et al. 2003). The software "grows" the crop in daily time increments, and therefore daily weather data are required. With climate models, we have only monthly statistics on the weather. DSSAT, however, overcomes this limitation by including a weather simulator that can convert monthly statistics into simulated daily weather data. In this analysis, the weather is simulated many different times and the outcome averaged over several growing seasons. The result is more of a long-term yield perspective that will not be unduly influenced by any individual stochastic extreme in the simulation.

The soil data used were adapted by John Dimes and Jawoo Koo from the *Harmonized World Soil Database* (Version 1.1) produced by FAO et al. (2009) and described by Batjes et al. (2009). They are simplified to 27 types of soil, each with high, medium, or low levels of soil organic carbon; deep, medium, or shallow rooting depth; and major components of sand, loam, or clay. Some grid cells had more than one soil type represented, and when that was the case, the dominant type was used.

DSSAT has parameters to model different varieties of each crop. For our work, we chose what seemed an appropriate variety and used it in all locations and time periods investigated. DSSAT requires the user to input the planting date of a crop. For rainfed crops, it is assumed that a crop is planted in the first month of a four-month period in which the monthly average maximum temperature does not exceed 37°C (about 99°F), the monthly average minimum temperature does not drop below 5°C (about 41°F), and monthly total precipitation is not less than 60 millimeters. In the tropics, the planting month begins with the rainy season. The particular mechanism for determining the start of the rainy season at any location is to look for the block of four months that gets the most rainfall. The month before that block is called the beginning of the rainy season. For irrigated crops, the first choice is the rainfed planting month.

DSSAT has an option to include CO_2 fertilization effects at different levels of CO_2 atmospheric concentration. For this study, all results use a setting of 369 parts per million, which was the concentration in the early 2000s. A short summary of the reasons for and against including CO_2 fertilization is found in Nelson et al. (2010, 14, text and footnote):

> Plants produce more vegetative matter as atmospheric concentrations of CO_2 increase. The effect depends on the nature of the photosynthetic process used by the plant species. So-called C3 plants use CO_2 less efficiently than C4 plants, so C3 plants are more sensitive to higher concentrations of CO_2. It remains an open question whether these laboratory results translate to actual field conditions. A recent report on field experiments on CO_2 fertilization (Long et al. 2006) finds that the effects in the field are approximately 50 percent less than in experiments in enclosed containers. Another report (Zavala et al. 2008) finds that higher levels of atmospheric CO_2 increase the susceptibility of soybean plants to the Japanese beetle and of maize to the western corn rootworm. Finally, a recent study (Bloom et al. 2010) finds that higher CO_2 concentrations inhibit the assimilation of nitrate into organic nitrogen compounds. So the actual field benefits of CO_2 fertilization remain uncertain.

Some use of nitrogen fertilizer is assumed in all our crop models. For almost all countries in Africa, the level of use is 20 kilograms of nitrogen per hectare (regardless of crop). For Madagascar and parts of South Africa, the level is 100 kilograms of nitrogen per hectare (regardless of crop).

DSSAT is used in two ways in this monograph. It is used directly for each country and for the region to compute changes in yields from the climate of 2000 to the climate of 2050. DSSAT is also used to provide results for each country of the world so that IMPACT can control for climate effects. The global work and the regional work were very similar though not perfectly identical because they were produced by two different teams. One example of the differences is the spatial resolution, which was 15 arc-minutes (30 kilometers) for the global team and 5 arc-minutes (10 kilometers) for the regional team. Some of the crops for West Africa were modeled by the global team, which is why the resolution in the maps varies among crops in some cases.

IMPACT

IMPACT was initially developed at IFPRI to project global food supply, food demand, and food security to the year 2020 and beyond (Rosegrant et al. 2008). It is a partial equilibrium agricultural model with 32 crop and livestock commodities, including cereals, soybeans, roots and tubers, meats, milk, eggs, oilseeds, oilcakes and meals, sugar, and fruits and vegetables. IMPACT has 115 regions, which are usually countries (though in a few cases several countries are aggregated together, with specified supply, demand, and prices for agricultural commodities.

Large regions are further divided into major river basins. The result, portrayed in Figure 2.2, is 281 spatial units called food production units (FPUs). The model links the various countries and regions through international trade using a series of linear and nonlinear equations to approximate the underlying production and demand relationships. World agricultural commodity prices are determined annually at levels that clear international markets. Growth in crop production in each country is determined by crop and input prices, exogenous rates of productivity growth and area expansion, investment in irrigation, and water availability. Demand is a function of prices, income, and population growth. We distinguish four categories of commodity demand: food, feed, biofuels feedstock, and other uses.

FIGURE 2.2   International Model for Policy Analysis of Agricultural Commodities and Trade (IMPACT) unit of analysis, the food production unit (FPU)

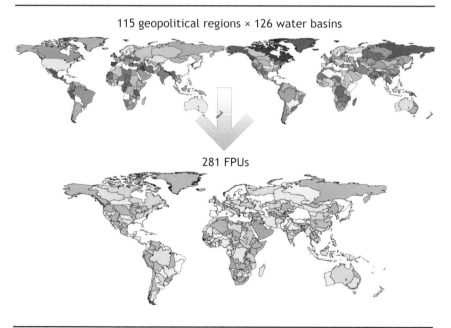

115 geopolitical regions × 126 water basins

281 FPUs

Source: Nelson et al. (2010).

From DSSAT to IMPACT

For input into the IMPACT model, DSSAT is run for five crops—rice, wheat, maize, soybeans, and groundnuts—at 15-arc-minute intervals for the locations where the SPAM dataset shows that each crop is currently grown. The results from this analysis are then aggregated to the IMPACT FPU level.

In extending these results to other crops in IMPACT, the primary assumption is that plants with the same photosynthetic metabolic pathway will react similarly to any given climate change effect in a particular geographic region. Millet, sorghum, sugarcane, and maize all use the C4 pathway. Millet and sugarcane are assumed to have the same productivity effects from climate change as maize in the same geographic regions. Sorghum effects for the Africa region were modeled explicitly, but for the rest of the world the maize productivity effects were assumed to apply to sorghum as well. The remainder of the crops use the C3 pathway. The climate effects for the C3 crops not directly modeled in DSSAT follow the average for wheat, rice, soy, and groundnuts from the same geographic region, with the following two exceptions. The IMPACT commodities of "other grains" and dryland legumes are directly mapped to the DSSAT results for wheat and groundnuts, respectively.

Income and Population Drivers

Differences in gross domestic product (GDP) and population growth define the overall scenarios, with all other driver values remaining the same across the three scenarios. Table 2.2 documents the GDP and population growth choices for the three overall scenarios.

TABLE 2.2   Gross domestic product (GDP) and population choices for the three overall scenarios

Category	Pessimistic	Baseline	Optimistic
GDP (constant 2000 US$)	Lowest of the four GDP growth rate scenarios from the Millennium Ecosystem Assessment GDP scenarios (Millennium Ecosystem Assessment 2005) and the rate used in the baseline (next column)	Based on rates from a World Bank Economics of Adaptation to Climate Change study (World Bank 2010), updated for Africa south of the Sahara and South Asian countries	Highest of the four GDP growth rates from the Millennium Ecosystem Assessment GDP scenarios (Millennium Ecosystem Assessment 2005) and the rate used in the baseline (previous column)
Population	UN high variant, 2008 revision	UN medium variant, 2008 revision	UN low variant, 2008 revision

Source: Nelson et al. (2010).

Notes: UN = United Nations; US$ = US dollars.

TABLE 2.3   Global average scenario per capita gross domestic product growth rate, 1990–2000 and 2010–50 (percent per year)

Category	1900–2000	2010–50		
		Pessimistic	Baseline	Optimistic
Developed countries	2.7	0.74	2.17	2.56
Developing countries	3.9	2.09	3.86	5.00
Low-income developing countries	4.7	2.60	3.60	4.94
Middle-income developing countries	3.8	2.21	4.01	5.11
World	2.9	0.86	2.49	3.22

Source: *World Development Indicators* for 1990–2000 (World Bank 2009) and Nelson et al. (2010) calculations for 2010–50.

The GDP and population growth rates combine to generate the three scenarios of per capita GDP growth. The growth rates in GDP per capita are shown in Table 2.3. The baseline scenario has just over 9 billion people in 2050; the optimistic scenario results in a substantially smaller number, 7.9 billion; the pessimistic scenario results in 10.4 billion people. For developed countries, the differences among the three scenarios are relatively small, with little overall population growth: population ranges from just over 1 billion to 1.3 billion in 2050, compared to 1 billion in 2010. For the developing countries as a group, the total 2010 population of 5.8 billion becomes 6.9–9 billion in 2050, depending on scenario.

As Table 2.4 shows, average world per capita income, beginning at $6,600 in 2010, ranges from $8,800 to $23,800 in 2050, depending on scenario.[3] The gap between average per capita income in developed and developing countries is large in 2010: developing countries' per capita income is only 5.6 percent of that in developed countries. Regardless of scenario, the relative difference is reduced over time: the developing-country income increases to between 8.6 percent and 14.0 percent of developed-country income in 2050, depending on overall scenario. Middle- and low-income developing countries' 2010 per capita income values are 6.5 percent and 2.6 percent, respectively, of the developed-country income. By 2050 the share increases to between 10.4 percent and 16.8 percent for middle-income developing countries, depending on overall scenario. For the low-income developing countries, however, the 2050 ratios remain low—between 2.5 percent and 4.8 percent.

The reader should be somewhat cautious in interpreting the results based on the three different scenarios. The optimistic scenario is optimistic not just

---

3 All references to dollars are to constant 2000 US dollars.

TABLE 2.4   Summary statistics for population and per capita gross domestic product, 2010 and 2050

Category	2010	2050 Optimistic	2050 Baseline	2050 Pessimistic
Population (millions)				
World	6,870	7,913	9,096	10,399
Developed countries	1,022	1,035	1,169	1,315
Developing countries	5,848	6,877	7,927	9,083
Middle-income developing countries	4,869	5,283	6,103	7,009
Low-income developing countries	980	1,594	1,825	2,074
East Africa	361.1	879.4	777.1	681.6
Southern Africa	141.7	276.2	240.2	207.0
West Africa	300.5	697.0	618.5	545.0
Income per capita (2000 US$)				
World	6,629	23,760	17,723	8,779
Developed countries	33,700	93,975	79,427	43,531
Developing countries	1,897	13,190	8,624	3,747
Middle-income developing countries	2,194	15,821	10,577	4,531
Low-income developing countries	420	4,474	2,094	1,101
East Africa	204	565	1,161	1,778
Southern Africa	1,961	2,725	5,892	11,499
West Africa	363	816	1,695	3,185

Source: Nelson et al. (2010).

Notes: 2010 income per capita is for the baseline scenario. US$ = US dollars.

for one country but for the entire world. This means that we cannot look at the impact from assuming that a single country is able to reduce its population growth rate or increase its GDP while the rest of the world continues at the same GDP and population growth rate. Rather, we have only the case in which all countries have a higher GDP and lower population growth rate as well. This means that changing scenarios changes supply and demand for the whole world, not just for one country.

Metrics for Human Well-being

Physical human well-being has many determinants. Calorie availability is a key element in low-income countries, where malnutrition and poverty are serious problems. Distribution, access, and supporting resources can enhance or reduce an individual's calorie availability. Similarly, child malnutrition has many determinants, including calorie intake (Rosegrant et al. 2008). The

TABLE 2.5 Noncaloric determinants of global child malnutrition, 2010 and 2050

Country category	Clean water access (percent)[a]		Female schooling (percent)[b]		Female relative life expectancy[c]	
	2010	2050	2010	2050	2010	2050
Middle-income countries	86.8	98.4	71.6	81.7	1.066	1.060
Low-income countries	69.0	85.8	54.9	61.6	1.044	1.048

Source: Population-weighted aggregations in Nelson et al. (2010) based on data from 2000 with expert extrapolations to 2050. Original data sources include the World Health Organization's Global Database on Child Growth Malnutrition (http://www.who.int/ nutgrowthdb/database/en/); the United Nations Administrative Committee on Coordination–Subcommittee on Nutrition; the World Bank's *World Development Indicators* (World Bank 2009); *FAOSTAT* (FAO 2010); and the United Nations Educational, Scientific and Cultural Organization *UNESCOSTAT* database. Aggregations are weighted by population shares and are based on the baseline population growth scenario.
[a] Share of population with access to safe water.
[b] Total female enrollment in secondary education (any age group) as a percentage of the female age group corresponding to national regulations for secondary education.
[c] Ratio of female to male life expectancy at birth.

relationship used to estimate the number of malnourished children is based on a cross-country regression relationship estimated by Smith and Haddad (2000) that takes into account female access to secondary education, the quality of maternal and child care, and health and sanitation.[4] The IMPACT model provides data on per capita calorie availability by country; the other determinants are assumed to remain the same across the overall scenarios. Table 2.5 shows the 2010 and 2050 values for the noncaloric determinants of child malnutrition, aggregated to low- and middle-income countries. The small decline in female relative life expectancy in 2050 for the middle-income countries is primarily caused by a decline in China, where it is expected that male life expectancy will gradually move up rather than female life expectancy moving down.

Agricultural Vulnerability to Climate Change

There are many dimensions of agricultural vulnerability to climate change: vulnerability of agricultural systems, communities, households, and individuals to climate change. Vulnerability is influenced by the degree of exposure and

---

4 Because it is a partial equilibrium model, IMPACT has no feedback mechanisms from climate change effects on productivity to income. This means that it cannot estimate directly the poverty effects of agricultural productivity declines from climate change. However, the reduced form function that relates child malnutrition to calorie availability and other determinants implicitly includes the effects of real income change on child malnutrition. Hertel, Burke, and Lobell (2010) use a general equilibrium model to estimate explicitly the effects of climate change on poverty. They find that the poverty impacts to 2030 "depend as much on where impoverished households earn their income as on the agricultural impacts themselves, with poverty rates in some non-agricultural household groups rising by 20–50 percent in parts of Africa and Asia under these price changes, and falling by equal amounts for agriculture-specialized households elsewhere in Asia and Latin America" (577).

sensitivity to that exposure. Household-level vulnerability is most often associated with threats to livelihoods. Livelihoods can be inadequate because of resource constraints and low productivity (e.g., farmers with too little land and no access to fertilizer) or because farmers operate in a risky environment (e.g., droughts that cause harvest failure).

Potential impacts of climate change on vulnerability to food insecurity include both direct nutritional effects (changes in consumption quantities and composition) and livelihood effects (changes in employment opportunities and the cost of acquiring adequate nutrition). Climate change can affect each of these dimensions. This monograph focuses on the productivity effects of climate change that translate into changes in calorie availability and to effects on child malnutrition. At this point the methodology and data to provide quantitative estimates of livelihood vulnerability are not available.

In some countries, calorie availability declined even though incomes were rising faster than food prices. This occurred almost exclusively in the pessimistic scenario that assumed low growth or declines in GDP per capita and high population growth. This outcome was driven by declining consumption of the key staple foods, which in turn was driven by high own-price elasticities in conjunction with low income elasticities for these staples.

Table 2.6 shows mean kilocalorie consumption per person per day from the IMPACT model for the year 2000, which is based on data from the FAO databases. We focused on the four leading sources of calories and the two leading meats. Rice and cassava were almost tied, closely followed by millet and sorghum, which were also nearly tied.

TABLE 2.6   Mean calorie consumption in West Africa, 2000

Food	Kilocalories per person per day
Beef	14
Poultry	6
Rice	316
Cassava	304
Millet	273
Sorghum	272
All foods	2,464

Source: Authors' calculations based on data from FAOSTAT.

TABLE 2.7   Mean price elasticities used for West African countries in IMPACT, 2010 and 2050

Food	2010		2050	
	Income	Own price	Income	Own price
Beef	1.038	−0.898	0.942	−0.849
Poultry	0.888	−0.605	0.795	−0.562
Rice	0.537	−0.889	0.471	−0.853
Cassava	0.191	−0.674	−0.006	−0.577
Millet	0.354	−0.584	0.079	−0.438
Sorghum	0.372	−0.577	0.100	−0.428

Source: Authors' calculations.

Notes: The numbers are weighted averages based on national consumption of each food item in 2000. IMPACT = International Model for Policy Analysis of Agricultural Commodities and Trade.

Table 2.7 shows the elasticities used in IMPACT. We note that by 2050, the income elasticity for cassava will actually be negative, and those for sorghum and millet will be very small. Own-price elasticities will generally be large in magnitude, especially for rice.

The IMPACT model is being improved continuously, and a comprehensive review of all income and price elasticities is part of the activities that will take place. The reader should assess carefully the mean calorie availability results for the pessimistic scenario presented in graphs in the chapters. A good rule of thumb is to compare changes in prices of key staples with changes in GDP per capita. If the latter are larger or are of comparable size to the price changes, one can conclude that mean calorie availability is projected to rise.

Travel Time Maps

We developed databases that show simulated travel time to towns and cities of various sizes. The analysis begins with information on how long it would take someone to travel through a small region, roughly 10 kilometers on a side. This information is developed by overlaying various spatial datasets, including ones for roads, rivers and other water bodies, urban areas, and international boundaries. Each feature has a particular speed associated with it, and there is a default speed for areas without detailed information.

Once the time to travel across the regions is developed, the only other data required are the locations of the towns and cities of interest. We used cities and towns from two sources: CIESIN et al. (2004) and the *World Gazetteer Database* (Helders 2005). ArcView 3.2 was used to calculate the shortest travel time to any point in the specified cities and towns dataset.

Box-and-Whisker Graphs

A box-and-whisker graph summarizes a variety of information for a variable in a relatively straightforward diagram. A sample box-and-whisker graph is shown in Figure 2.3. The horizontal lines at the top and bottom of the diagram are the "whiskers" and show the minimum and maximum values of the variable. The top and bottom edges of the rectangle, the "box," show the 75th and 25th percentiles, respectively, of the variable under consideration. The horizontal divider line inside the box represents the median value of the data.

These graphs were generated using Stata (StataCorp 2009) with Tukey's (1977) formula for setting the upper and lower whisker values, which Stata calls "adjacent values."

Now that we have given a general overview of the models and some of the data reviewed in this monograph, we are ready to see the results of the models applied to each of the countries studied in the chapters that follow.

FIGURE 2.3   Sample box-and-whisker graph

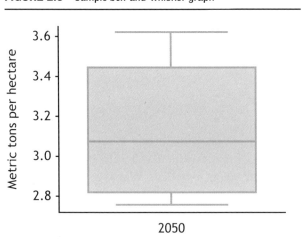

Sources: Authors, using StataCorp (2009) and Tukey (1977).

References

Batjes, N., K. Dijkshoorn, V. van Engelen, G. Fischer, A. Jones, L. Montanarella, M. Petri, et al. 2009. *Harmonized World Soil Database*. Laxenburg, Austria: International Institute for Applied Systems Analysis (IIASA).

Bloom, A. J., M. Burger, R. Assensio, J. Salvador, and A. B. Cousins. 2010. "Carbon Dioxide Enrichment Inhibits Nitrate Assimilation in Wheat and Arabidopsis." *Science* 328: 899–902.

CIESIN (Center for International Earth Science Information Network, Columbia University), Columbia University, IFPRI (International Food Policy Research Institute), World Bank, and CIAT (Centro Internacional de Agricultura Tropical). 2004. *Global Rural–Urban Mapping Project, Version 1 (GRUMPv1)*. Palisades, NY, US: Socioeconomic Data and Applications Center (SEDAC), Columbia University. http://sedac.ciesin.columbia.edu/gpw.

FAO (Food and Agriculture Organization of the United Nations). 2010. *FAOSTAT Database on Agriculture*. Rome.

FAO, IIASA (International Institute for Applied Systems Analysis), ISRIC (World Data Center for Soils), ISS-CAS (Institute of Soil Science–Chinese Academy of Sciences), JRC (Joint Research Centre). 2009. *Harmonized World Soil Database* (Version 1.1). Rome and Laxenburg, Austria: FAO and IIASA.

Helders, S. 2005. *World Gazetteer Database*. Accessed June 7, 2007. http://world-gazetteer.com/.

Hertel, T. M., M. B. Burke, and D. B. Lobell. 2010. "The Poverty Implications of Climate-Induced Crop Yield Changes by 2030." *Global Environmental Change* 20 (4): 577–585.

Jones, J. W., G. Hoogenboom, C. H. Porter, K. J. Boote, W. D. Batchelor, L. A. Hunt, P. W. Wilkens, et al. 2003. "The DSSAT Cropping System Model." *European Journal of Agronomy* 18 (3–4): 235–265.

Jones, P. G., P. K. Thornton, and J. Heinke. 2009. "Generating Characteristic Daily Weather Data Using Downscaled Climate Model Data from the IPCC's Fourth Assessment." Project report for the International Institute for Land Reclamation and Improvement, Wageningen, the Netherlands. Accessed May 7, 2010. www.ccafs-climate.org/pattern_scaling/.

Long, S. P., E. A. Ainsworth, A.D.B. Leakey, J. Nosberger, and D. R. Ort. 2006. "Food for Thought: Lower-than-Expected Crop Yield Stimulation with Rising CO_2 Concentrations." *Science* 312 (5782): 1918–1921. doi:10.1126/science.1114722.

Millennium Ecosystem Assessment. 2005. *Ecosystems and Human Well-being: Synthesis*. Washington, DC: Island Press. http://www.maweb.org/en/Global.aspx.

Nakicenovic, N., et al. (2000). *Special Report on Emissions Scenarios: A Special Report of Working Group III of the Intergovernmental Panel on Climate Change*. Cambridge: Cambridge University Press. http://www.grida.no/climate/ipcc/emission/index.htm.

Nelson, G. C., M. W. Rosegrant, A. Palazzo, I. Gray, C. Ingersoll, R. Robertson, S. Tokgoz, et al. 2010. *Food Security, Farming, and Climate Change to 2050: Scenarios, Results, Policy Options.* Washington, DC: International Food Policy Research Institute.

Rosegrant, M. W., S. Msangi, C. Ringler, T. B. Sulser, T. Zhu, and S. A. Cline. 2008. *International Model for Policy Analysis of Agricultural Commodities and Trade (IMPACT): Model Description.* Washington, DC: International Food Policy Research Institute. www.ifpri.org/themes/impact/impactwater.pdf.

Smith, L., and L. Haddad. 2000. *Explaining Child Malnutrition in Developing Countries: A Cross-Country Analysis.* Washington, DC: International Food Policy Research Institute.

StataCorp. 2009. Stata: Release 11. Statistical Software. College Station, TX, US.

Tukey, J. W. 1977. *Exploratory Data Analysis.* Reading, MA, US: Addison-Wesley.

World Bank. 2009. *World Development Indicators.* Accessed May 2011. http://data.worldbank.org/data-catalog/world-development-indicators.

———. 2010. *Economics of Adaptation to Climate Change: Synthesis Report.* Washington: World Bank. http://climatechange.worldbank.org/content/economics-adaptation-climate-change-study-homepage.

You, L., and S. Wood. 2006. "An Entropy Approach to Spatial Disaggregation of Agricultural Production." *Agricultural Systems* 90 (1–3): 329–347.

You, L., S. Wood, and U. Wood-Sichra. 2006. "Generating Global Crop Distribution Maps: From Census to Grid." Paper presented at the International Association of Agricultural Economists Conference, Brisbane, Australia, August 11–18.

———. 2009. "Generating Plausible Crop Distribution and Performance Maps for Sub-Saharan Africa Using a Spatially Disaggregated Data Fusion and Optimization Approach." *Agricultural Systems* 99 (2–3): 126–140.

Zavala, J. A., C. L. Casteel, E. H. DeLucia, and M. R. Berenbaum. 2008. "Anthropogenic Increase in Carbon Dioxide Compromises Plant Defense against Invasive Insects." *Proceedings of the National Academy of Sciences, USA* 105 (13): 5129–5133. doi:10.1073/pnas.0800568105.

Chapter 3

BENIN

Agnidé Emmanuel Lawin, P. B. Irénikatché Akponikpè, Abdulai Jalloh,
Gerald C. Nelson, and Timothy S. Thomas

Benin covers a land area of 114,763 square kilometers and occupies a long stretch of land perpendicular to the coast of the Gulf of Guinea in West Africa. It is bordered on the north by Burkina Faso and the Republic of Niger, on the east by the Federal Republic of Nigeria, and on the west by the Republic of Togo. With a 124-kilometer coastline, it stretches north to south some 672 kilometers and east to west 324 kilometers at its widest point. Most of the country experiences transitional tropical conditions, with less rainfall than in other areas at the same latitude—a climate known as the Benin variant, marked by a dry season from November to early April and a rainy season from mid-April to October.

Climate change, as a worldwide concern, implies generally warmer temperatures as well as changes in precipitation patterns, with more extreme weather events and shifting seasons. Agriculture is especially vulnerable, and climate change will thus disproportionately affect the poor, who depend on agriculture for their livelihoods and who have a lower capacity to adapt. The population of Benin is projected to at least double (to 18 million) or possibly more than triple (to 25 million) by 2050, with increasingly densely populated urban areas. The share of agriculture in gross domestic product (GDP) is expected to stagnate or increase, indicating that nonagricultural sectors of the economy will be stagnant at best. This chapter assesses the vulnerability of the agricultural sector of Benin to climate change to provide the basis for designing informed policies to meet those challenges. The study focuses on Benin's main foodcrops: yams, cassava, maize, and other roots and tubers.

The climate models show different outcomes for precipitation levels in Benin in 2050. CNRM-CM3 and ECHAM 5 show increased precipitation, while the two other models (CSIRO Mark 3 and MIROC 3.2) show areas of precipitation decrease, mainly in the south.[1] All four general circulation models (GCMs) show an increase in the normal annual maximum temperature for the whole country, ranging from slight (1°–1.5°C for MIROC 3.2) to substantial (2.5°–3.0°C for ECHAM 5). These changes in climate affect crop production simulations in varying ways. For instance, for a given GCM the modeled spatial changes in maize production generally track changes in precipitation.

The purpose of this chapter is to help policymakers and researchers better understand and anticipate the likely impacts of climate change on agriculture, as well as on vulnerable households in Benin. The study on which it is based reviewed current data on agriculture and economic development and modeled the effects of anticipated changes in climate between now and 2050 using crop models to assess the impact of climate changes on agricultural production. The study further modeled future supply and demand for food to show trends in food prices and trade. Policy options are presented for reducing the impacts of climate change on agriculture in Benin.

Review of the Current Situation

Population

Figure 3.1 shows trends in the size of the total population and the rural population (left axis), along with the share of the urban population (right axis). According to the third census of Benin (Benin, INSAE 2003), the country's total population was 6.8 million in 2003. From about 27 percent in 1980, the share of urban population rose to 40 percent in 2008 (see Figure 3.1). The rural sector, though declining in percentage of population, will continue to play an important role in providing the agricultural workforce as well as in creating potential demand for goods and services. Benin's population growth rate increased from 1.9 during 1960–69 to 3.3 during 1990–99 (Table 3.1).

Figure 3.2 shows the geographic distribution of Benin's population as of 2000. The population is unevenly distributed between the southern and northern regions and between rural and urban areas. The share of the population per region decreases going from the south (51.5 percent) to the north (31.7 percent). Most of the population is concentrated in the southern region, between latitudes 6.35°N and 7.18°N.

---

1   CNRM-CM3 is National Meteorological Research Center–Climate Model 3. ECHAM 5 is a fifth-generation climate model developed at the Max Planck Institute for Meteorology in Hamburg. CSIRO Mark 3 is a climate model developed at the Australia Commonwealth Scientific and Industrial Research Organisation. MIROC 3.2 is the Model for Interdisciplinary Research on Climate, developed at the University of Tokyo Center for Climate System Research.

FIGURE 3.1 Population trends in Benin: Total population, rural population, and percent urban, 1960–2008

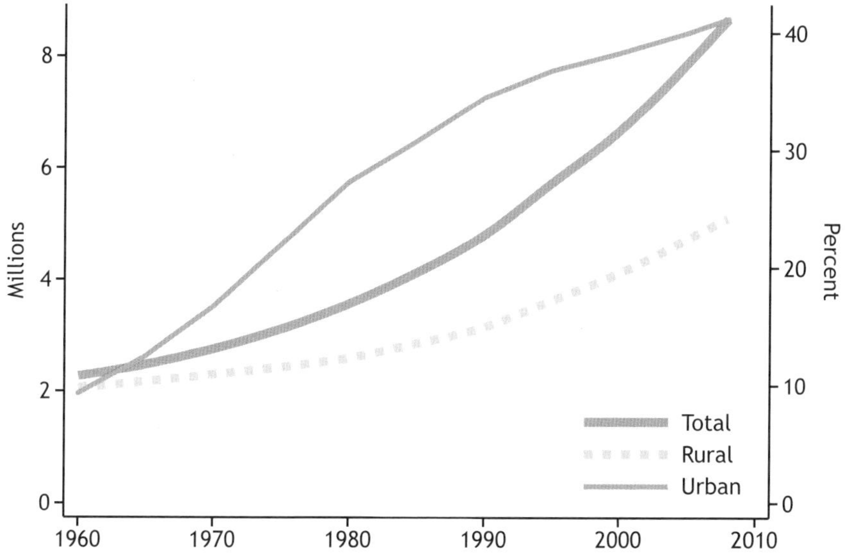

Source: World Development Indicators (World Bank 2009).

TABLE 3.1 Population growth rates in Benin, 1960–2008 (percent)

Decade	Total growth rate	Rural growth rate	Urban growth rate
1960–69	1.9	1.1	7.8
1970–79	2.5	1.2	7.5
1980–89	2.9	1.9	5.3
1990–99	3.3	2.7	4.4
2000–2008	3.3	2.7	4.2

Source: Authors' calculations based on World Development Indicators (World Bank 2009).

Income

The level of income available to an individual is a widely used indicator of resilience to stresses. Figure 3.3 shows trends in Benin's GDP per capita as well as the proportion of GDP from agriculture (agriculture GDP). The share of income earned in agriculture shows the importance of the agricultural sector for the economy. In general, as development increases, the importance of agriculture in GDP tends to decline.

FIGURE 3.2   Population distribution in Benin, 2000 (persons per square kilometer)

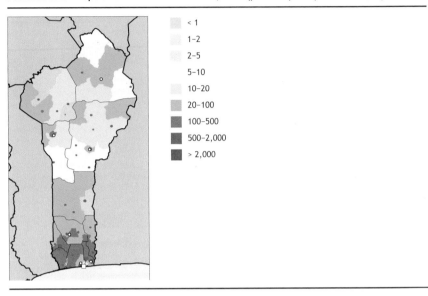

Source: CIESIN et al. (2004).

The share of GDP from agriculture steadily decreased from the mid-1960s to the mid-1970s; agriculture GDP has since fluctuated between 30 and 38 percent. Per capita GDP fluctuated between 1960 and 1990, but with a slight upward trend. Since 1990 there has been a steadier increase in per capita GDP, which rose to $360 in 2008,[2] an increase that can be attributed to the liberalization of the country's economy.

Vulnerability to Climate Change

Vulnerability has many dimensions. This chapter focuses on income as a determinant of vulnerability or resilience, addressing both level and source of income. Table 3.2 provides some data on additional indicators of the vulnerability and resilience of the population to economic shocks: education level, literacy, and concentration of labor in poorer or less dynamic sectors of the economy.

Benin's primary school enrollment, at 95.9 percent, is among the highest in the region. However, the secondary school enrollment rate is still low (32.5 percent), as in most other countries in the region. The adult literacy rate is also low, at 40.5 percent. The under-five malnutrition rate is high (21.5 percent in 2001), correlated with high adult illiteracy and low per capita GDP.

---

2 All dollar figures are constant 2000 US dollars.

FIGURE 3.3   Per capita GDP in Benin (constant 2000 US$) and share of GDP from agriculture (percent), 1960–2008

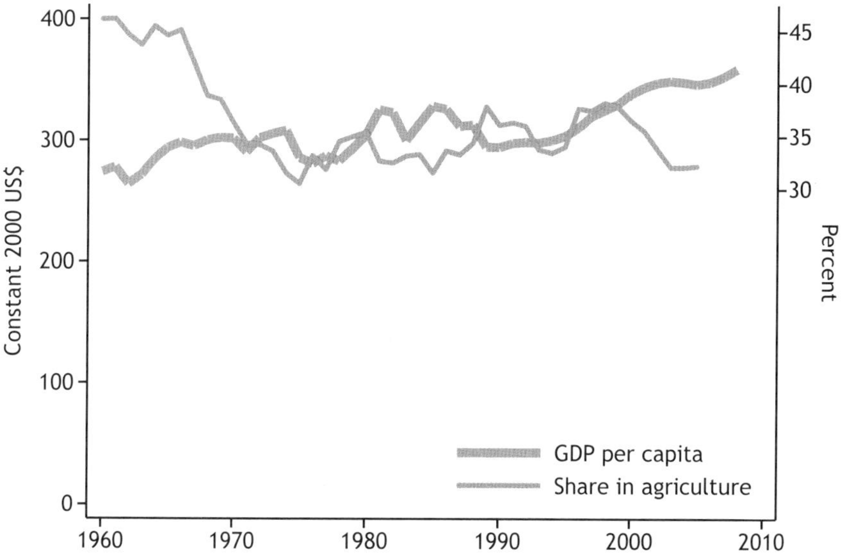

Source: World Development Indicators (World Bank 2009).
Notes: GDP = gross domestic product; US$ = US dollars.

TABLE 3.2   Education and labor statistics for Benin, 1990s and 2000s

Indicator	Year	Percent
Primary school enrollment (percent gross, three-year average)	2006	95.9
Secondary school enrollment (percent gross, three-year average)	2005	32.5
Adult literacy rate	2007	40.5
Percent employed in agriculture	1995	70.0
Under-five malnutrition (weight for age)	2001	21.5

Source: Authors' calculations based on World Development Indicators (World Bank 2009).

Although living conditions in Benin remain underdeveloped, there has been considerable improvement since the 1960s, as shown in Figure 3.4. The under-five mortality rate has decreased by half, from more than 250 per 1,000 in the late 1960s to about 125 per 1,000 in 2008; life expectancy at birth increased by half between 1964 and 2008, from 40 to 60 years. These positive developments are the result of multiple livelihood-improvement policy actions, including a food security program as well as health programs to

FIGURE 3.4   Well-being indicators in Benin, 1960–2008

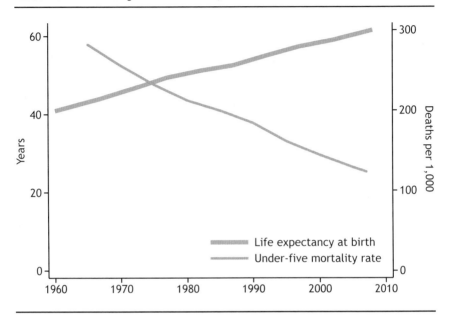

Source: World Development Indicators (World Bank 2009).

address malaria, AIDS, poliomyelitis, and child healthcare issues. The recently implemented free-of-charge Caesarean delivery program is expected to further improve child delivery conditions.

The high percentage of the population living on less than US$2 (US dollars) per day illustrates the general poverty level of the country (Figure 3.5). Poverty is acute in the northernmost part of Benin as well as in parts of the coastal area. Note that the Atlantique-Littoral region and other southern regions, with a lower percentage of people living on less than US$2, host a majority of the population.

Review of Land Use and Agriculture

Land Use Overview

Although the southern part of Benin is situated within the evergreen forest belt of West Africa, the coastal areas of the country (and neighboring Togo), with northern savannalike vegetation, form part of the notably dry Dahomey Gap (Salzmann and Hoelzmann 2005). In general, Benin is dominated by

FIGURE 3.5   Poverty in Benin, circa 2005 (percentage of population below US$2 per day)

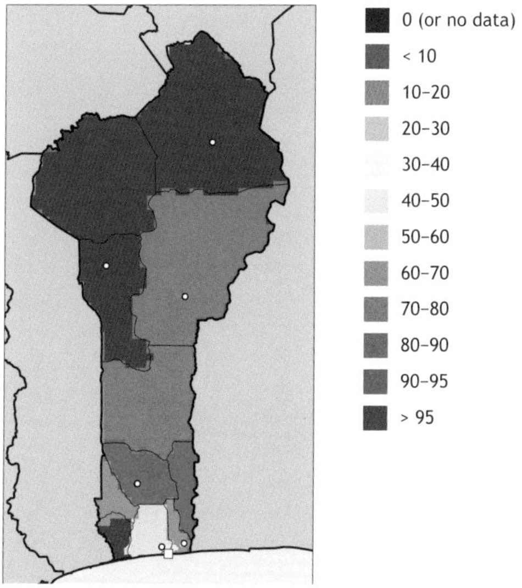

- 0 (or no data)
- < 10
- 10–20
- 20–30
- 30–40
- 40–50
- 50–60
- 60–70
- 70–80
- 80–90
- 90–95
- > 95

Source: Wood et al. (2010).
Note: Based on 2005 US$ (US dollars) and on purchasing power parity value.

shrub cover (closed-open, deciduous), followed by broadleaved tree cover and mosaic systems (cropland and shrub) (Figure 3.6). The country has several protected areas concentrated in the central and the northern parts of the country, as well as two main cross-border national parks (Pendjari and W) in the far northwest (see Figure 3.7).[3]

Figure 3.8 shows the stylized travel times to urban areas of various sizes. These four maps may be helpful for the reader to approximate the transport costs of agricultural inputs and consumables to farms and of farm output to markets. The larger cities of greater population density and size (500,000 or more) are concentrated in the south: Cotonou, Godomey, Calavi, and Porto-Novo (see Figure 3.8). It is a challenge to transport agricultural produce from the north to the urban centers in the south and imported goods in the reverse direction. The situation is somewhat better for the medium-sized and small cities distributed across the country (populations between 25,000 and 10,000); however, the market is smaller in these regions.

---

3 The International Union for Conservation of Nature (IUCN) classifies protected areas according to their management objectives. The protected area categories are outlined at www.iucn.org/about/work/programmes/pa/pa_products/wcpa_categories/.

FIGURE 3.6   Land cover and land use in Benin, 2000

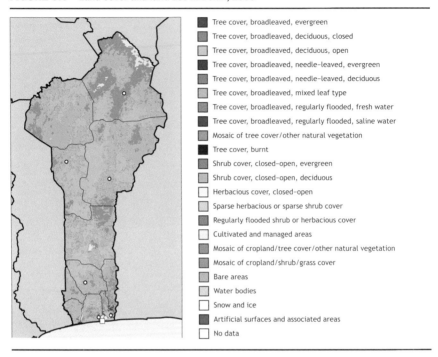

■ Tree cover, broadleaved, evergreen
☐ Tree cover, broadleaved, deciduous, closed
☐ Tree cover, broadleaved, deciduous, open
■ Tree cover, broadleaved, needle-leaved, evergreen
☐ Tree cover, broadleaved, needle-leaved, deciduous
☐ Tree cover, broadleaved, mixed leaf type
☐ Tree cover, broadleaved, regularly flooded, fresh water
■ Tree cover, broadleaved, regularly flooded, saline water
☐ Mosaic of tree cover/other natural vegetation
■ Tree cover, burnt
☐ Shrub cover, closed–open, evergreen
☐ Shrub cover, closed–open, deciduous
☐ Herbacious cover, closed–open
☐ Sparse herbacious or sparse shrub cover
☐ Regularly flooded shrub or herbacious cover
☐ Cultivated and managed areas
☐ Mosaic of cropland/tree cover/other natural vegetation
☐ Mosaic of cropland/shrub/grass cover
☐ Bare areas
☐ Water bodies
☐ Snow and ice
■ Artificial surfaces and associated areas
☐ No data

Source: GLC2000 (Bartholome and Belward 2005).

FIGURE 3.7   Protected areas in Benin, 2009

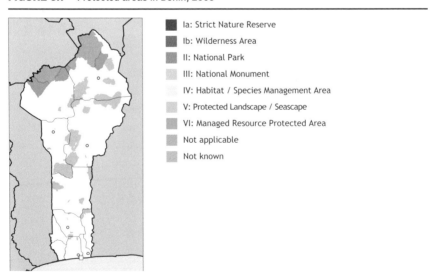

■ Ia: Strict Nature Reserve
■ Ib: Wilderness Area
▨ II: National Park
▨ III: National Monument
▨ IV: Habitat / Species Management Area
☐ V: Protected Landscape / Seascape
▨ VI: Managed Resource Protected Area
▨ Not applicable
▨ Not known

Sources: Protected areas are from the World Database on Protected Areas (UNEP and IUCN 2009). Water bodies are from the World Wildlife Fund's Global Lakes and Wetlands Database (Lehner and Döll 2004).

FIGURE 3.8 Travel time to urban areas of various sizes in Benin, circa 2000

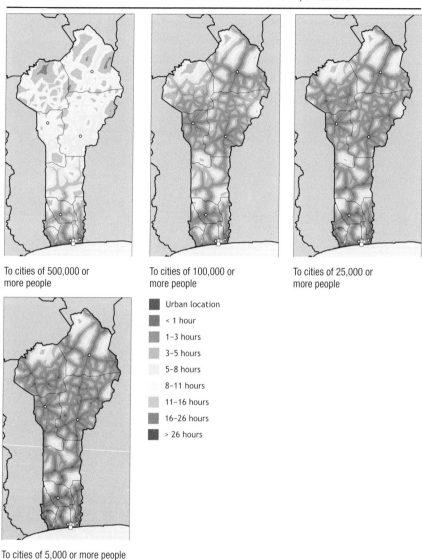

To cities of 500,000 or
more people

To cities of 100,000 or
more people

To cities of 25,000 or
more people

■ Urban location

■ < 1 hour

■ 1–3 hours

■ 3–5 hours

5–8 hours

8–11 hours

11–16 hours

■ 16–26 hours

■ > 26 hours

To cities of 5,000 or more people

Source: Authors' calculations.

Agriculture Overview

Maize, yams, and cassava are the three major foodcrops cultivated in Benin (Table 3.3). Seed cotton is the major cash crop grown in the country, followed by cashew nuts. Yams and cassava are the major staple foodcrops, followed by maize (Table 3.4).

TABLE 3.3   Harvest area of leading agricultural commodities in Benin, 2006–08 (thousands of hectares)

Rank	Crop	Percent of total	(Thousands of hectares)
	Total	100.0	2,222
1	Maize	30.6	679
2	Seed cotton	10.1	225
3	Cashew nuts	9.5	212
4	Yams	8.3	185
5	Cassava	7.9	175
6	Sorghum	6.7	149
7	Beans	6.5	145
8	Groundnuts	5.2	116
9	Millet	1.9	42
10	Other pulses	1.4	31

Source: FAOSTAT (FAO 2010).
Note: All values are based on the three-year average for 2006–08.

TABLE 3.4   Consumption of leading food commodities in Benin, 2003–05 (thousands of tons)

Rank	Crop	Percent of total	Food consumption (thousands of hectares)
	Total	100.0	4,176
1	Yams	25.1	1,048
2	Cassava	25.0	1,044
3	Maize	11.4	475
4	Rice	4.8	200
5	Other vegetables	4.7	197
6	Tomatoes	3.6	152
7	Sorghum	3.1	131
8	Other fruits	2.6	108
9	Pineapples	2.4	100
10	Chicken	1.7	72

Source: FAOSTAT (FAO 2010).
Note: All values are based on the three-year average for 2003–05.

FIGURE 3.9   Yield (metric tons per hectare) and harvest area density (hectares) for rainfed maize in Benin, 2000

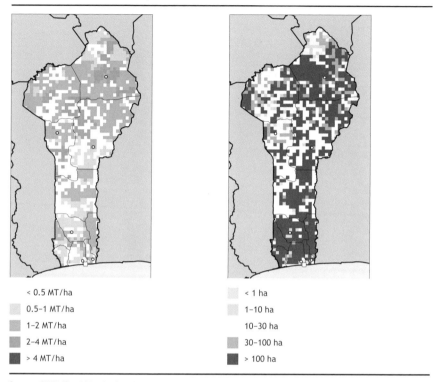

< 0.5 MT/ha	< 1 ha
0.5–1 MT/ha	1–10 ha
1–2 MT/ha	10–30 ha
2–4 MT/ha	30–100 ha
> 4 MT/ha	> 100 ha

Sources: SPAM (Spatial Production Allocation Model) (You and Wood 2006; You, Wood, and Wood-Sichra 2006, 2009).
Notes: ha = hectare; MT/ha = metric tons per hectare.

Figures 3.9–3.11 show the estimated yield and growing areas for key crops in Benin. Maize is more widely cultivated in the southern regions than in the central zones (see Figure 3.9). The production profiles for yams, sweet potatoes, and cassava are similar, although yam and sweet potato production is limited to the southeast and northwestern areas (see Figure 3.10), while cassava is quite rare in the north of the country (see Figure 3.11). Maize yields range from 1 to 2 metric tons per hectare, while the yields of fresh roots and tubers range from 7 to 10 metric tons per hectare across the country.[4]

---

4 All tons are metric tons.

FIGURE 3.10   Yield (metric tons per hectare) and harvest area density (hectares) for rainfed yams and sweet potatoes in Benin, 2000

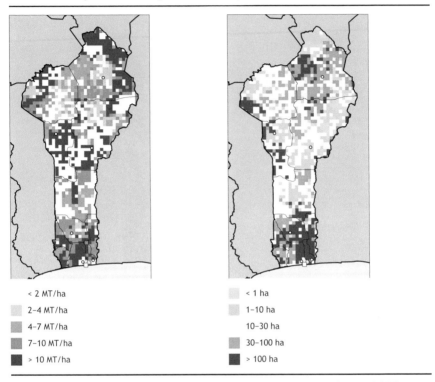

< 2 MT/ha	< 1 ha
2–4 MT/ha	1–10 ha
4–7 MT/ha	10–30 ha
7–10 MT/ha	30–100 ha
> 10 MT/ha	> 100 ha

Sources: SPAM (Spatial Production Allocation Model) (You and Wood 2006; You, Wood, and Wood-Sichra 2006, 2009).
Notes: ha = hectare; MT = metric tons.

Economic and Demographic Scenarios

Population

The population of Benin, projected by the government to be 8.5 million for 2010 (Benin, INSAE 2003) and projected by the United Nations to be 10.0 million (UNPOP 2009), is expected to at least double and possibly grow to more than two and a half times that size by 2050: the low variant is approximately 21 million, while the high variant is almost 27 million (Figure 3.12). These projections correspond to average densities of 186 and 237 people per square kilometers for the low and high variants, respectively.

FIGURE 3.11   Yield (metric tons per hectare) and harvest area density (hectares) for rainfed cassava in Benin, 2000

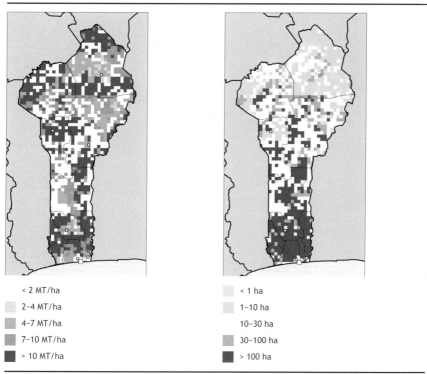

< 2 MT/ha	< 1 ha
2–4 MT/ha	1–10 ha
4–7 MT/ha	10–30 ha
7–10 MT/ha	30–100 ha
> 10 MT/ha	> 100 ha

Sources: SPAM (Spatial Production Allocation Model) (You and Wood 2006; You, Wood, and Wood-Sichra 2006, 2009).
Notes: ha = hectare; MT = metric tons.

Income

Figure 3.13 presents three scenarios for GDP per capita, derived by combining three GDP projections with the three population projections of Figure 3.12 (based on United Nations population data). The optimistic scenario combines high GDP with low population, the baseline scenario combines the medium GDP projection with the medium population projection, and the pessimistic scenario combines the low GDP projection with the high population projection. The agricultural modeling in the next section uses these scenarios.

Benin's GDP per capita has been steadily increasing since 1990 and is presently around US$360. According to both the optimistic and the baseline scenarios, GDP is projected to increase. According to the pessimistic scenario, however, per capita GDP will actually decline.

FIGURE 3.12   Population projections for Benin, 2010–50

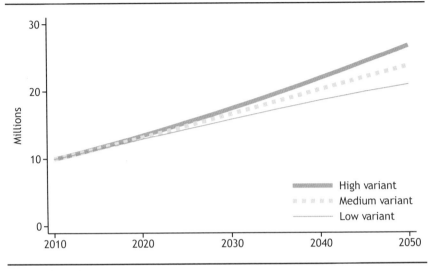

Source: UNPOP (2009).

FIGURE 3.13   Gross domestic product (GDP) per capita in Benin, future scenarios, 2010–50

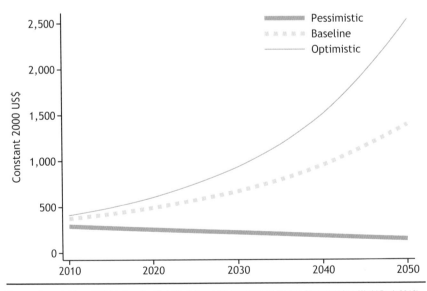

Sources: Computed from GDP data from the World Bank Economic Adaptation to Climate Change project (World Bank 2010), from the Millennium Ecosystem Assessment (2005) reports, and from population data from the United Nations (UNPOP 2009).
Note: US$ = US dollars.

Biophysical Scenarios

Climate Scenarios

Precipitation

Figure 3.14 shows precipitation changes predicted for Benin in the four downscaled climate models we use in this chapter for the A1B scenario.[5] CNRM-CM3 and ECHAM 5 show increased rainfall for some parts of the country and no significant decline for any part of the country. However, the two other models show a precipitation decrease in either most of the country (CSIRO) or just the southern region (MIROC). Although the MIROC model shows less rainfall in the most agriculturally productive part of the country, it also shows increased rainfall in sections that currently experience low rainfall. If this model proves to be most accurate, that should imply that some of the agricultural production for the country will shift northward. On the other hand, livestock production adapted to the relatively drier northern region could be affected by the possible increase in the incidence of pests and diseases associated with wet conditions. Adapting to such changes would require appropriate crop varieties and animal breeds as well as matching management practices, including efficient management of water in drought conditions and control of floods.

Temperature

Figure 3.15 shows how the daily high temperatures would change during the warmest month in the A1B scenario. The models show an increase in temperature ranging from 1°–1.5°C (based on MIROC 3.2, medium resolution) to 2.0°–2.5°C (based on CNRM-CM3). CSIRO Mark 3 shows a rise of 1.5°–2.0°C in most parts of the country except for the coastal areas, which have a lower temperature, while ECHAM 5 shows a rise of 2.0°–2.5°C for the northernmost part of the country and 1.5°–2.0°C for the rest of the country. Such increases in temperature could pose a serious threat to the productivity as well as the survival of certain crop species and to biodiversity in general, on which farmers in the country rely heavily. Consequently, adaptation to increases in temperature would require the development of crop varieties that could tolerate such conditions.

---

5 The A1B scenario is a greenhouse gas emissions scenario that assumes fast economic growth, a population that peaks midcentury, and the development of new and efficient technologies, along with a balanced use of energy sources.

FIGURE 3.14   Changes in mean annual precipitation in Benin, 2000–2050, A1B scenario (millimeters)

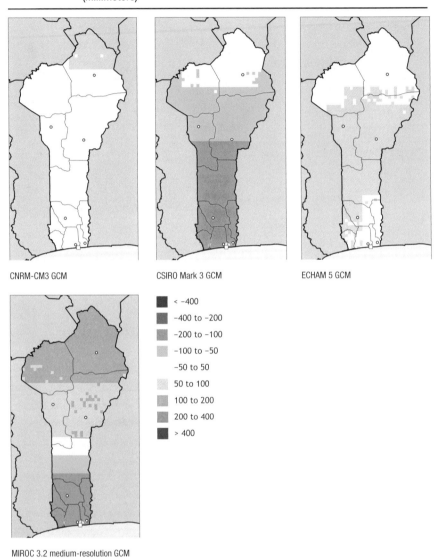

CNRM-CM3 GCM   CSIRO Mark 3 GCM   ECHAM 5 GCM

■ < –400
■ –400 to –200
■ –200 to –100
■ –100 to –50
   –50 to 50
   50 to 100
■ 100 to 200
■ 200 to 400
■ > 400

MIROC 3.2 medium-resolution GCM

Source: Authors' calculations based on Jones, Thornton, and Heinke (2009).

Notes: A1B = greenhouse gas emissions scenario that assumes fast economic growth, a population that peaks midcentury, and the development of new and efficient technologies, along with a balanced use of energy sources; CNRM-CM3 = National Meteorological Research Center–Climate Model 3; CSIRO = climate model developed at the Australia Commonwealth Scientific and Industrial Research Organisation; ECHAM 5 = fifth-generation climate model developed at the Max Planck Institute for Meteorology (Hamburg); GCM = general circulation model; MIROC = Model for Interdisciplinary Research on Climate, developed by the University of Tokyo Center for Climate System Research.

FIGURE 3.15   Change in monthly mean maximum daily temperature in Benin for the warmest month, 2000–2050, A1B scenario (°C)

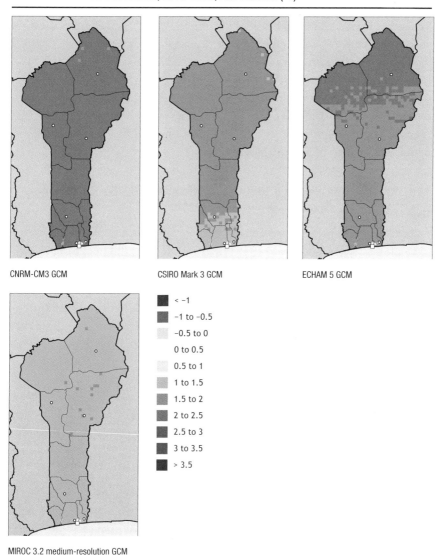

CNRM-CM3 GCM

CSIRO Mark 3 GCM

ECHAM 5 GCM

■ < –1
■ –1 to –0.5
□ –0.5 to 0
  0 to 0.5
□ 0.5 to 1
□ 1 to 1.5
□ 1.5 to 2
■ 2 to 2.5
■ 2.5 to 3
■ 3 to 3.5
■ > 3.5

MIROC 3.2 medium-resolution GCM

Source: Authors' calculations based on Jones, Thornton, and Heinke (2009).

Notes: A1B = greenhouse gas emissions scenario that assumes fast economic growth, a population that peaks midcentury, and the development of new and efficient technologies, along with a balanced use of energy sources; CNRM-CM3 = National Meteorological Research Center–Climate Model 3; CSIRO = climate model developed at the Australia Commonwealth Scientific and Industrial Research Organisation; ECHAM 5 = fifth-generation climate model developed at the Max Planck Institute for Meteorology (Hamburg); GCM = general circulation model; MIROC = Model for Interdisciplinary Research on Climate, developed at the University of Tokyo Center for Climate System Research.

Crop Physiological Responses to Climate Change

The yield results from the Decision Support Software for Agrotechnology Transfer (DSSAT) using 2050 climate from each GCM were compared to the yields simulated with unchanged (2000) climate.

The output for rainfed maize yields is mapped in Figure 3.16. DSSAT outputs for all four GCMs show a slight increase in maize yield (5–25 percent of baseline) for the far northern part of the country. For the central and the southern parts of the country (covering the most productive zone of maize), the models show significant maize yield reductions (5–25 percent of baseline), with CSIRO Mark 3 showing greater losses.

Agricultural Vulnerability Scenarios (Crop-Specific)

Maize

Figure 3.17 shows the combined effects of climate change and economic developments on maize from now to 2050. There is little or no difference among the scenarios for maize area, production, and yield. All the scenarios show the harvested area for maize increasing slightly in the near future and stagnating after 2020 (at around 800,000 hectares). The maize yield is shown to significantly improve, doubling to 2 tons per hectare, effecting an increase in overall production. It should be noted that there are currently maize varieties that have a yield potential higher than 2 tons per hectare; achieving these yields will depend on improved management practices. Projected net export levels differ, however. In the baseline and optimistic scenarios, maize exports rise steadily; the pessimistic scenario shows a modest increase in exports followed by a decrease to just above the current level—despite the modeled increase in the world price of maize. This trend could be explained by the increase in population, and hence increased domestic consumption, in the pessimistic scenario.

Yams and sweet potatoes

For yams and sweet potatoes the three scenarios produce almost identical results for all areas of Benin. According to all the scenarios, yam and sweet potato production will almost double, increasing to close to 4 million tons as a consequence of significant yield improvement (doubling from 11 to 20 tons per hectare)—even though the harvested area is shown to slightly decrease after 2020 (Figure 3.18). Net exports are shown to stagnate until 2025 and then decrease, with the country importing yams and sweet potatoes by 2050. The country is likely to face a difficult situation, because the world price will significantly increase according to all three scenarios.

FIGURE 3.16 Yield change under climate change: Rainfed maize in Benin, 2000–2050, A1B scenario

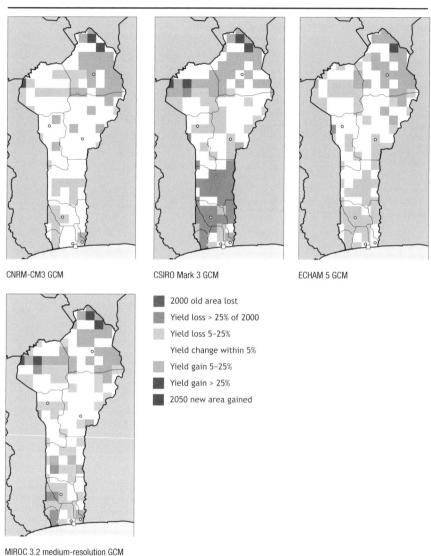

CNRM-CM3 GCM

CSIRO Mark 3 GCM

ECHAM 5 GCM

■ 2000 old area lost
■ Yield loss > 25% of 2000
▫ Yield loss 5–25%
  Yield change within 5%
▪ Yield gain 5–25%
■ Yield gain > 25%
■ 2050 new area gained

MIROC 3.2 medium-resolution GCM

Source: Authors' estimates.

Notes: A1B = greenhouse gas emissions scenario that assumes fast economic growth, a population that peaks midcentury, and the development of new and efficient technologies, along with a balanced use of energy sources; CNRM-CM3 = National Meteorological Research Center–Climate Model 3; CSIRO = climate model developed at the Australia Commonwealth Scientific and Industrial Research Organisation; ECHAM 5 = fifth-generation climate model developed at the Max Planck Institute for Meteorology (Hamburg); GCM = general circulation model; MIROC = Model for Interdisciplinary Research on Climate, developed at the University of Tokyo Center for Climate System Research.

FIGURE 3.17   Impact of changes in GDP and population on maize in Benin, 2010–50

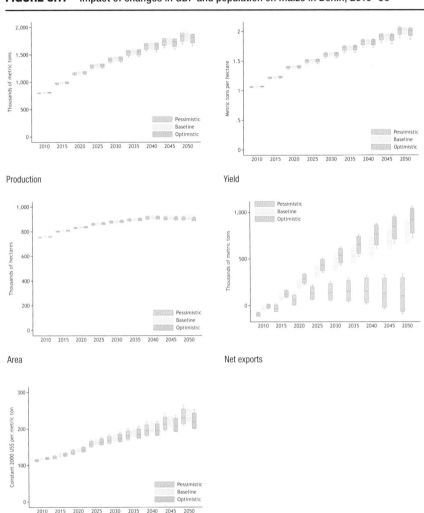

Source: Based on analysis conducted for Nelson et al. (2010).

Notes: The box and whiskers plot for each socioeconomic scenario shows the range of effects from the four future climate scenarios. GDP = gross domestic product; US$ = US dollars.

FIGURE 3.18   Impact of changes in GDP and population on yams and sweet potatoes in Benin, 2010–50

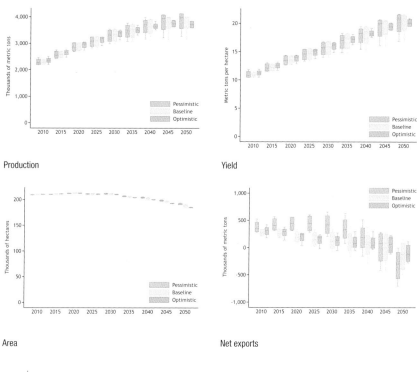

Production

Yield

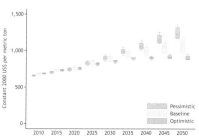

Area

Net exports

Prices

Source: Based on analysis conducted for Nelson et al. (2010).

Notes: The box and whiskers plot for each socioeconomic scenario shows the range of effects from the four future climate scenarios. GDP = gross domestic product; US$ = US dollars.

Cassava and Other Roots and Tubers

Cassava production and yield are shown to improve until 2030 and then stagnate, at between 3 and 4 million metric tons and at just over 15 tons per hectare, respectively (Figure 3.19). The harvested area does not change much over 2010–50 in any of the scenarios. Net exports of cassava and other roots and tubers will decrease significantly, from an initial zero level. The resulting growth in imports will be at a steady or modestly increasing world price, with detrimental consequences for the economy.

Human Vulnerability Scenarios

In Figure 3.20 we see that the scenarios have dramatically different outcomes for the number of malnourished children under age five. In the baseline scenario, the number is shown to slightly increase; in the pessimistic scenario, the number almost doubles by 2050; and in the optimistic scenario, the number of malnourished children under age five in Benin would continue to increase slightly until 2030 and then decline to about 400,000.

Similarly, the availability of kilocalories per capita is shown to decrease slightly in the baseline scenario and decline significantly in the pessimistic scenario. In the optimistic scenario, a significant increase is foreseen after 2030 (Figure 3.21). These results of IMPACT clearly indicate that there is a vital need for Benin to develop and implement a food security policy with enabling conditions for resource-poor farmers, including safety nets.

Conclusions and Policy Recommendations

The total population of Benin is increasing rapidly, at a rate of 3.3 percent. There will therefore be a growing number of mouths to feed against the background of the adverse effects of climate on food production. In some scenarios, the most productive zone for staple crops could experience reduced precipitation as well as an average increase of 2°C in temperature, with substantial negative effects on staple yields (e.g., a decline of 5–25 percent for maize).

Yams, cassava, and maize are currently the main food products consumed in the country. Net exports of maize are shown to increase, either significantly (in the optimistic and baseline scenarios) or slightly (in the pessimistic scenario). For tubers and root crops (yams, sweet potatoes, cassava, and others), imports will grow in all scenarios. Because the world price of all these commodities will increase, exports of maize will benefit the country, while imports of tubers and root crops will negatively affect the balance of trade. Investment

FIGURE 3.19 Impact of changes in GDP and population on cassava in Benin, 2010–50

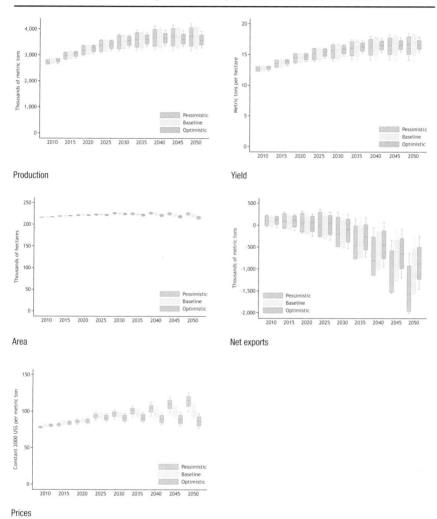

Production

Yield

Area

Net exports

Prices

Source: Based on analysis conducted for Nelson et al. (2010).

Notes: The box and whiskers plot for each socioeconomic scenario shows the range of effects from the four future climate scenarios. GDP = gross domestic product; US$ = US dollars.

FIGURE 3.20   Number of malnourished children under five years of age in Benin in multiple income and climate scenarios, 2010–50

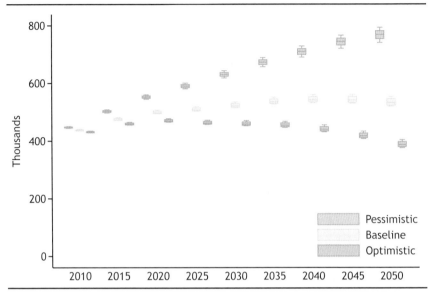

Source: Based on analysis conducted for Nelson et al. (2010).
Note: The box and whiskers plot for each socioeconomic scenario shows the range of effects from the four future climate scenarios.

in agricultural productivity for these crops could help raise farmers' incomes and reduce imports and maximize exports.

Our policy recommendations for adapting to the agricultural effects of climate change are as follows:

- Take appropriate steps to monitor climate and provide relevant information for early warning of likely climate change and adverse consequences.

- Support agricultural research efforts aimed at developing and identifying crop varieties of the major staples that could be more adaptive to climate change.

- Promote the development and adoption of more efficient water-use techniques.

- Support the capacity building of farmers with regard to access to and improved use of climate information.

- Establish crop marketing networks and access to inputs that will ensure improved marketing to stimulate agricultural production.

FIGURE 3.21   Kilocalories per capita in Benin in multiple income and climate scenarios, 2010–50

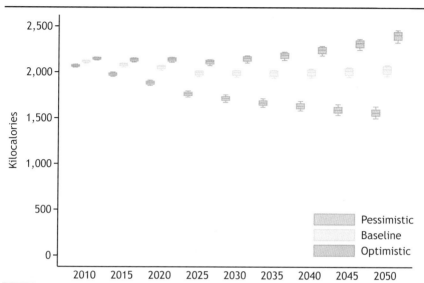

Source: Based on analysis conducted for Nelson et al. (2010).

Note: The box and whiskers plot for each socioeconomic scenario shows the range of effects from the four future climate scenarios.

- Take adequate steps to slow population growth and thus avoid imposing tremendous pressure on the natural resource base for food production.

These approaches are widely recognized as essential to support agriculture.

References

Bartholome, E., and A. S. Belward. 2005. "GLC2000: A New Approach to Global Land Cover Mapping from Earth Observation Data." *International Journal of Remote Sensing* 26 (9): 1959–1977.

Benin, INSAE (Institut National de la Statistique et de l'Analyse Economique). 2003. *Troisième recensement général de la population et de l'habitat.* Cotonou.

CIESIN (Center for International Earth Science Information Network, Columbia University), Columbia University, IFPRI (International Food Policy Research Institute), World Bank, and CIAT (Centro Internacional de Agricultura Tropical). 2004. *Global Rural–Urban Mapping Project, Version 1 (GRUMPv1).* Palisades, NY, US: Socioeconomic Data and Applications Center (SEDAC), Columbia University. http://sedac.ciesin.columbia.edu/gpw.

FAO (Food and Agriculture Organization of the United Nations). 2010. *FAOSTAT Database on Agriculture.* Rome.

Jones, P. G., P. K. Thornton, and J. Heinke. 2009. "Generating Characteristic Daily Weather Data Using Downscaled Climate Model Data from the IPCC's Fourth Assessment." Project report for the International Institute for Land Reclamation and Improvement, Wageningen, the Netherlands. Accessed May 7, 2010. www.ccafs-climate.org/pattern_scaling/.

Lehner, B., and P. Döll. 2004. "Development and Validation of a Global Database of Lakes, Reservoirs, and Wetlands." *Journal of Hydrology* 296 (1–4): 1–22.

Millennium Ecosystem Assessment. 2005. *Ecosystems and Human Well-being: Synthesis.* Washington, DC: Island Press. http://www.maweb.org/en/Global.aspx.

Nelson, G. C., M. W. Rosegrant, A. Palazzo, I. Gray, C. Ingersoll, R. Robertson, S. Tokgoz, et al. 2010. *Food Security, Farming, and Climate Change to 2050: Scenarios, Results, Policy Options.* Washington, DC: International Food Policy Research Institute.

Salzmann, U., and P. Hoelzmann. 2005. "The Dahomey Gap: An Abrupt Climatically Induced Rain Forest Fragmentation in West Africa during the Late Holocene." *Holocene* 15 (2): 190–199.

UNEP and IUCN (United Nations Environment Programme and International Union for the Conservation of Nature). 2009. *World Database on Protected Areas* (*WDPA*): *Annual Release.* Accessed 2009. www.wdpa.org/protectedplanet.aspx.

UNPOP (United Nations Department of Economic and Social Affairs–Population Division). 2009. *World Population Prospects: The 2008 Revision.* New York. http://esa.un.org/unpd/wpp/.

Wood, S., G. Hyman, U. Deichmann, E. Barona, R. Tenorio, Z. Guo, et al. 2010. *Sub-national Poverty Maps for the Developing World Using International Poverty Lines: Preliminary Data Release.* Washington, DC: Harvest Choice and International Food Policy Research Institute. http://labs.harvestchoice.org/2010/08/poverty-maps/.

World Bank. 2009. *World Development Indicators.* Accessed May 2011. http://data.worldbank.org/data-catalog/world-development-indicators.

———. 2010. *Economics of Adaptation to Climate Change: Synthesis Report.* Washington, DC. http://climatechange.worldbank.org/content/economics-adaptation-climate-change-study-homepage.

You, L., and S. Wood. 2006. "An Entropy Approach to Spatial Disaggregation of Agricultural Production." *Agricultural Systems* 90 (1–3): 329–347.

You, L., S. Wood, U. Wood-Sichra. 2006. "Generating Global Crop Distribution Maps: From Census to Grid." Paper presented at the International Association of Agricultural Economists Conference, Brisbane, Australia, August 11–18.

———. 2009. "Generating Plausible Crop Distribution and Performance Maps for Sub-Saharan -Africa Using a Spatially Disaggregated Data Fusion and Optimization Approach." *Agricultural Systems* 99 (2–3): 126–140.

Chapter 4

BURKINA FASO

Léopold Somé, Abdulai Jalloh, Robert Zougmoré, Gerald C. Nelson, and
Timothy S. Thomas

B urkina Faso is a landlocked country in West Africa covering about
274,000 square kilometers. It is bordered by the Republic of Mali on the
north and west; by Cote d'Ivoire on the Southwest; by Ghana, Togo, and
Benin on the South; and by Niger on the east. The country has a dry tropical climate with two contrasting seasons. The rainy season generally lasts from
May to October, but its duration decreases progressively from the southwest,
amounting to only three months in the northern part of the country.

Agriculture accounts for 40 percent of the gross domestic product (GDP)
and 60 percent of the total exports of Burkina Faso. Its cropped area is 3.5–
4.0 million hectares, representing about 13 percent of the country's total area
and one-third of the arable land. Rainfed agriculture dominates, with largely
rudimentary agricultural techniques prevailing among small-scale farmers.
Crop production is more diversified in the Sudanian zone (in the southwest),
with a variety of roots and tubers (yams, sweet potatoes, and cocoyams), fruits
(mangoes, bananas, and citrus fruits), cashews, and sugarcane. The major cash
crops are cotton, groundnuts, cowpeas, and sesame.

Review of the Current Situation

On the basis of its annual average distribution of rainfall, the country can be
divided into three ecoclimatic zones: (1) the Sahelian zone, where the total
annual rainfall is below 600 millimeters and occurs over a period of three to
four months; (2) the Sudan-Sahelian zone, with total rainfall of 600–900 millimeters during four to five months of the year; and (3) the Sudanian zone,
where the annual average rainfall is more than 900 millimeters and occurs in
five to six months of the year.

Three river basins drain the country: the Volta basin (63 percent of the
total area), the Niger basin (30 percent), and the Comoe basin (7 percent).
This hydrographic network is quite dense, but most of the rivers are not

permanent, limiting the possibilities for irrigation. Several dams and small reservoirs support agricultural activities in the country.

Population

The most recent general population census, held in 2006, estimated the population of Burkina Faso at 14.1 million, with an average density of 51.8 inhabitants per square kilometer (Burkina Faso, INSD 2009). The majority of the population is young, with more than 30 percent under 10 years of age and 46.6 percent under 15 years. Figure 4.1 shows the numbers of the total and rural population (left axis) as well as the share of urban population (right axis). The percentage of the population living in urban areas increased sharply in the mid-1970s, possibly as a result of the severe drought in 1972/1973, which affected the livelihoods of farm families, forcing many to go to the urban areas for alternative livelihoods. Another episode of drought occurred between 1983 and 1987.

Population migration as a consequence of climate variability and change has been clearly identified by the Burkina Faso National Adaptation Programme of Action initiative (Burkina Faso, MECV 2007). However, the

FIGURE 4.1 Population trends in Burkina Faso: Total population, rural population, and percent urban, 1960–2008

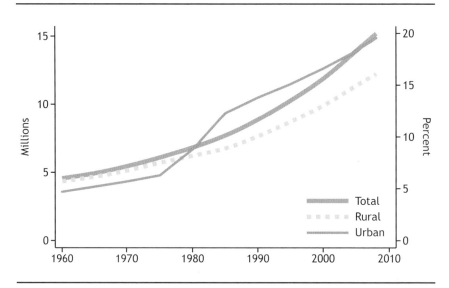

Source: World Development Indicators (World Bank 2009).

TABLE 4.1 Population growth rates in Burkina Faso, 1960–2008 (percent)

Decade	Total growth rate	Rural growth rate	Urban growth rate
1960–69	1.7	1.6	3.7
1970–79	2.3	2.0	6.4
1980–89	2.6	2.0	7.3
1990–99	2.9	2.6	4.8
2000–2008	3.1	2.7	5.1

Source: Authors' calculations based on World Development Indicators (World Bank 2009).

urban population is currently only about 20 percent of the population of the country, less than most of the countries in the region. The total growth rate of the population, at 4.1 percent per year (Table 4.1), seems to be higher than the growth rate of the economy.

Table 4.1 provides additional information concerning rates of population growth in Burkina Faso. Uncharacteristically for any nation, we see that not only the population but also the growth rate has increased in every decade since the 1960s. Although the rural growth rate lags the urban growth rate, it is still increasing at a steady rate.

Figure 4.2 shows the geographic distribution of the population in Burkina Faso. Population density is relatively higher in the provinces along the White Volta River and those along the principal road from Ghana through the capital city to Mali. Bobo-Dioulasso Province, in the western part of the country, also shows a relatively high population density, hosting the second capital city.

Income

The share of income earned in agriculture shows the importance of the agricultural sector in the economy of Burkina Faso. Figure 4.3 shows trends in GDP per capita and the proportion of GDP from agriculture.

Per capita GDP has generally increased since 1960. However, the increase was relatively small until the mid-1990s, increasing from about $130 to about $180 between 1960 and 1994. The rate of growth increased around 1994, with GDP per capita rising to $220 in 2000 and then to more than $260 in 2008. The improvement in per capita GDP could be explained by the devaluation of the CFA franc in January 1994, more favorable climatic conditions, and the boom in the mineral sector. The share of GDP from agriculture has generally been between 30 and 40 percent, declining from 1960 to the early 1980s, rising in the early and mid-1990s, and again declining after 1998 due to the growth in the service sector (see Figure 4.3).

FIGURE 4.2   Population distribution in Burkina Faso, 2000 (persons per square kilometer)

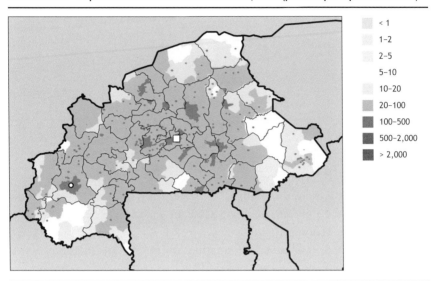

Source: CIESIN et al. (2004).

FIGURE 4.3   Per capita GDP in Burkina Faso (constant 2000 US$) and share of GDP from agriculture (percent), 1960–2008

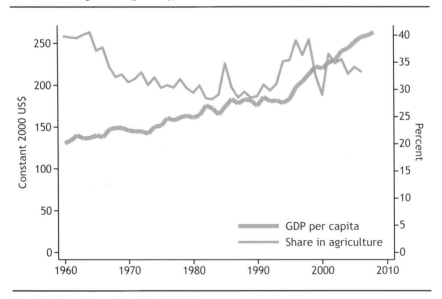

Source: World Development Indicators (World Bank 2009).

Notes: GDP = gross domestic product; US$ = US dollars.

Vulnerability to Climate Change

Vulnerability is the inability to recover from stress. Poor people are vulnerable to many different kinds of stresses because they lack the financial resources to respond. In agriculture, poor people are particularly vulnerable to the stresses of an uncertain climate. At the national level, vulnerability arises from the interactions among population and income growth and the availability or scarcity of natural and manufactured resources.

Vulnerability has many dimensions. In this chapter the focus is on income and then nonincome indicators of life expectancy at birth and the under-five mortality rate displayed in Figure 4.4. Table 4.2 provides some data on additional indicators of vulnerability and resiliency to economic shocks: the level of education of the population, literacy, and the concentration of labor in poorer or less dynamic sectors. There is a significant drop in secondary school enrollment compared to that for primary school in Burkina Faso. The adult literacy rate is also very low. Agriculture employs the bulk of the population, who are generally resource poor and produce less than a subsistence level. The lack of financial resources severely limits the ability of these poor farmers to use much-needed inputs like the improved seeds, fertilizer, and pesticides that will ensure increased agricultural production.

FIGURE 4.4   Well-being indicators in Burkina Faso, 1960–2008

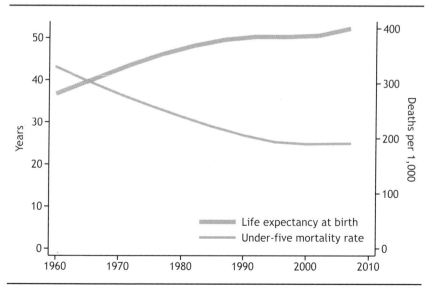

Source: World Development Indicators (World Bank 2009).

TABLE 4.2   Education and labor statistics for Burkina Faso, 1990s and 2000s

Indicator	Year	Percent
Primary school enrollment (percent gross, three-year average)	2008	71.0
Secondary school enrollment (percent gross, three-year average)	2008	18.1
Adult literacy rate	2007	28.7
Percent employed in agriculture	1994	88.8
Under-five malnutrition (weight for age)	2003	35.2

Source: Authors' calculations based on World Development Indicators (World Bank 2009).

Figure 4.4 shows two noneconomic correlates of poverty: life expectancy and under-five mortality. This figure shows a general improvement in both of these well-being indictors. Life expectancy at birth increased from less than 40 years in 1960 (the year of Burkina Faso's independence) to 53 years in 2008. During the same period, the under-five mortality rate decreased from more than 300 to fewer than 200 per 1,000 in the mid-1990s. Among the important factors contributing to this increase has been the control of diseases that affect children, like measles and poliomyelitis, particularly through vaccination.

FIGURE 4.5   Poverty in Burkina Faso, circa 2005 (percentage of population below US$2 per day)

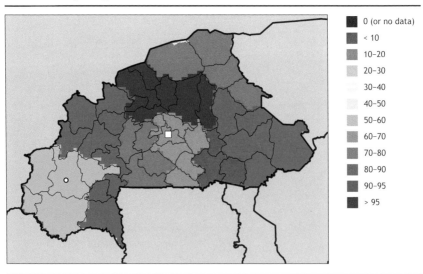

Source: Wood et al. (2010).
Note: Based on 2005 US$ (US dollars) and on purchasing power parity value.

Figure 4.5 shows the proportion of the population in Burkina Faso living on less than US$2 (US dollars) per day, which exceeds 50 percent of the population in all parts of the country. Poverty is relatively less pronounced in the provinces adjacent to the two major cities and more severe in the provinces with higher population densities.

Review of Land Use and Agriculture

Land Use Overview

Figure 4.6 shows the land cover and land use in Burkina Faso as of 2000. Natural vegetation varies with the three ecoclimatic zones in the country—steppe in the north, shrubs and annual grasses in the center, and various trees and perennial grasses in the south and southwest (Guinko 1984). The northern, Sahelian region is characterized variously by herbaceous cover, closed–open vegetation, and scrubland steppe. It is mainly devoted to pasture, but due to the harsh climate and overgrazing the vegetation is often thorny and stunted. The most common species found in this area include *Acacia* spp., *Balanitesaegyptiaca, Bauhinia rufescens,* and *Ziziphusmauritiania.* The annual grasses form a discontinuous cover except in the clayey soil depressions.

The Sudan region of Burkina Faso, in the southwest, is characterized by species like Shea trees (*Vitellaria paradoxa*), nere (*Parkia biglobosa*), and other Sudan species. Perennial grasses (*Andropogongayanus* and *Cymbopogon* spp.) are abundant; during the rainy season, they form a continuous cover. The Sudan–Guinean zone is characterized by ligneous species whose density and height are significantly greater than in the other two domains. Most of the species found in the Sudanian zone are present in this region. Characteristic species here include *Burkea africana, Isoberlinia doka,* and *Detarium microcarpum.* There are also several forest galleries along the perennial rivers.

Figure 4.7 shows protected areas, including parks and reserves. These fragile environmental areas may also be important for the tourism industry.

Figure 4.8 shows travel time to the larger cities, which offer potential markets for agricultural products. Policymakers need to keep in mind the importance of transport costs when considering potential for agricultural expansion. Fertile unused land that is far from markets represents potential areas of expansion only if transportation infrastructure is in place (and, of course, if expansion does not conflict with preservation priorities as shown in Figure 4.7). In general, the travel time to major towns and cities is 1–3 hours. There is a

FIGURE 4.6   Land cover and land use in Burkina Faso, 2000

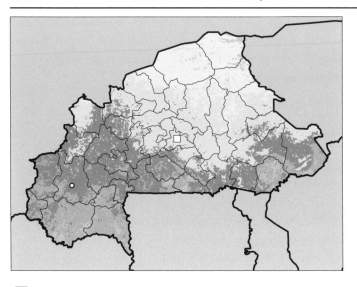

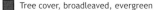

■ Tree cover, broadleaved, evergreen

■ Tree cover, broadleaved, deciduous, closed

□ Tree cover, broadleaved, deciduous, open

■ Tree cover, broadleaved, needle-leaved, evergreen

■ Tree cover, broadleaved, needle-leaved, deciduous

□ Tree cover, broadleaved, mixed leaf type

■ Tree cover, broadleaved, regularly flooded, fresh water

■ Tree cover, broadleaved, regularly flooded, saline water

■ Mosaic of tree cover/other natural vegetation

■ Tree cover, burnt

■ Shrub cover, closed-open, evergreen

■ Shrub cover, closed-open, deciduous

□ Herbacious cover, closed-open

□ Sparse herbacious or sparse shrub cover

■ Regularly flooded shrub or herbacious cover

□ Cultivated and managed areas

■ Mosaic of cropland/tree cover/other natural vegetation

■ Mosaic of cropland/shrub/grass cover

■ Bare areas

■ Water bodies

□ Snow and ice

■ Artificial surfaces and associated areas

□ No data

Source: GLC2000 (Global Land Cover 2000) (Bartholome and Belward 2005).

FIGURE 4.7 Protected areas in Burkina Faso, 2009

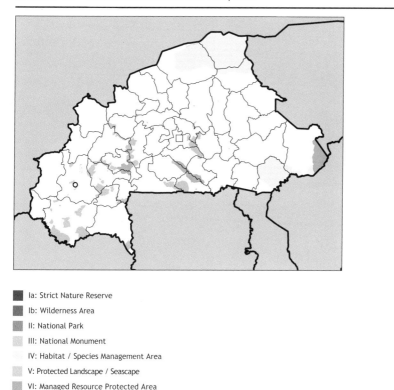

- Ia: Strict Nature Reserve
- Ib: Wilderness Area
- II: National Park
- III: National Monument
- IV: Habitat / Species Management Area
- V: Protected Landscape / Seascape
- VI: Managed Resource Protected Area
- Not applicable
- Not known

Sources: Protected areas are from the World Database on Protected Areas (UNEP and IUCN 2009). Water bodies are from the World Wildlife Fund's Global Lakes and Wetlands Database (Lehner and Döll 2004).

good network of roads around the first and second capital cities. Only in Pama Province is the road network relatively underdeveloped.

Agriculture Overview

The next three tables show key agricultural commodities in terms of area harvested (Table 4.3), the value of the harvest (Table 4.4), and the provision of food for human consumption (ranked by weight) (Table 4.5). Sorghum and millet are the major staples in Burkina Faso, while cotton is the major cash crop. Maize, cowpeas, and groundnuts are also important crops grown and consumed in the country.

FIGURE 4.8   Travel time to urban areas of various sizes in Burkina Faso, circa 2000

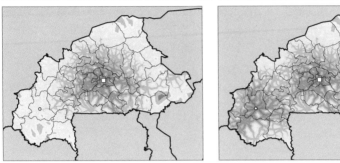

To cities of 500,000 or more people

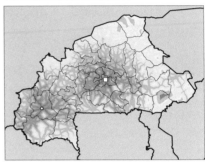

To cities of 100,000 or more people

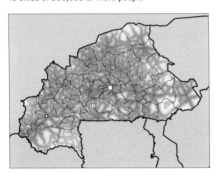

To towns and cities of 25,000 or more people

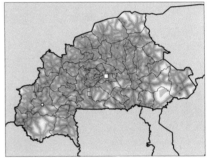

To towns and cities of 10,000 or more people

- Urban location
- < 1 hour
- 1–3 hours
- 3–5 hours
- 5–8 hours
- 8–11 hours
- 11–16 hours
- 16–26 hours
- > 26 hours

Source: Authors' calculations.

TABLE 4.3 Harvest area of leading agricultural commodities in Burkina Faso, 2006–08 (thousands of hectares)

Rank	Crop	Percent of total	Harvest area
	Total	100.0	5,316
1	Sorghum	30.4	1,613
2	Millet	25.0	1,328
3	Cowpeas	13.2	702
4	Maize	9.6	509
5	Seed cotton	9.1	483
6	Groundnuts	7.2	385
7	Sesame seed	1.0	51
8	Rice	1.0	51
9	Bambara beans	0.8	44
10	Karite nuts	0.5	28

Source: FAOSTAT (FAO 2010).
Note: All values are based on the three-year average for 2006–08.

TABLE 4.4 Value of production of leading agricultural commodities in Burkina Faso, 2005–07 (millions of US$)

Rank	Crop	Percent of total	Value of production
	Total	100.0	1,214.6
1	Sorghum	23.8	289.6
2	Millet	17.0	206.7
3	Seed cotton	16.7	202.4
4	Maize	12.3	150.0
5	Cowpeas	9.6	116.0
6	Other fresh vegetables	3.6	43.4
7	Rice	3.2	39.2
8	Groundnuts	2.8	34.1
9	Sugarcane	1.8	21.7
10	Onions	1.2	14.4

Source: FAOSTAT (FAO 2010).
Note: All values are based on the three-year average for 2005–07. US$ = US dollars.

TABLE 4.5   Consumption of leading food commodities in Burkina Faso, 2003–05 (thousands of metric tons)

Rank	Crop	Percentage of total	Food consumption
	Total	100.0	4,946
1	Sorghum	24.2	1,195
2	Millet	19.5	962
3	Fermented beverages	13.7	678
4	Maize	12.6	625
5	Rice	4.8	238
6	Other vegetables	4.1	204
7	Groundnuts	3.6	178
8	Other pulses	3.2	156
9	Beef	2.0	101
10	Wheat	1.4	69

Source: FAOSTAT (FAO 2010).
Note: All values are based on the three-year average for 2003–05.

The next four figures show the estimated yields and growing areas of key crops in Burkina Faso in 2000. Sorghum (Figure 4.9) and millet (Figure 4.10) are cultivated in almost all parts of the country except the southwest; sorghum is more widely cultivated than millet. Yields of both crops range from 0.5 to 1.0 metric tons per hectare. Cotton (Figure 4.11) and maize (Figure 4.12) are mainly grown in the southwest, with maize cultivation extending to the central part of the country. Yields of both crops range from 1.0 to 2.0 metric tons per hectare.

Economic and Demographic Scenarios

Population
Figure 4.13 shows population projections for Burkina Faso by 2050 according to the United Nations (UN) population office. The projections of the national statistics and demography institute in Burkina Faso show the total population increasing to 21.5 million by 2020 (Burkina Faso, INSD 2009). The UN projections are in agreement, showing a total population greater than 30 million in 2050. An increasing population will impose severe pressure on the natural resource base as well as on public and social services, presenting a growing challenge for the government.

FIGURE 4.9 Yield (metric tons per hectare) and harvest area density (hectares) for rainfed sorghum in Burkina Faso, 2000

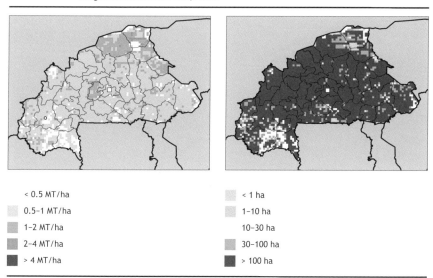

< 0.5 MT/ha	< 1 ha
0.5–1 MT/ha	1–10 ha
1–2 MT/ha	10–30 ha
2–4 MT/ha	30–100 ha
> 4 MT/ha	> 100 ha

Sources: SPAM (Spatial Production Allocation Model) (You and Wood 2006; You, Wood, and Wood-Sichra 2006, 2009).
Notes: ha = hectare; MT = metric tons.

FIGURE 4.10 Yield (metric tons per hectare) and harvest area density (hectares) for rainfed millet in Burkina Faso, 2000

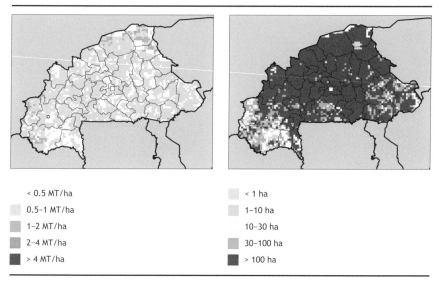

< 0.5 MT/ha	< 1 ha
0.5–1 MT/ha	1–10 ha
1–2 MT/ha	10–30 ha
2–4 MT/ha	30–100 ha
> 4 MT/ha	> 100 ha

Source: SPAM (Spatial Production Allocation Model) (You and Wood 2006; You, Wood, and Wood-Sichra 2006, 2009).
Notes: ha = hectare; MT = metric tons.

FIGURE 4.11   Yield (metric tons per hectare) and harvest area density (hectares) for rainfed cotton in Burkina Faso, 2000

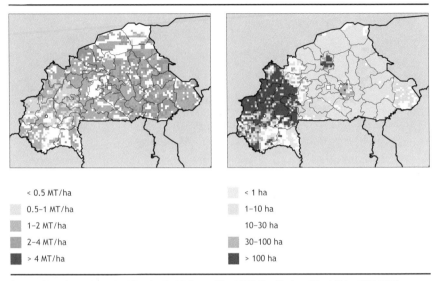

< 0.5 MT/ha	< 1 ha
0.5–1 MT/ha	1–10 ha
1–2 MT/ha	10–30 ha
2–4 MT/ha	30–100 ha
> 4 MT/ha	> 100 ha

Sources: SPAM (Spatial Production Allocation Model) (You and Wood 2006; You, Wood, and Wood-Sichra 2006, 2009).
Notes: ha = hectare; MT = metric tons.

FIGURE 4.12   Yield (metric tons per hectare) and harvest area density (hectares) for rainfed maize in Burkina Faso, 2000

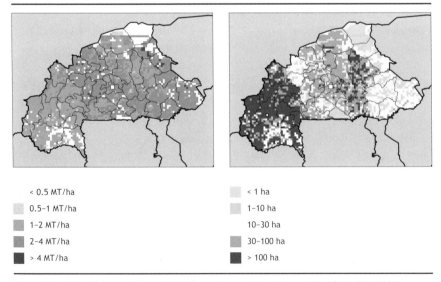

< 0.5 MT/ha	< 1 ha
0.5–1 MT/ha	1–10 ha
1–2 MT/ha	10–30 ha
2–4 MT/ha	30–100 ha
> 4 MT/ha	> 100 ha

Source: SPAM (Spatial Production Allocation Model) (You and Wood 2006; You, Wood, and Wood-Sichra 2006, 2009).
Notes: ha = hectare; MT = metric tons.

FIGURE 4.13   Population projections for Burkina Faso, 2010–50

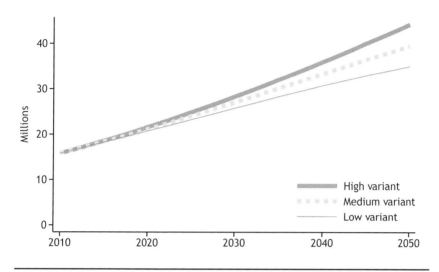

Source: UNPOP (2009).

Income

Figure 4.14 presents three scenarios for future national GDP per capita, derived by combining three GDP projections with three population projections from the UN. The optimistic scenario combines high GDP with low population; the baseline scenario combines the medium GDP projection with the medium population projection; and the pessimistic scenario combines the low GDP projection with the high population projection. (The agricultural modeling in the next section will use these scenarios as well.)

The economy of Burkina Faso depends on the agricultural sector (mainly cotton and livestock) and recently has depended on the mineral sector (mainly gold). Burkina Faso has very limited natural resources, and unless new mineral resources are discovered, it will be almost impossible to realize the optimistic scenario and the associated growth in GDP per capita. The pessimistic scenario predicts a rather small improvement in per capita GDP, which will rise above US$500 only after 2040 and still be below US$1,000 in 2050. The optimistic scenario predicts a rapid increase in per capita GDP between 2030 and 2050, from US$800 in 2030 to above US$2,500 in 2050.

FIGURE 4.14   Gross domestic product (GDP) per capita in Burkina Faso, future scenarios, 2010–50

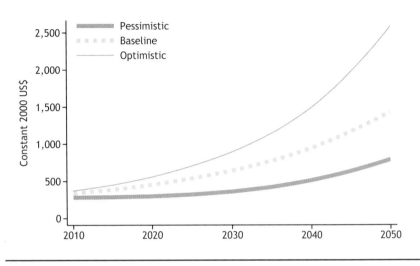

Sources: Computed from GDP data from the World Bank Economic Adaptation to Climate Change project (World Bank 2010), from the Millennium Ecosystem Assessment (2005), reports, and from population data from the United Nations (UNPOP 2009). Note: US$ = US dollars.

Biophysical Scenarios

Climate Scenarios

Figure 4.15 shows precipitation changes in Burkina Faso in the four downscaled general circulation models (GCMs) using the A1B scenario.[1] CNRM-CM3 and MIROC 3.2 medium resolution show an increase in rainfall in large areas of the country, with MIROC 3.2 medium resolution predicting wetter conditions. CSIRO Mark 3 shows drier conditions (−200 to −100 millimeters of rainfall) in the central and southwestern part of the country, whereas ECHAM 5 shows a uniform −50 to 50 millimeters for the entire country.[2]

---

1   The A1B scenario is a greenhouse gas emissions scenario that assumes fast economic growth, a population that peaks midcentury, and the development of new and efficient technologies, along with a balanced use of energy sources.

2   CNRM-CM3 is National Meteorological Research Center–Climate Model 3. MIROC 3.2 medium resolution is the Model for Interdisciplinary Research on Climate, developed at the University of Tokyo Center for Climate System Research. CSIRO Mark 3 is a climate model developed at the Australia Commonwealth Scientific and Industrial Research Organisation. ECHAM 5 is a fifth-generation climate model developed at the Max Planck Institute for Meteorology in Hamburg.

FIGURE 4.15 Changes in mean annual precipitation in Burkina Faso, 2000–2050, A1B scenario (millimeters)

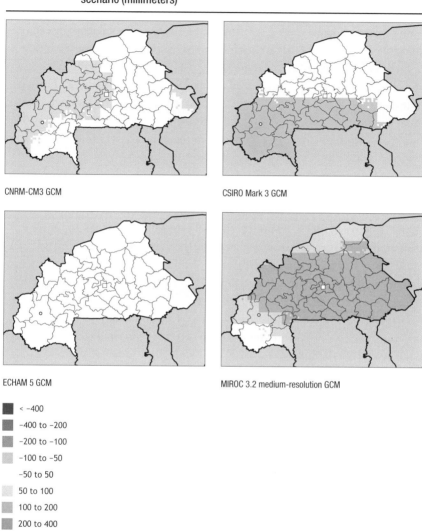

CNRM-CM3 GCM

CSIRO Mark 3 GCM

ECHAM 5 GCM

MIROC 3.2 medium-resolution GCM

- < −400
- −400 to −200
- −200 to −100
- −100 to −50
- −50 to 50
- 50 to 100
- 100 to 200
- 200 to 400
- > 400

Source: Authors' calculations based on Jones, Thornton, and Heinke (2009).

Notes: A1B = greenhouse gas emissions scenario that assumes fast economic growth, a population that peaks midcentury, and the development of new and efficient technologies, along with a balanced use of energy sources; CNRM-CM3 = National Meteorological Research Center–Climate Model 3; CSIRO = climate model developed at the Australia Commonwealth Scientific and Industrial Research Organisation; ECHAM 5 = fifth-generation climate model developed at the Max Planck Institute for Meteorology (Hamburg); GCM = general circulation model; MIROC = Model for Interdisciplinary Research on Climate, developed at the University of Tokyo Center for Climate System Research.

Figure 4.16 shows the change in average daily maximum temperature in the A1B scenario according to the four GCMs. The increases in temperature range from 1.1° to 2.7°C. CNRM-CM3 and ECHAM 5 show a relatively greater increase (2.5°–3.0°C). CSIRO Mark 3 and MIROC 3.2 medium resolution show an increase of 2.0°–2.5°C and 1.0°–1.5°C, respectively. Temperature increases in the tropics generally lead to a reduction in crop yields and production. Most of the cereal crops grown in Burkina Faso can withstand temperature increases if sufficient water is available. However, taking into account the lack of irrigation possibilities, crop yields in these models would be expected to decrease unless rainfall increased enough to compensate.

Crop Physiological Response to Climate Change

We used the Decision Support Software for Agrotechnology Transfer (DSSAT) crop model to compute crop yields in Burkina Faso in the current temperature and precipitation regimes. We then repeated the exercise for each of the four GCMs for the year 2050, with crop variety, soil, and management practices held constant for all locations. The future yield results from DSSAT were compared to the current or baseline yield results from DSSAT. The next two figures show the output for two key crops, sorghum and maize, comparing crop yields for 2050 with climate change to the crop yields assuming an unchanged (2000) climate.

Figure 4.17 shows a yield loss of 5–25 percent of baseline for sorghum according to all the models. Additionally, ECHAM 5 and MIROC 3.2 medium resolution show a yield loss greater than 25 percent in various parts of the country, particularly the central to southwestern regions. All models also indicate a loss of cropping area in the northernmost regions of the country. The loss is greatest based on ECHAM 5. However, in small areas scattered in the central region, there may also be a yield gain.

All scenarios show a significant area of the country where the maize yields will increase by 5–25 percent, with greater than 25 percent increases in some areas (Figure 4.18). However, all the models also show a reduction in the maize yields in the current maize-growing areas. The increase in maize yields in other parts of the country might be partially explained by the possible increase in rainfall in those areas during critical growth phases, or perhaps increased solar radiation will be responsible for increasing the growth rates and yields.

FIGURE 4.16   Change in monthly mean maximum daily temperature in Burkina Faso for the warmest month, 2000–2050, A1B scenario (°C)

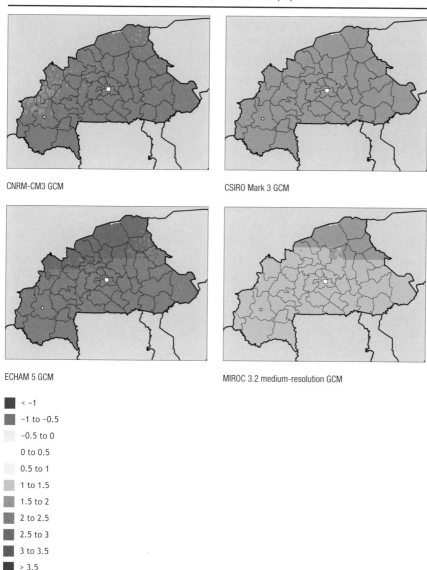

CNRM-CM3 GCM

CSIRO Mark 3 GCM

ECHAM 5 GCM

MIROC 3.2 medium-resolution GCM

■ < −1
■ −1 to −0.5
  −0.5 to 0
  0 to 0.5
  0.5 to 1
  1 to 1.5
■ 1.5 to 2
■ 2 to 2.5
■ 2.5 to 3
■ 3 to 3.5
■ > 3.5

Source: Authors' calculations based on Jones, Thornton, and Heinke (2009).

Notes: A1B = greenhouse gas emissions scenario that assumes fast economic growth, a population that peaks midcentury, and the development of new and efficient technologies, along with a balanced use of energy sources; CNRM-CM3 = National Meteorological Research Center–Climate Model 3; CSIRO = climate model developed at the Australia Commonwealth Scientific and Industrial Research Organisation; ECHAM 5 = fifth-generation climate model developed at the Max Planck Institute for Meteorology (Hamburg); GCM = general circulation model; MIROC = Model for Interdisciplinary Research on Climate, developed at the University of Tokyo Center for Climate System Research.

FIGURE 4.17   Yield change under climate change: Rainfed sorghum in Burkina Faso, 2000–2050, A1B scenario

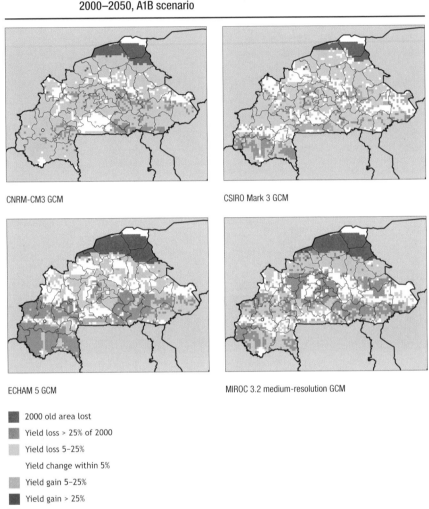

CNRM-CM3 GCM

CSIRO Mark 3 GCM

ECHAM 5 GCM

MIROC 3.2 medium-resolution GCM

- ■ 2000 old area lost
- ■ Yield loss > 25% of 2000
- ▢ Yield loss 5–25%
- Yield change within 5%
- ▢ Yield gain 5–25%
- ■ Yield gain > 25%
- ■ 2050 new area gained

Source: Authors' estimates.

Notes: A1B = greenhouse gas emissions scenario that assumes fast economic growth, a population that peaks midcentury, and the development of new and efficient technologies, along with a balanced use of energy sources; CNRM-CM3 = National Meteorological Research Center–Climate Model 3; CSIRO = climate model developed at the Australia Commonwealth Scientific and Industrial Research Organisation; ECHAM 5 = fifth-generation climate model developed at the Max Planck Institute for Meteorology (Hamburg); GCM = general circulation model; MIROC = Model for Interdisciplinary Research on Climate, developed at the University of Tokyo Center for Climate System Research.

FIGURE 4.18   Yield change under climate change: Rainfed maize in Burkina Faso, 2000–2050, A1B scenario

CNRM-CM3 GCM

CSIRO Mark 3 GCM

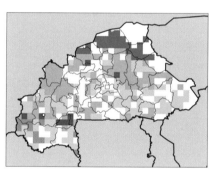

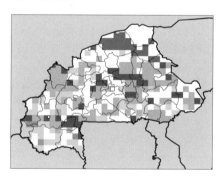

ECHAM 5 GCM

MIROC 3.2 medium-resolution GCM

- 2000 old area lost
- Yield loss > 25% of 2000
- Yield loss 5–25%
- Yield change within 5%
- Yield gain 5–25%
- Yield gain > 25%
- 2050 new area gained

Source: Authors' estimates.

Notes: A1B = greenhouse gas emissions scenario that assumes fast economic growth, a population that peaks midcentury, and the development of new and efficient technologies, along with a balanced use of energy sources; CNRM-CM3 = National Meteorological Research Center–Climate Model 3; CSIRO = climate model developed at the Australia Commonwealth Scientific and Industrial Research Organisation; ECHAM 5 = fifth-generation climate model developed at the Max Planck Institute for Meteorology (Hamburg); GCM = general circulation model; MIROC = Model for Interdisciplinary Research on Climate, developed at the University of Tokyo Center for Climate System Research.

Agricultural Vulnerability Scenarios (Crop-Specific)

The next four figures show simulation results from IMPACT associated with key agricultural crops in Burkina Faso. The figure for each featured crop has five graphs showing production, yield, area, net exports, and world price. Sorghum production—based on area cultivated as well as productivity per unit area—increases in all of the scenarios (Figure 4.19). This increase will primarily be led by increases in sorghum yield but will also be due to increases in sorghum area planted. The improvement in sorghum crop yield can perhaps be attributed to the anticipated selection and breeding effort of the agricultural research service and to the use of adaptive technologies by farmers. Net exports of sorghum increase after 2035 in both the optimistic and the baseline scenarios but to decrease in the pessimistic scenario. The increase in exports due to rising production is plausible with an increase in trade in the subregion.

Similar to the case of sorghum, the area under production and the yield for millet are shown to increase in all the scenarios (Figure 4.20). The millet yield, like that of sorghum, can be further improved by the selection and breeding efforts of the agricultural research service and by the use of adaptive technologies by farmers. However, unlike in the case of sorghum, all the scenarios show an increase in the net export of millet between 2040 and 2050.

Trends for cotton are similar in all the scenarios and are also similar to those for millet. Recently Burkina Faso adopted highly productive genetically modified cotton, supporting the plausibility of the production and yield trends shown in Figure 4.21.

The trends for maize production—in area of production, yield, net exports, and world price—are also similar in all the scenarios (Figure 4.22). Although maize production is shown to increase due to increased productivity, the area planted with the crop will decline slightly. The increase in productivity will be due to improved management practices as well as technological improvements. Maize varieties are currently available in Burkina Faso that yield much more than the yield projected for 2050. Maize consumption in urban areas has risen in the past five years; with the projected increase in population, domestic demand for maize should continue to increase. The increase in local demand will mean a decrease in net exports, despite an increase in the world price of maize.

Human Vulnerability Scenarios

Figure 4.23 shows the impact of future GDP and population scenarios on under-five malnutrition rates in Burkina Faso. The box-and-whisker plots

FIGURE 4.19   Impact of changes in GDP and population on sorghum in Burkina Faso,
2010–50

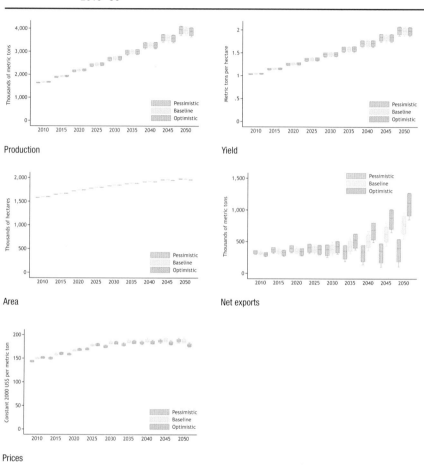

Source: Based on analysis conducted for Nelson et al. (2010).

Notes: The box and whiskers plot for each socioeconomic scenario shows the range of effects from the four future climate scenarios. GDP = gross domestic product; US$ = US dollars.

FIGURE 4.20   Impact of changes in GDP and population on millet in Burkina Faso, 2010–50

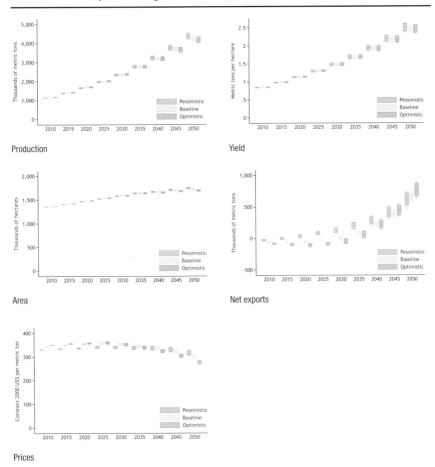

Source: Based on analysis conducted for Nelson et al. (2010).

Notes: The box and whiskers plot for each socioeconomic scenario shows the range of effects from the four future climate scenarios. GDP = gross domestic product; US$ = US dollars.

FIGURE 4.21   Impact of changes in GDP and population on cotton in Burkina Faso, 2010–50

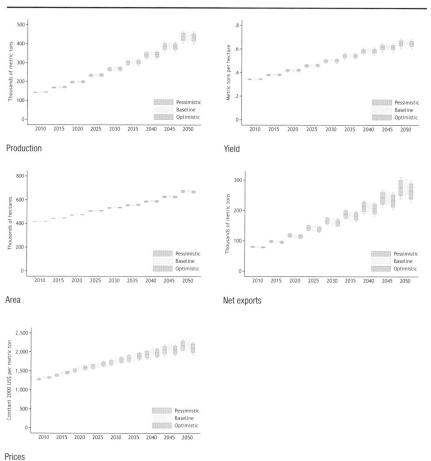

Production

Yield

Area

Net exports

Prices

Source: Based on analysis conducted for Nelson et al. (2010).

Notes: The box and whiskers plot for each socioeconomic scenario shows the range of effects from the four future climate scenarios. GDP = gross domestic product; US$ = US dollars.

FIGURE 4.22   Impact of changes in GDP and population on maize in Burkina Faso, 2010–50

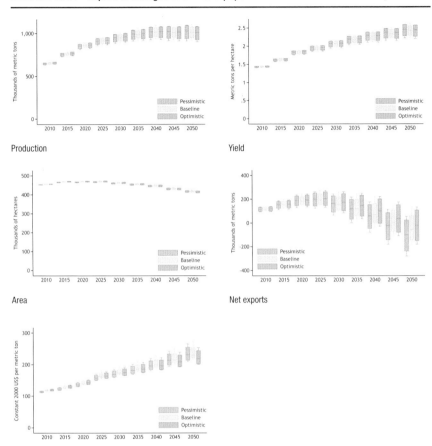

Production

Yield

Area

Net exports

Prices

Source: Based on analysis conducted for Nelson et al. (2010).

Notes: The box and whiskers plot for each socioeconomic scenario shows the range of effects from the four future climate scenarios. GDP = gross domestic product; US$ = US dollars.

in the figure indicate the range of climate scenario effects. All scenarios show an increase in the number of malnourished children under age five in the near future, at least until 2025. Only the optimistic scenario has a lower number in 2050 than at present. Although the number of malnourished children increases in the baseline and pessimistic scenarios, it is likely that the *proportion* of children who are malnourished will decline in all scenarios, because the population is projected to increase at a larger rate than the number of malnourished children is projected to increase.

Figure 4.24 shows the available kilocalories per capita. The pessimistic scenario shows only a small increase by 2050, with a declining trend in calories until 2025. The other scenarios, however, paint a much brighter future. The optimistic scenario shows the largest increase, perhaps explaining the decline in the number of malnourished children shown in Figure 4.23.

FIGURE 4.23   Number of malnourished children under five years of age in Burkina Faso in multiple income and climate scenarios, 2010–50

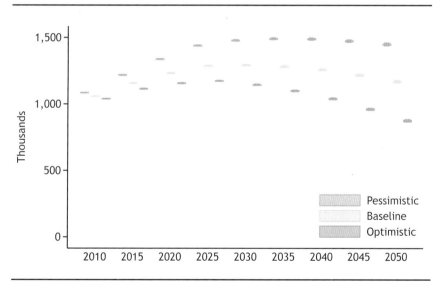

Source: Based on analysis conducted for Nelson et al. (2010).

Note: The box and whiskers plot for each socioeconomic scenario shows the range of effects from the four future climate scenarios.

FIGURE 4.24   Kilocalories per capita in Burkina Faso in multiple income and climate scenarios, 2010–50

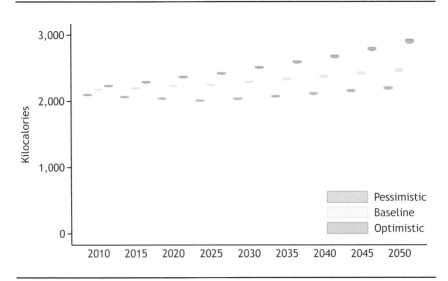

Source: Based on analysis conducted for Nelson et al. (2010).

Note: The box and whiskers plot for each socioeconomic scenario shows the range of effects from the four future climate scenarios.

Conclusions and Policy Recommendations

This chapter outlines Burkina Faso's current vulnerability to climate change with respect to land use and agriculture and analyzes the potential impact of climate change on crop production. The results of the study on which the chapter is based confirm the high level of uncertainty in rainfall for Burkina Faso indicated by the Intergovernmental Panel for Climate Change (Parry et al. 2007) for all of West Africa. The study results also highlight the challenges Burkina Faso faces regarding the availability of data for climate change analysis. The lack of data for forecasting models creates a handicap for long-term forecasting efforts and thus for the efficient use of scenarios. There is thus an urgent need to support the meteorological and hydrological services.

Our analysis also points to the following policy implications:

- Support is needed for the agricultural research system to continue its efforts in developing crop varieties tolerant of or resistant to changing climatic conditions of temperature and rainfall.

- Capacity building is needed for all stakeholders—particularly farmers—to enable them to adequately manage crops so that optimum productivity levels can be achieved in view of the challenges of climate change.

- Control (mobilization and distribution) of surface water and groundwater is essential for the supply of water, not only to populations and animals but also to crops. Irrigation during dry spells in the rainy season and full irrigation in the dry season are needed in order to improve the food security of the country.

- Permanent availability of water and other inputs, such as fertilizers and pesticides, will ensure the development of garden market crops. High priority must be granted to this activity, because it appears to present one of the best opportunities for women and young people to improve their incomes.

- It will be helpful to promote the widespread adoption and use of appropriate and proven field water harvesting technologies, such as *zai,* combined with stony lines, half- moons, mulching, and the like.[3] These techniques are also designed to control the runoff and erosion phenomenon which contributes largely to land degradation.

Our study should improve the level of understanding of climate change issues for all the stakeholders, in particular for decisionmakers engaged in planning to meet the UN's Millennium Development Goals.

References

Bartholome, E., and A. S. Belward. 2005. "GLC2000: A New Approach to Global Land Cover Mapping from Earth Observation Data." *International Journal of Remote Sensing* 26 (9): 1959–1977.

Burkina Faso, INSD (Institut National de la Statistique et de la Démographie). 2009. *Annuaire statistique edition 2008.* Ouagadougou.

---

3 The traditional method for constructing zai consists of digging tiny pits 10 centimeters in diameter and 5 centimeters deep with hoes to break the surface crust during the dry season. The Harmattan wind transports sand and organic materials into the pits. Improved technology involves digging larger pits, 20–50 centimeters in diameter and 10–25 centimeters deep, to store more rainfall and runoff. Animal manure added after the first rains complements the work of the wind and makes nutrients more available to crops (Reij and Toulmin 1996). Half-moons are a technology applied on the Arenosols of the Sahelian zone and on the ferruginous soils in the savannah. It consists of the construction of semicircular structures 15–20 centimeters deep, with the remaining soil arranged as a contour bund on the curved side with a diameter of 3–4 meters.

Burkina Faso, MECV (Ministère de l'Environnement et du Cadre de Vie). 2007. *Programme d'action national e d'adaptation (PANA) à la variabilité et aux changements climatiques.* Ouagadougou.

CIESIN (Center for International Earth Science Information Network, Columbia University), Columbia University, IFPRI (International Food Policy Research Institute), World Bank, and CIAT (Centro Internacional de Agricultura Tropical). 2004. *Global Rural–Urban Mapping Project, Version 1 (GRUMPv1).* Palisades, NY, US: Socioeconomic Data and Applications Center (SEDAC), Columbia University. http://sedac.ciesin.columbia.edu/gpw.

FAO (Food and Agriculture Organization of the United Nations). 2010. *FAOSTAT Database on Agriculture.* Rome.

Guinko, S. 1984. "Végétation de la haute Volta." Dissertation, Université de Bordeaux III, France.

Jones, P. G., P. K. Thornton, and J. Heinke. 2009. "Generating Characteristic Daily Weather Data Using Downscaled Climate Model Data from the IPCC's Fourth Assessment." Project report for the International Institute for Land Reclamation and Improvement, Wageningen, the Netherlands. Accessed May 7, 2010. www.ccafs-climate.org/pattern_scaling/.

Lehner, B., and P. Döll. 2004. "Development and Validation of a Global Database of Lakes, Reservoirs, and Wetlands." *Journal of Hydrology* 296 (1–4): 1–22.

Millennium Ecosystem Assessment. 2005. *Ecosystems and Human Well-being: Synthesis.* Washington, DC: Island Press. http://www.maweb.org/en/Global.aspx.

Nelson, G. C., M. W. Rosegrant, A. Palazzo, I. Gray, C. Ingersoll, R. Robertson, S. Tokgoz, et al. 2010. *Food Security, Farming, and Climate Change to 2050: Scenarios, Results, Policy Options.* Washington, DC: International Food Policy Research Institute.

Parry, M., O. F. Canaziani, J. P. Palutikof, P. J. van der Linden, and C. E. Hanson. 2007. "Technical Summary." In *Climate Change 2007: Impacts, Adaptation and Vulnerability.* Contribution of Working Group II to the Fourth Assessment Report of the Intergovernmental Panel on Climate Change, edited by M. Parry, O. F. Canaziani, J. P. Palutikof, P. J. Van der Linden, and C. E. Hanson. Cambridge, UK: Cambridge University Press.

Reij, C. I., and C. Toulmin. 1996. *Sustaining the Soil: Indigenous Soil and Water Conservation in Africa.* London: Earthscan.

UNEP and IUCN (United Nations Environment Programme and International Union for the Conservation of Nature). 2009. *World Database on Protected Areas (WDPA): Annual Release.* Accessed 2009. www.wdpa.org/protectedplanet.aspx.

UNPOP (United Nations Department of Economic and Social Affairs–Population Division). 2009. *World Population Prospects: The 2008 Revision.* New York. Downloaded from http://esa.un.org/unpd/wpp/.

Wood, S., G. Hyman, U. Deichmann, E. Barona, R. Tenorio, Z. Guo, et al. 2010. *Sub-national Poverty Maps for the Developing World Using International Poverty Lines: Preliminary Data Release.* Washington, DC: Harvest Choice and International Food Policy Research Institute. http:// labs.harvestchoice.org/2010/08/poverty-maps/.

World Bank. 2009. *World Development Indicators.* Accessed May 2011. http://data.worldbank.org/ data-catalog/world-development-indicators.

———. 2010. *Economics of Adaptation to Climate Change: Synthesis Report.* Washington, DC. http://climatechange.worldbank.org/content/economics-adaptation-climate-change-study -homepage.

You, L., and S. Wood. 2006. "An Entropy Approach to Spatial Disaggregation of Agricultural Production." *Agricultural Systems* 90 (1–3): 329–347.

You, L., S. Wood, and U. Wood-Sichra. 2006. "Generating Global Crop Distribution Maps: From Census to Grid." Paper presented at the International Association of Agricultural Economists Conference, Brisbane, Australia, August 11–18.

———. 2009. "Generating Plausible Crop Distribution and Performance Maps for Sub-Saharan Africa Using a Spatially Disaggregated Data Fusion and Optimization Approach." *Agricultural Systems* 99 (2–3): 126–140.

Chapter 5

CÔTE D'IVOIRE

Kadio Ahossane, Abdulai Jalloh, Gerald C. Nelson, and Timothy S. Thomas

The West African state of Côte d'Ivoire has an area of 322,465 square kilometers, with a coastline of 540 kilometers along the Gulf of Guinea. It shares borders with Liberia in the southwest, Guinea in the northwest, Mali and Burkina Faso in the north, and Ghana in the east. The southern part of Côte d'Ivoire borders the Atlantic Ocean. In the western part of the coastal areas, there are only two seasons—wet and dry. Moving inland toward the east, a short dry season occurs during the middle of the wet season, creating an annual cycle of four seasons.

The entire country enjoys a humid climate, with at least seven rainy months and not less than 1,000 millimeters of annual rainfall. Most of the interior has an annual rainfall of between 1,000 and 1,500 millimeters. Temperatures are remarkably constant throughout the year, with the mean temperatures of the warmest and coldest months very close: 27°C and 24°C for Bouaké and Tabou, 28°C and 25°C for Abidjan, and 29°C and 26°C for Ferkessédougou. In the capital city, Abidjan, the mean annual air temperature is 26.2°C; March is the warmest month there, and August is the coolest month.

Review of the Current Situation

Population

In 2009 the estimated population of Côte d'Ivoire was 20.6 million. The population has doubled every 20 years since the country became independent in 1960, increasing from about 4 million in 1960 to 8 million in 1980 and 16 million in 2000. Figure 5.1 shows trends for the total population and the rural population (left axis), as well as the share of urban population (right axis). Côte d'Ivoire is one of the countries with a very large immigrant population from neighboring countries, as well as a non-African expatriate community composed of approximately 10,000 French nationals and as many as 60,000 Lebanese nationals.

FIGURE 5.1   Population trends in Côte d'Ivoire: Total population, rural population, and percent urban, 1960–2008

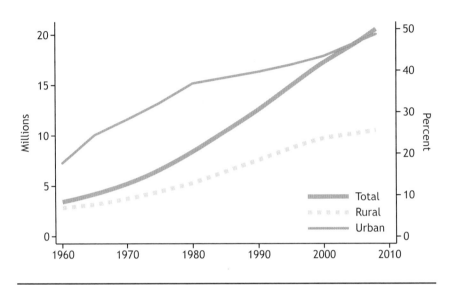

Source: World Development Indicators (World Bank 2009).

Urbanization has increased in Côte d'Ivoire since 1960, when only 20 percent of the population lived in urban areas. In 2008 almost 50 percent of the Ivorian population lived in urban areas. The high urban population growth rate is reflected in Table 5.1. Between 2000 and 2008, the urban population growth rate was four times higher than rural population growth rate. Rural-to-urban migration as well as improved health conditions in the urban areas may be important factors in the rapid urban population growth.

TABLE 5.1   Population growth rates in Côte d'Ivoire, 1960–2008 (percent)

Decade	Total growth rate	Rural growth rate	Urban growth rate
1960–69	4.2	2.7	9.0
1970–79	4.8	3.5	7.5
1980–89	4.1	3.6	4.8
1990–99	3.2	2.6	4.1
2000–2008	2.2	0.9	3.6

Source: Authors' calculations based on World Development Indicators (World Bank 2009).

FIGURE 5.2   Population distribution in Côte d'Ivoire, 2000 (persons per square kilometer)

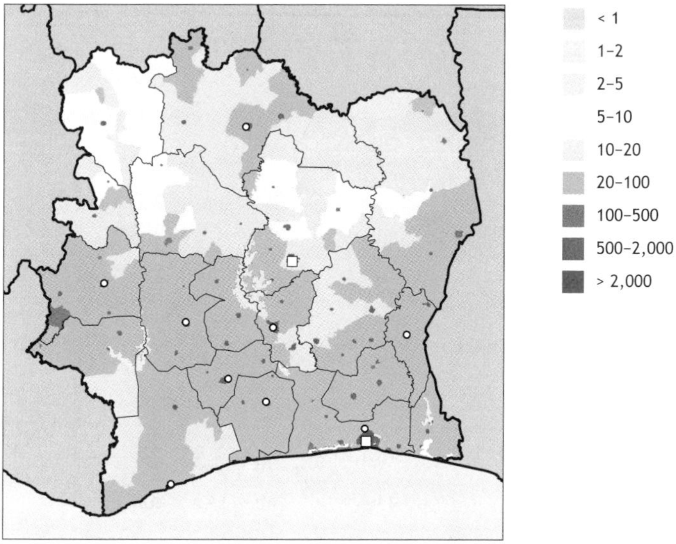

Legend:
- < 1
- 1–2
- 2–5
- 5–10
- 10–20
- 20–100
- 100–500
- 500–2,000
- > 2,000

Source: CIESIN et al. (2004).

Figure 5.2 shows the geographic distribution of the population in Côte d'Ivoire. Population density is higher in the southern part of the country, which has more urban areas as well as large cocoa plantations that attract migrant labor, particularly from neighboring Burkina Faso.

Income

Figure 5.3 shows trends in the gross domestic product (GDP) per capita and the proportion of GDP from agriculture. Côte d'Ivoire produces 40 percent of the world's cocoa crop and is a major exporter of other agricultural produce, as well as tropical wood products and tuna. However, reliance on commodity exports exposes the economy to international price swings. The GDP per capita increased in the 1960s and 1970s but then dropped dramatically. Conversely, the contribution of agriculture to GDP declined steadily from 1960 to 1980 as the manufacturing and service sectors of the economy improved after independence, then began to increase in the 1980s as other sectors of the economy continued to decline. Nevertheless, at the end of the first decade after independence, the government's strategy for economic growth and development was proving successful. The production of cash crops expanded, and with the revenues from commodity sales the government

FIGURE 5.3   Per capita GDP in Côte d'Ivoire (constant 2000 US$) and share of GDP from
agriculture (percent), 1960–2008

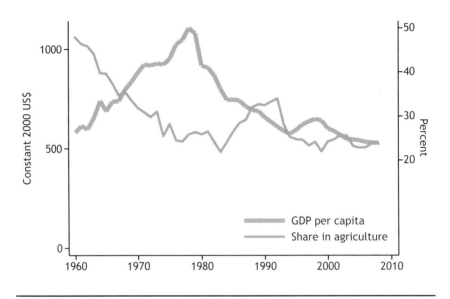

Source: World Development Indicators (World Bank 2009).
Notes: GDP = gross domestic product; US$ = US dollars.

upgraded roads, improved communications, and raised the educational level of
the workforce.

Increased aid flows, rigorous macroeconomic policies, and high international commodity prices, along with devaluation, yielded 6–7 percent annual
GDP growth rates in 1994–98. Since that time, however, economic decline
has resulted in declining living standards. Falling commodity prices, along
with government corruption and fiscal mismanagement, had brought the
economy to its knees by the end of 1999. At that point, a coup d'état and
the installation of a military junta caused the cancellation of foreign assistance. Private foreign investment declined sharply, while the government's
internal and external debt ballooned. As a result, the economy contracted by
−2.3 percent in 2000. Thereafter the economic situation further deteriorated
as the political situation culminated in a division of the country between the
North and the South, controlled by dissident soldiers and the government-
backed army, respectively. However, stability is gradually being restored following the installation of a civilian government after the elections in 2010.

Vulnerability to Climate Change

Table 5.2 provides some data on Côte d'Ivoire's performance on indicators of a country's vulnerability or resiliency to economic shocks beyond that of income level: level of education, literacy, and concentration of labor in poorer or less dynamic sectors. Côte d'Ivoire, like other countries in the region, has a relatively higher enrollment in primary school (72.1 percent) than in secondary schools (24.6 percent). Adult literacy, although low, is relatively higher than in many countries in the region. The majority of the population is engaged in agriculture.

Figure 5.4 shows data for Côte d'Ivoire on two noneconomic correlates of poverty: life expectancy and under-five mortality. The Ivorian government recognized very early the need to invest in the social sectors—notably education, health, and basic socioeconomic infrastructure—in order to improve the population's standard of living. After independence, life expectancy at birth increased from 40 years to 55 years in the late 1970s, while the under-five mortality rate decreased sharply, from 300 per 1,000 in the 1960s to less than 200 per 1,000 in 1980 and 125 per 1,000 in 2008.

As for poverty levels based on consumption measures, Wood et al. (2010) report that slightly fewer than half of Côte d'Ivoire's 20 million people live below the poverty threshold based on the 2005 US dollar and the purchasing power parity measure.

Review of Land Use and Agriculture

Land Use Overview

Figure 5.5 shows land cover and land use in Côte d'Ivoire as of 2000. The southern part of the country is characterized by mosaic terrain, with cropland, trees, and other natural vegetation along with patches of tree cover

TABLE 5.2 Education and labor statistics for Côte d'Ivoire, 1990s and 2000s

Indicator	Year	Percent
Primary school enrollment (percent gross, three-year average)	2007	72.1
Secondary school enrollment (percent gross, three-year average)	2002	24.6
Adult literacy rate	2000	48.7
Percent employed in agriculture	1996	60.0
Under-five malnutrition (weight for age)	2006	16.7

Source: Authors' calculations based on World Development Indicators (World Bank 2009).

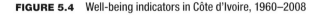

FIGURE 5.4   Well-being indicators in Côte d'Ivoire, 1960–2008

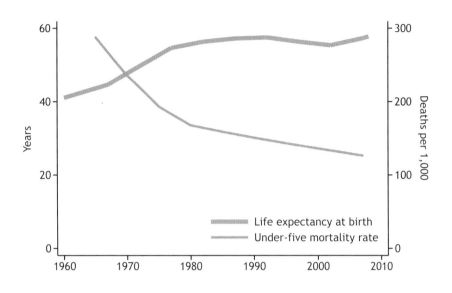

Source: World Development Indicators (World Bank 2009).

(broadleaved evergreen forests). The northern region is characterized by tree cover (broadleaved, deciduous, open). Fifty-two percent of the total land area of more than 322,000 square kilometers is considered agricultural land, amounting to slightly more than 3.6 hectares per capita.

Figure 5.6 shows protected areas, including parks and reserves. These fragile environmental areas may also be important for the tourism industry. Côte d'Ivoire has nine parks and reserves. Tai National Park covers an area of approximately 536,000 hectares and is located in the southwestern department of Guiglo (Roth et al. 1979; UICN/BRAO 2008). It represents over 50 percent of the total West African forest areas given high protection status and is the largest intact rainforest in West Africa (Myers 1990). Tai National Park was classified as a Biosphere Reserve in 1978 and a World Heritage site in 1983.

Abokonamekro Game Reserve is located 60 kilometers from Yamoussoukro and covers 20,430 hectares. It hosts elephants, buffaloes, cobs de buffon, rhinos, and giraffes (UICN/BRAO 2008). Asagny National Park is located 100 kilometers from Abidjan, at the mouth of the Bandama River, and covers 19,400 hectares; it is mainly marshy savannah with palm trees. Elephants, bush pigs, buffaloes, monkeys, and several species of birds live there in harmony (UICN/BRAO 2008).

FIGURE 5.5   Land cover and land use in Côte d'Ivoire, 2000

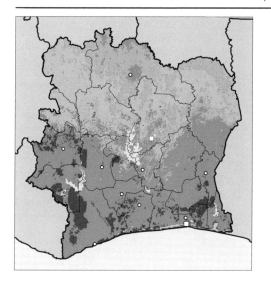

 Tree cover, broadleaved, evergreen

☐ Tree cover, broadleaved, deciduous, closed

☐ Tree cover, broadleaved, deciduous, open

■ Tree cover, broadleaved, needle-leaved, evergreen

☐ Tree cover, broadleaved, needle-leaved, deciduous

☐ Tree cover, broadleaved, mixed leaf type

☐ Tree cover, broadleaved, regularly flooded, fresh water

☐ Tree cover, broadleaved, regularly flooded, saline water

☐ Mosaic of tree cover/other natural vegetation

■ Tree cover, burnt

☐ Shrub cover, closed-open, evergreen

☐ Shrub cover, closed-open, deciduous

☐ Herbacious cover, closed-open

☐ Sparse herbacious or sparse shrub cover

☐ Regularly flooded shrub or herbacious cover

☐ Cultivated and managed areas

☐ Mosaic of cropland/tree cover/other natural vegetation

☐ Mosaic of cropland/shrub/grass cover

☐ Bare areas

☐ Water bodies

☐ Snow and ice

■ Artificial surfaces and associated areas

☐ No data

Source: GLC2000 (Global Land Cover 2000) (Bartholome and Belward 2005).

FIGURE 5.6   Protected areas in Côte d'Ivoire, 2009

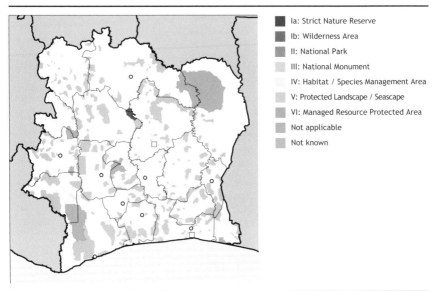

Ia: Strict Nature Reserve
Ib: Wilderness Area
II: National Park
III: National Monument
IV: Habitat / Species Management Area
V: Protected Landscape / Seascape
VI: Managed Resource Protected Area
Not applicable
Not known

Source: Protected areas are from the World Database on Protected Areas (UNEP and IUCN 2009). Water bodies are from the World Wildlife Fund's Global Lakes and Wetlands Database (Lehner and Döll 2004).

Comoé National Park, founded in 1968 as the "Book of Bouna," is located in Bouna and is the oldest and largest park in Côte d'Ivoire, at 1,149,250 hectares (UICN/BRAO 2008). The park has 500 kilometers of tracks suitable for motor vehicles and is home to a wide variety of wildlife: elephants, buffaloes, cobs de buffon, lions, hippos, cynocephali, and several species of birds (Chape et al. 2003). Other major national parks include Marahoué (101,000 hectares), located in the center-west region of Bouaflé, and Mount Sangbe National Park, located north of Man in the western part of the country (95,000 hectares) (UICN/BRAO 2008).

Figure 5.7 shows the travel time to urban areas, which are potential markets for agricultural products and sources of agricultural inputs and consumer goods for farmers. The road network is fairly good in Côte d'Ivoire, and all major towns are fairly well connected. The plantations are also accessible. The majority of the population lives either in or close to cities of 100,000 people or more. These urban areas and their immediate surrounding areas are associated with a variety of crop production activities. Average travel times are inversely related to population density: areas with larger populations have better road networks and therefore experience less travel time to nearby cities.

FIGURE 5.7   Travel time to urban areas of various sizes in Côte d'Ivoire, circa 2000

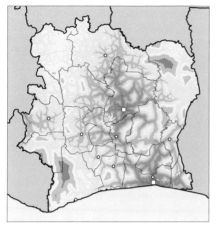

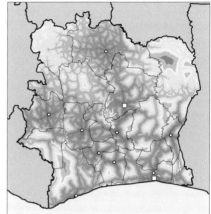

To cities of 500,000 or more people

To cities of 100,000 or more people

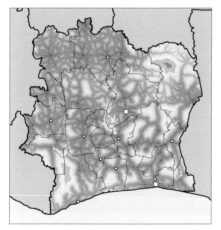

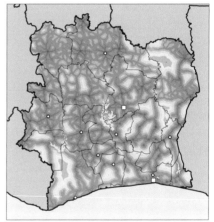

To towns and cities of 25,000 or more people

To towns and cities of 10,000 or more people

- ■ Urban location
- ■ < 1 hour
- ■ 1–3 hours
- ■ 3–5 hours
- ■ 5–8 hours
- ■ 8–11 hours
- ■ 11–16 hours
- ■ 16–26 hours
- ■ > 26 hours

Source: Authors' calculations.

Agriculture Overview

Tables 5.3–5.5 show key agricultural commodities in terms of the area harvested, the value of the harvest, and the provision of food for human consumption (ranked by weight). Cocoa is the major cash crop and occupies the largest

TABLE 5.3   Harvest area of leading agricultural commodities in Côte d'Ivoire, 2006–08 (thousands of hectares)

Rank	Crop	Percent of total	Harvest area
	Total	100.0	6,940
1	Cocoa beans	31.0	2,151
2	Yams	10.4	723
3	Cashew nuts	9.5	657
4	Coffee	8.4	585
5	Plantains	5.5	382
6	Rice	5.4	375
7	Cassava	4.9	339
8	Maize	4.2	292
9	Seed cotton	3.6	247
10	Oil palm fruit	3.1	212

Source: FAOSTAT (FAO 2010).
Note: All values are based on the three-year average for 2006–08.

TABLE 5.4   Value of production of leading agricultural commodities in Côte d'Ivoire, 2005–07 (millions of US$)

Rank	Crop	Percent of total	Value of production
	Total	100.0	3,871.4
1	Cocoa beans	24.5	949.2
2	Yams	22.4	869.0
3	Cassava	8.8	339.6
4	Plantains	7.8	303.8
5	Bananas	4.8	186.5
6	Rice	3.7	143.3
7	Coffee	3.6	139.1
8	Maize	3.1	121.7
9	Rubber	2.8	110.2
10	Seed cotton	2.3	89.8

Source: FAOSTAT (FAO 2010).
Note: All values are based on the three-year average for 2005–07. US$ = US dollars.

TABLE 5.5   Consumption of leading food commodities in Côte d'Ivoire, 2003–05 (thousands of metric tons)

Rank	Crop	Percent of total	Food consumption
	Total	100.0	11,068
1	Yams	29.8	3,298
2	Cassava	17.2	1,899
3	Plantains	10.9	1,210
4	Rice	7.7	855
5	Other vegetables	5.7	636
6	Fermented beverages	4.0	446
7	Beer	3.4	380
8	Maize	3.4	380
9	Wheat	2.6	293
10	Sugar	1.8	203

Source: FAOSTAT (FAO 2010).
Note: All values are based on the three-year average for 2003–05.

area under cultivation, whereas yams occupy the largest area planted with foodcrops. Yams, cassava, and plantains are the major staples in Côte d'Ivoire. Other foodcrops include taro (in the south) and varieties of millet and sorghum (in the north).

The next four figures show the estimated current yields and growing areas for key crops. Yams and sweet potatoes are produced in all parts of the country (Figure 5.8), with yields ranging from 7 to 10 metric tons per hectare and production concentrated in the forest region, which is also the main region for cassava and plantain production (Figures 5.9 and 5.10). Cassava root yields range from 4 to 7 metric tons per hectare, and plantain and banana yields range from 2 to 4 metric tons per hectare. Coffee is grown mainly in the northern part of the country (Figure 5.11), with yields of less than 1 metric ton per hectare.

Economic and Demographic Scenarios

Population

Figure 5.12 shows population projections for Côte d'Ivoire by the United Nations (UN) population office (UNPOP 2009) through 2050. All three scenarios show an increasing population until 2050—with the current population doubling by 2043 (based on the high variant) or by 2050 (based on the medium variant). Rapid increases in population have consequences for

FIGURE 5.8   Yield (metric tons per hectare) and harvest area density (hectares) for rainfed yams and sweet potatoes in Côte d'Ivoire, 2000

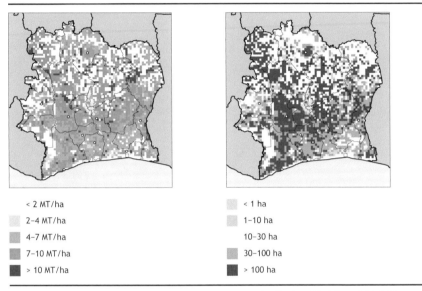

< 2 MT/ha	< 1 ha
2–4 MT/ha	1–10 ha
4–7 MT/ha	10–30 ha
7–10 MT/ha	30–100 ha
> 10 MT/ha	> 100 ha

Sources: SPAM (Spatial Production Allocation Model) (You and Wood 2006; You, Wood, and Wood-Sichra 2006, 2009).
Notes: ha = hectare; MT = metric tons.

FIGURE 5.9   Yield (metric tons per hectare) and harvest area density (hectares) for rainfed cassava in Côte d'Ivoire, 2000

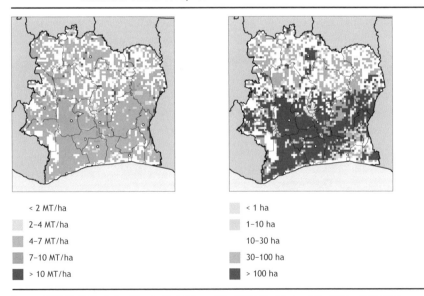

< 2 MT/ha	< 1 ha
2–4 MT/ha	1–10 ha
4–7 MT/ha	10–30 ha
7–10 MT/ha	30–100 ha
> 10 MT/ha	> 100 ha

Sources: SPAM (Spatial Production Allocation Model) (You and Wood 2006; You, Wood, and Wood-Sichra 2006, 2009).
Notes: ha = hectare; MT = metric tons.

FIGURE 5.10 Yield (metric tons per hectare) and harvest area density (hectares) for rainfed plantains and bananas in Côte d'Ivoire, 2000

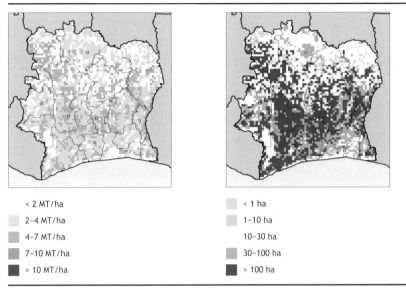

< 2 MT/ha		< 1 ha
2–4 MT/ha		1–10 ha
4–7 MT/ha		10–30 ha
7–10 MT/ha		30–100 ha
> 10 MT/ha		> 100 ha

Sources: SPAM (Spatial Production Allocation Model) (You and Wood 2006; You, Wood, and Wood-Sichra 2006, 2009).
Notes: ha = hectare; MT = metric tons.

FIGURE 5.11 Yield (metric tons per hectare) and harvest area density (hectares) for rainfed coffee in Côte d'Ivoire, 2000

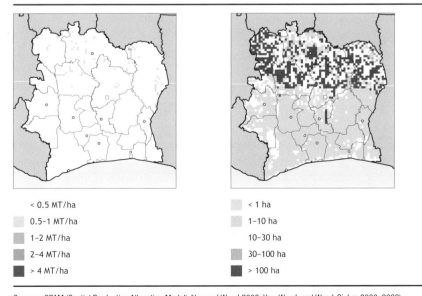

< 0.5 MT/ha		< 1 ha
0.5–1 MT/ha		1–10 ha
1–2 MT/ha		10–30 ha
2–4 MT/ha		30–100 ha
> 4 MT/ha		> 100 ha

Sources: SPAM (Spatial Production Allocation Model) (You and Wood 2006; You, Wood, and Wood-Sichra 2006, 2009).
Notes: ha = hectare; MT = metric tons.

FIGURE 5.12 Population projections for Côte d'Ivoire, 2010–50

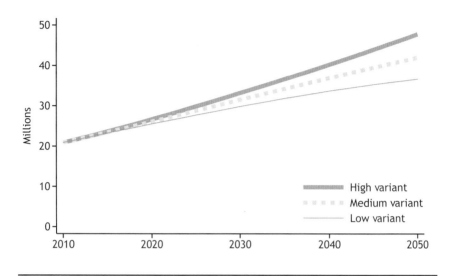

Source: UNPOP (2009).

agriculture and for standards of living. Access to natural resources—especially agricultural land—will become increasingly difficult, and nutritional adequacy may suffer as a consequence. Increasing access to employment, as well as developing infrastructure for roads and social services such as schools and health centers, are additional challenges the country will face.

Income

Figure 5.13 presents three overall scenarios for Côte d'Ivoire's GDP per capita, derived by combining three GDP scenarios with the three population scenarios of Figure 5.12 (based on UN population data). The optimistic scenario combines high GDP with low population scenarios for all countries, the baseline scenario combines the medium GDP projection with the medium population scenario, and the pessimistic scenario combines the low GDP scenario with the high population scenario. The agricultural modeling in the next section uses these scenarios.

The pessimistic scenario shows a relatively insignificant increase in GDP per capita, whereas the optimistic scenario shows per capita GDP more than doubling by 2030 and increasing sharply thereafter, reaching more than US$6,000 (US dollars) by 2050.

FIGURE 5.13   Gross domestic product (GDP) per capita in Côte d'Ivoire, future scenarios, 2010–50

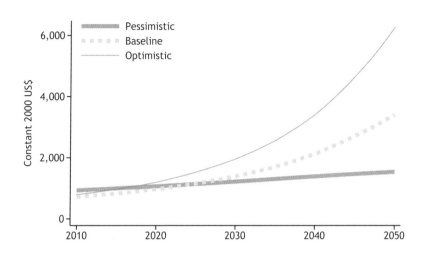

Sources: Computed from GDP data from the World Bank Economic Adaptation to Climate Change project (World Bank 2010), from the Millennium Ecosystem Assessment (2005), reports, and from population data from the United Nations (UNPOP 2009).
Note: US$ = US dollars.

Biophysical Scenarios

Climate Scenarios

Figure 5.14 shows projected annual precipitation changes under the four downscaled general circulation models (GCMs) in the A1B scenario.[1] CNRM-CM3 and ECHAM 5 show generally higher rainfall than CSIRO Mark 3 and MIROC 3.2.[2] CNRM-CM3 shows an increase in precipitation of 50–100 millimeters in the north and on the coast; ECHAM 5 shows a similar increase in the southwest. CSIRO Mark 3 shows a decrease in precipitation of –200 to –100 millimeters in the north, whereas MIROC 3.2 shows a decrease

---

1   The A1B scenario is a greenhouse gas emissions scenario that assumes fast economic growth, a population that peaks midcentury, and the development of new and efficient technologies, along with a balanced use of energy sources.

2   CNRM-CM3 is National Meteorological Research Center–Climate Model 3. ECHAM 5 is a fifth-generation climate model developed at the Max Planck Institute for Meteorology in Hamburg. CSIRO is a climate model developed at the Australia Commonwealth Scientific and Industrial Research Organisation. MIROC is the Model for Interdisciplinary Research on Climate, developed at the University of Tokyo Center for Climate System Research.

FIGURE 5.14 Changes in mean annual precipitation in Côte d'Ivoire, 2000–2050, A1B
scenario (millimeters)

CNRM-CM3 GCM

CSIRO Mark 3 GCM

ECHAM 5 GCM

MIROC 3.2 medium-resolution GCM

■ < –400
□ –400 to –200
□ –200 to –100
□ –100 to –50
  –50 to 50
□ 50 to 100
□ 100 to 200
□ 200 to 400
■ > 400

Source: Authors' calculations based on Jones, Thornton, and Heinke (2009).

Notes: A1B = greenhouse gas emissions scenario that assumes fast economic growth, a population that peaks midcentury,
and the development of new and efficient technologies, along with a balanced use of energy sources; CNRM-CM3 = National
Meteorological Research Center–Climate Model 3; CSIRO = climate model developed at the Australia Commonwealth Scientific and Industrial Research Organisation; ECHAM 5 = fifth-generation climate model developed at the Max Planck Institute
for Meteorology (Hamburg); GCM = general circulation model; MIROC = Model for Interdisciplinary Research on Climate,
developed at the University of Tokyo Center for Climate System Research.

of up to −400 millimeters in the southwest and −200 to −100 millimeters in the southeast.

Figure 5.15 shows the change in the average daily maximum temperature for the warmest month of the year modeled on the basis of the A1B scenario. The CNRM-CM3 model shows an increase of 2.0°–2.5°C all over the country, whereas the ECHAM 5 GCM shows the same for only the northern part of the country but predicts that the southern half will experience an increase of only 1.5°–2.0°C. The CSIRO GCM has a spatial distribution similar to that of ECHAM 5 but predicts that temperatures will be a half-degree cooler across the board. The MIROC 3.2 medium-resolution GCM is the least pessimistic, showing a maximum rise in temperature of only 1.0°–1.5°C, with a substantial patch in the south projected to experience an increase of only 0.5°–1.0°C.

Crop Physiological Response to Climate Change

The effect of climate change on key crops is mapped in the next two sets of figures. Crop yields with 2050 climate are compared to the yields assuming an unchanged (2000) climate. The CSIRO, ECHAM 5, and MIROC 3.2 GCMs show a yield loss of 5–25 percent of baseline for rice in the central and northeast regions of the country (Figure 5.16). MIROC 3.2 shows a yield loss greater than 25 percent in a portion of the central part of the country. In contrast, CNRM-CM3 shows a yield gain of 5–25 percent of baseline in many parts of the country, with a small portion of the country showing losses of between 5 and 25 percent.

All models present a relatively more pessimistic scenario for maize compared to rice in Côte d'Ivoire (Figure 5.17). ECHAM 5 in particular predicts that most of the northwest quadrant will have a yield loss of greater than 25 percent, while CNRM predicts as many areas of gains as of losses.

Agricultural Vulnerability Scenarios (Crop-Specific)

The next four figures show simulation results from the IMPACT model associated with key agricultural crops of Côte d'Ivoire. The figure for each featured crop has five graphs: production, yield, area, net exports, and world price.

All scenarios show similar trends for sweet potatoes and yams in production, area under production, and net exports (Figure 5.18). Sweet potato and yam production is shown to increase slightly, to a maximum of 3.5–4.0 million

FIGURE 5.15   Change in monthly mean maximum daily temperature in Côte d'Ivoire for the warmest month, 2000–2050, A1B scenario (°C)

CNRM-CM3 GCM

CSIRO Mark 3 GCM

ECHAM 5 GCM

MIROC 3.2 medium-resolution GCM

  < –1

   –1 to –0.5

   –0.5 to 0

   0 to 0.5

   0.5 to 1

   1 to 1.5

   1.5 to 2

   2 to 2.5

   2.5 to 3

   3 to 3.5

   > 3.5

Source: Authors' calculations based on Jones, Thornton, and Heinke (2009).

Notes: A1B = greenhouse gas emissions scenario that assumes fast economic growth, a population that peaks midcentury, and the development of new and efficient technologies, along with a balanced use of energy sources; CNRM-CM3 = National Meteorological Research Center–Climate Model 3; CSIRO = climate model developed at the Australia Commonwealth Scientific and Industrial Research Organisation; ECHAM 5 = fifth-generation climate model developed at the Max Planck Institute for Meteorology (Hamburg); GCM = general circulation model; MIROC = Model for Interdisciplinary Research on Climate, developed at the University of Tokyo Center for Climate System Research.

FIGURE 5.16   Yield change under climate change: Rainfed rice in Côte d'Ivoire, 2010–50, A1B scenario

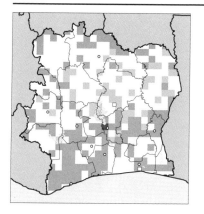

CNRM-CM3 GCM

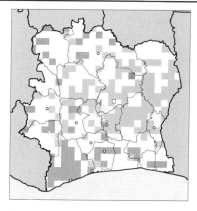

CSIRO Mark 3 GCM

ECHAM 5 GCM

MIROC 3.2 medium-resolution GCM

■ 2000 old area lost

▨ Yield loss > 25% of 2000

▨ Yield loss 5–25%

Yield change within 5%

▨ Yield gain 5–25%

■ Yield gain > 25%

■ 2050 new area gained

Source: Authors' estimates.

Notes: A1B = greenhouse gas emissions scenario that assumes fast economic growth, a population that peaks midcentury, and the development of new and efficient technologies, along with a balanced use of energy sources; CNRM-CM3 = National Meteorological Research Center–Climate Model 3; CSIRO = climate model developed at the Australia Commonwealth Scientific and Industrial Research Organisation; ECHAM 5 = fifth-generation climate model developed at the Max Planck Institute for Meteorology (Hamburg); GCM = general circulation model; MIROC = Model for Interdisciplinary Research on Climate, developed at the University of Tokyo Center for Climate System Research.

FIGURE 5.17   Yield change under climate change: Rainfed maize in Côte d'Ivoire, 2010–50, A1B scenario

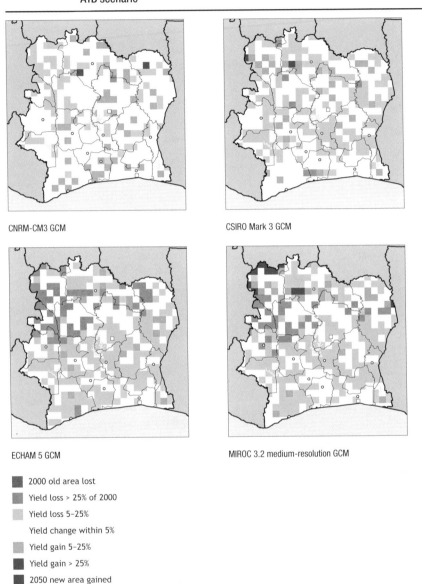

CNRM-CM3 GCM

CSIRO Mark 3 GCM

ECHAM 5 GCM

MIROC 3.2 medium-resolution GCM

■ 2000 old area lost
■ Yield loss > 25% of 2000
▫ Yield loss 5–25%
Yield change within 5%
▫ Yield gain 5–25%
■ Yield gain > 25%
■ 2050 new area gained

Source: Authors' estimates.

Notes: A1B = greenhouse gas emissions scenario that assumes fast economic growth, a population that peaks midcentury, and the development of new and efficient technologies, along with a balanced use of energy sources; CNRM-CM3 = National Meteorological Research Center–Climate Model 3; CSIRO = climate model developed at the Australia Commonwealth Scientific and Industrial Research Organisation; ECHAM 5 = fifth-generation climate model developed at the Max Planck Institute for Meteorology (Hamburg); GCM = general circulation model; MIROC = Model for Interdisciplinary Research on Climate, developed at the University of Tokyo Center for Climate System Research.

metric tons in 2025, then to decrease to 3.0 million metric tons in 2050. The area planted with the crop is shown to decrease from 435,000 hectares in 2010 to 400,000 hectares in 2050; the yield per hectare will range between 8 and 10 metric tons. Net exports are projected to decline progressively despite the increase in world prices. From 2035 to 2050, the projected world prices for sweet potatoes and yams diverge increasingly between the pessimistic and optimistic scenarios.

Similar to the cases of sweet potatoes and yams, the production, land area, productivity, and world price for cassava increase in all the scenarios (Figure 5.19). Production of cassava and other roots and tubers in Côte d'Ivoire is shown to increase from 2.2 million metric tons in 2010 to 2.5–3.0 million metric tons from 2030 to 2050. The land area under cassava is not projected to change, while net exports will progressively decrease despite the increase in world price. A greater increase in population relative to the increase in cassava production could account for the declining net exports.

Trends for total rice production, yield per hectare, and area of production are similar in all the scenarios (Figure 5.20). Both total production and productivity are shown increasing, while the area devoted to the crop will increase by a very small amount. Production is predicted to grow from 700,000 metric tons in 2010 to close to 1.2 million metric tons in 2050 in the pessimistic scenario and to around 1.1 million metric tons in the optimistic scenario. Although net exports decrease in all scenarios, the decrease will be greater in the optimistic scenario than in the pessimistic scenario. This could be attributed to the lower projected world price in the optimistic scenario.

The trends for production, productivity, area cultivated, and the world market price of maize in Côte d'Ivoire are similar to those for both roots and tubers and rice (Figure 5.21). For exports, however—unlike in the case of rice and roots and tubers—the net maize exports are shown to increase initially and then fall after 2035. However, there is an increasing uncertainty in the trends for net exports and world prices in all of the scenarios as climate change effects become more pronounced.

Human Vulnerability Scenarios

Figure 5.22 shows the impact of future GDP and population scenarios on under-five malnutrition rates in Côte d'Ivoire. The box-and-whisker plots in the figure indicate the range of climate scenario effects. The number of malnourished children under five years of age decreases in both the baseline and the optimistic scenarios but to increase in the pessimistic scenario. The

FIGURE 5.18   Impact of changes in GDP and population on yams and sweet potatoes in
Côte d'Ivoire, 2010–50

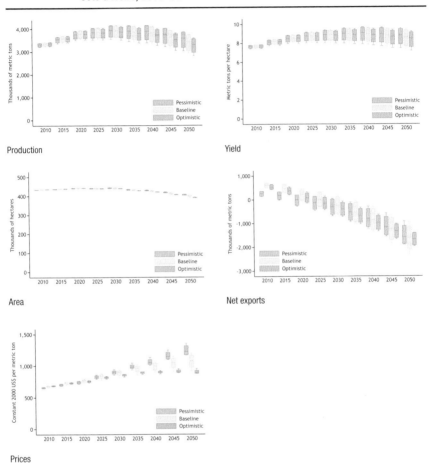

Source: Based on analysis conducted for Nelson et al. (2010).

Notes: The box and whiskers plot for each socioeconomic scenario shows the range of effects from the four future climate scenarios. GDP = gross domestic product; US$ = US dollars.

FIGURE 5.19 Impact of changes in GDP and population on cassava in Côte d'Ivoire, 2010–50

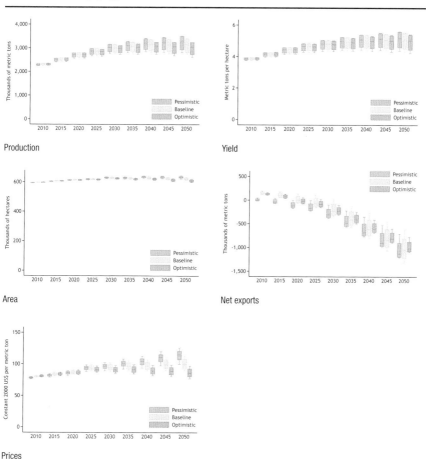

Production

Yield

Area

Net exports

Prices

Source: Based on analysis conducted for Nelson et al. (2010).

Notes: The box and whiskers plot for each socioeconomic scenario shows the range of effects from the four future climate scenarios. GDP = gross domestic product; US$ = US dollars.

FIGURE 5.20   Impact of changes in GDP and population on rice in Côte d'Ivoire, 2010–50

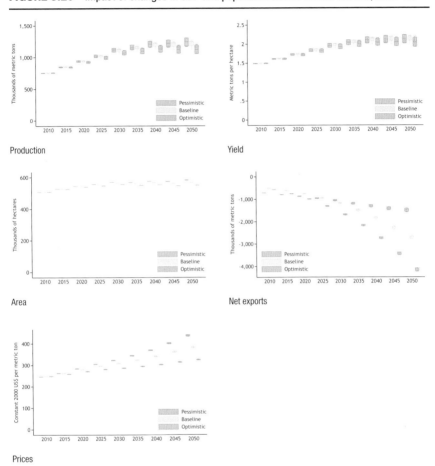

Production

Yield

Area

Net exports

Prices

Source: Based on analysis conducted for Nelson et al. (2010).

Notes: The box and whiskers plot for each socioeconomic scenario shows the range of effects from the four future climate scenarios. GDP = gross domestic product; US$ = US dollars.

FIGURE 5.21 Impact of changes in GDP and population on maize in Côte d'Ivoire, 2010–50

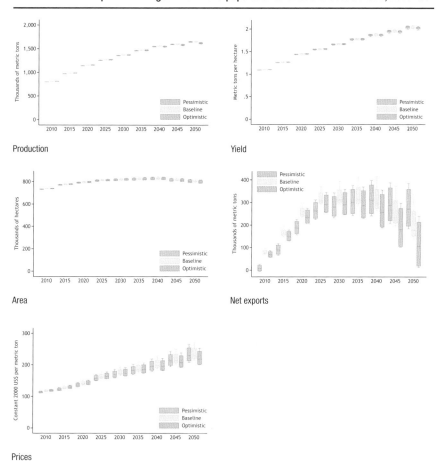

Production

Yield

Area

Net exports

Prices

Source: Based on analysis conducted for Nelson et al. (2010).

Notes: The box and whiskers plot for each socioeconomic scenario shows the range of effects from the four future climate scenarios. GDP = gross domestic product; US$ = US dollars.

FIGURE 5.22   Number of malnourished children under five years of age in Côte d'Ivoire in multiple income and climate scenarios, 2010–50

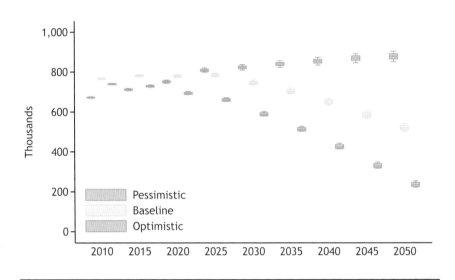

Source: Based on analysis conducted for Nelson et al. (2010).
Note: The box and whiskers plot for each socioeconomic scenario shows the range of effects from the four future climate scenarios.

optimistic scenario shows a decrease in malnourished children under age five, from 740,000 in 2010 to 240,000 in 2050, whereas the pessimistic scenario shows an increase to 880,000 in 2050. With the increase in population, even this increase in numbers of malnourished represents a decrease in percentage of children under 5 who are malnourished.

Figure 5.23 shows the available kilocalories per capita. The pessimistic scenario shows this indicator decreasing, from 2,400 in 2010 to 2,000 in 2050. The optimistic scenario shows an increase, to 3,000 in 2043 and 3,600 in 2050. These trends correlate with the scenarios for malnourished children under age five.

Conclusions and Policy Recommendations

Increased food production is needed to feed the rising population in Côte d'Ivoire, with the majority concentrated in urban areas. This challenge will require appropriate research interventions to ensure sustainable crop production without adversely affecting the natural resource base, particularly against the background of climate change challenges. Some models show a decrease

FIGURE 5.23   Kilocalories per capita in Côte d'Ivoire in multiple income and climate scenarios, 2010–50

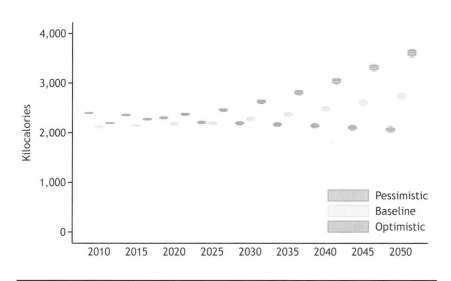

Source: Based on analysis conducted for Nelson et al. (2010).

Note: The box and whiskers plot for each socioeconomic scenario shows the range of effects from the four future climate scenarios.

in precipitation, and all show an increase in temperature, with some showing increases of up to 2.5°C by 2050. The maize crop is shown to be particularly vulnerable to these adverse climatic conditions.

In view of the significant proportion of the population of Côte d'Ivoire deriving their livelihoods from the agricultural sector, government policies relating to agriculture should be re-examined and revised where necessary to support an environment and activities that will ensure the resilience of farmers in regard to the natural recourses base so that sustainable food production might be maintained against the background of a changing climate.

The Government of Côte d'Ivoire should reflect the importance of agriculture in the overall economy by formulating and supporting policies to slow population growth, support rapid agricultural growth, and provide a solid foundation for the growth of other sectors of the economy. Such policies should include measures to accomplish the following:

• Improve the system for recording daily weather data as well as developing seasonal predictions to help farmers select more appropriate technologies for the anticipated weather.

- Improve market infrastructure, including appropriate storage facilities and rural roads, to facilitate easy transport and storage of produce. Reliable communication networks will greatly enhance farmers' ability to access relevant market information.

- Increase the funding to agricultural research and extension to support the development of appropriate technologies and management practices designed to optimize productivity in the face of climate change and consider whether incentives could be created to enhance participation in the development and distribution of such technologies by both the private and the nongovernmental sectors.

Possible agricultural interventions include the following:

- Developing varieties of major crops, particularly maize, that are adaptable to the changing climate and are compatible with associated crops.

- Determining appropriate times and patterns of planting in the changing climate.

- In addition to developing policies directly supporting agricultural adaptation, providing support for family planning and other interventions to slow population growth, which might reduce the demand for food and enhance food security for the nation.

Finally, policies for mitigating climate change, such as policies encouraging reforestation, augmentation of soil organic carbon, and modification of livestock management practices, might be considered, some of which would also improve yields. With a supportive policy environment and improved research and extension, farmers will have greater hope of adapting to the changing climate in the coming decades.

References

Bartholome, E., and A. S. Belward. 2005. "GLC2000: A New Approach to Global Land Cover Mapping from Earth Observation Data." *International Journal of Remote Sensing* 26 (9): 1959–1977.

Chape, S., S. Blyth, L. Fish, P. Fox, and M. Spalding, compilers. 2003. *2003 United Nations List of Protected Areas.* Gland, Switzerland, and Cambridge, UK: International Union for Conservation of Nature (IUCN); Cambridge, UK: United Nations Environment Programme–World Conservation Monitoring Centre (UNEP–WCMC). ix + 44 pp.

CIESIN (Center for International Earth Science Information Network, Columbia University), Columbia University, IFPRI (International Food Policy Research Institute), World Bank, and CIAT (Centro Internacional de Agricultura Tropical). 2004. *Global Rural–Urban Mapping Project, Version 1 (GRUMPv1)*. Palisades, NY, US: Socioeconomic Data and Applications Center (SEDAC), Columbia University. http://sedac.ciesin.columbia.edu/gpw.

FAO (Food and Agriculture Organization of the United Nations). 2010. *FAOSTAT Database on Agriculture*. Rome.

Jones, P. G., P. K. Thornton, and J. Heinke. 2009. "Generating Characteristic Daily Weather Data Using Downscaled Climate Model Data from the IPCC's Fourth Assessment." Project report for the International Institute for Land Reclamation and Improvement, Wageningen, the Netherlands. Accessed May 7, 2010. www.ccafs-climate.org/pattern_scaling/.

Lehner, B., and P. Döll. 2004. "Development and Validation of a Global Database of Lakes, Reservoirs, and Wetlands." *Journal of Hydrology* 296 (1–4): 1–22.

Millennium Ecosystem Assessment. 2005. *Ecosystems and Human Well-being: Synthesis.* Washington, DC: Island Press. http://www.maweb.org/en/Global.aspx.

Myers, N. 1990. "The Biodiversity Challenge: Expanded Hotspot Analysis." *Environmentalist* 10: 243.

Nelson, G. C., M. W. Rosegrant, A. Palazzo, I. Gray, C. Ingersoll, R. Robertson, S. Tokgoz, et al. 2010. *Food Security, Farming, and Climate Change to 2050: Scenarios, Results, Policy Options.* Washington, DC: International Food Policy Research Institute.

Roth, H. H., M. Mühlenberg, P. Roben, and W. Barthlott. 1979. *Etat actuel des parcs nationaux de la Comoé et de Taï ainsi que de la Réserve d'Azagny et propositions visant à leur conservation et à leur développement aux fins de promotion du tourisme.* P.N. 73.2085.6. 4 vols. Kronberg: FGU.

UICN/BRAO (Union Internationale pour la Conservation de la Nature/Bureau Régional pour l'Afrique de l'Ouest). 2008. *Evaluation de l'efficacité de la gestion des aires protégées: Parcs et réserves de Côte d'Ivoire.* Programme Aires protégées. Ouagadougou, Burkina Faso. http://data.iucn.org/dbtw-wpd/edocs/2008-008.pdf.

UNEP and IUCN (United Nations Environment Programme and International Union for the Conservation of Nature). 2009. *World Database on Protected Areas (WDPA): Annual Release.* Accessed 2009. www.wdpa.org/protectedplanet.aspx.

UNPOP (United Nations Department of Economic and Social Affairs–Population Division). 2009. *World Population Prospects: The 2008 Revision.* New York. http://esa.un.org/unpd/wpp/.

Wood, S., G. Hyman, U. Deichmann, E. Barona, R. Tenorio, Z. Guo, et al. 2010. *Sub-national Poverty Maps for the Developing World Using International Poverty Lines: Preliminary Data Release.* Washington, DC: Harvest Choice and International Food Policy Research Institute. http://labs.harvestchoice.org/2010/08/poverty-maps/.

World Bank. 2009. *World Development Indicators.* Accessed May 2011. http://data.worldbank.org/data-catalog/world-development-indicators.

———. 2010. *Economics of Adaptation to Climate Change: Synthesis Report.* Washington, DC. http://climatechange.worldbank.org/content/economics-adaptation-climate-change-study-homepage.

You, L., and S. Wood. 2006. "An Entropy Approach to Spatial Disaggregation of Agricultural Production." *Agricultural Systems* 90 (1–3): 329–347.

You, L., S. Wood, and U. Wood-Sichra. 2006. "Generating Global Crop Distribution Maps: From Census to Grid." Paper presented at the International Association of Agricultural Economists Conference, Brisbane, Australia, August 11–18.

———. 2009. "Generating Plausible Crop Distribution and Performance Maps for Sub-Saharan Africa Using a Spatially Disaggregated Data Fusion and Optimization Approach." *Agricultural Systems* 99 (2–3): 126–140.

Chapter 6

GHANA

Delali Kofi Nutsukpo, Abdulai Jalloh, Robert Zougmoré, Gerald C. Nelson, and Timothy S. Thomas

Including inland water bodies, Ghana covers 238,539 square kilometers and is located on the south central coast of West Africa. The country shares borders in the east with Togo, in the north with Burkina Faso, and in the west with Côte d'Ivoire. The topography of Ghana is mainly undulating, with most slopes less than 5 percent and many not exceeding 1 percent. The topography of the high rainforest is, however, mainly strongly rolling. The uplifted edges of the Voltarian basin give rise to narrow plateaus between 300 and 600 meters in elevation (Boateng 1998). Moving from the rainforest zone in the south to the Sahara Desert in the north, rainfall generally decreases and temperature increases. Rainfall is the most important climatic factor influencing vegetation in Ghana. The wettest area is in the extreme southwest, where the rainfall is over 2,000 millimeters per year. In the extreme north, the annual rainfall is less than 1,100 millimeters. The driest area is at the southeastern coastal tip, where the rainfall is about 750 millimeters. Much of the rain falls in intense storms of short duration, especially at the beginning of the season, resulting in heavy runoff and erosion. The annual mean relative humidity is about 80 percent in the south and 44 percent in the north (Dickson and Benneh 1988). The mean monthly temperature for the entire country is 25°C. Although temperatures are uniformly moderate, there are important variations over different parts of the country, reflecting altitude and distance from the sea.

The agricultural sector in Ghana includes crops, livestock, and fisheries, all contributing to national food security. Ghanaian agriculture is rainfed, with only 4 percent of its irrigation potential developed (Ghana, MOFA 2009). As the backbone of the national economy, agriculture provides employment to over 50 percent of the country's workforce and supplies over 70 percent of the national food requirements. The potential impacts of global climate change (such as unpredictable rainfall, increasing temperatures, and longer dry periods) add to the vulnerability of Ghanaian agricultural production systems. Although the general consequences of climate change are becoming better known, great uncertainty remains about how climate change will affect specific locations.

Review of the Current Situation

Population

Figure 6.1 shows trends in the total population and rural population of Ghana (left axis), as well as the shares of the rural and urban populations (right axis), and Table 6.1 shows the population growth rates between 1960 and 2008. The urban population of Ghana has been growing faster than the rural population since the country's independence in 1957, and it is now about half of the total population. The rural population has also grown steadily, peaking at 2.4 percent growth in 1990. The urban population growth rate, by contrast, although higher than that of rural areas over the entire period, fell from 4.7 percent between 1960 and 1969 to 3.8 percent between 2000 and 2008.

Figure 6.2 shows the geographic distribution of the population in Ghana. The rising urban growth rate is reflected in the population increases in several towns in the southern sector of the country—Accra, Tema, and Kumasi—with population densities greater than 2,000 persons per square kilometer. Tamale is also becoming an important growth center in the northern part of the country. Increases in the urban population are also spilling over into

FIGURE 6.1   Population trends in Ghana: Total population, rural population, and percent urban, 1960–2008

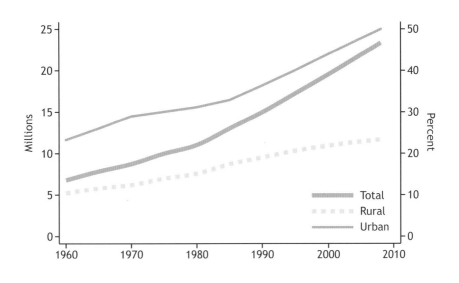

Source: World Development Indicators (World Bank 2009).

TABLE 6.1   Population growth rates in Côte d'Ivoire, 1960–2008 (percent)

Decade	Total growth rate	Rural growth rate	Urban growth rate
1960–69	2.5	1.8	4.7
1970–79	2.3	2.0	3.1
1980–89	3.1	2.4	4.6
1990–99	2.7	1.4	4.6
2000–2008	2.2	0.8	3.8

Source: Authors' calculations based on World Development Indicators (World Bank 2009).

adjacent periurban areas, with population densities of 100–500 per square kilometer. Although the slowing growth rate in rural populations and the relatively smaller increase in the total rural population compared to urban areas may potentially reduce the agricultural workforce, there may be a compensating expansion in periurban agriculture to meet the food demands of urban populations, especially for vegetables.

FIGURE 6.2   Population distribution in Ghana, 2000 (persons per square kilometer)

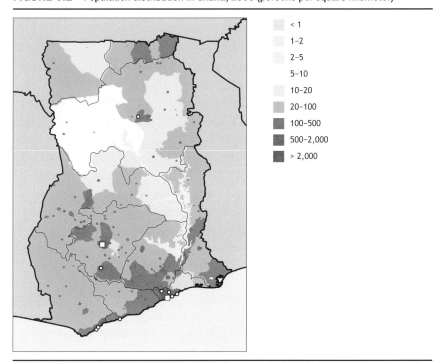

< 1
1–2
2–5
5–10
10–20
20–100
100–500
500–2,000
> 2,000

Source: CIESIN et al. (2004).

FIGURE 6.3   Per capita GDP in Ghana, 1960–2008 (constant 2000 US$) and share of GDP from agriculture (percent)

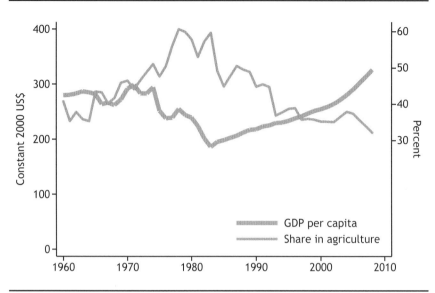

Source: World Development Indicators (World Bank 2009).
Notes: GDP = gross domestic product; US$ = US dollars.

Income

The share of income earned in agriculture shows the importance of agriculture as a sector of the economy in Ghana. Figure 6.3 shows trends in gross domestic product (GDP) per capita and in the proportion of GDP from agriculture. The agricultural sector's contribution to GDP increased from 1960 until the late 1970s, when the sector was the largest single contributor to GDP. After the mid-1980s, however, agricultural GDP declined to less than 50 percent of the country's total GDP. Agricultural GDP has continued to decline, while per capita GDP has increased. The rapid increases in per capita GDP after 2000 may reflect the development of the service sector, especially the rapid growth in the telecommunications subsector (Ghana, GSS 2010).

Vulnerability to Climate Change

Table 6.2 provides some data on Ghana's performance on indicators of a population's vulnerability or resilience to economic shocks beyond that of income level: level of education, literacy, and concentration of labor in poorer or less dynamic sectors. The table indicates that there is nearly universal enrollment in primary

TABLE 6.2   Education and labor statistics for Ghana, 1990s and 2000s

Indicator	Year	Percent
Primary school enrollment (percent gross, three-year average)	2008	103.7
Secondary school enrollment (percent gross, three-year average)	2008	53.3
Adult literacy rate	2007	65.0
Percent employed in agriculture	1999	55.0
Under-five malnutrition (weight for age)	2008	13.9

Source: Authors' calculations based on World Development Indicators (World Bank 2009).

school (three-year average) and that more than 50 percent of children gained access to secondary education in 2008. These improvements in access to formal education are reflected in the adult literacy rate of 65 percent in 2007. Literacy has the potential of reducing the population's vulnerability to economic shocks through improved access to income sources other than agriculture.

Figure 6.4 shows data for Ghana on two noneconomic correlates of poverty: life expectancy and under-five mortality. The correlates are widely used as indicators of well-being. Life expectancy rose from 45 years in 1960 to almost 60 years in 1990 but declined to 57 years in 2009. Under-five mortality

FIGURE 6.4   Well-being indicators in Ghana, 1960–2008

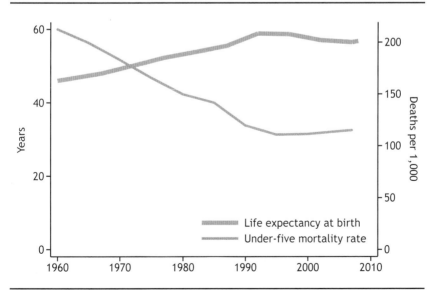

Source: World Development Indicators (World Bank 2009).

decreased from 200 deaths per 1,000 births in 1960 to 120 deaths per 1,000 births in 2008–09.

Figure 6.5 shows the proportion of the Ghanaian population living on less than US$2 (US dollars) per day. Poverty is endemic in the three northern regions, where more than 95 percent of the population is living on less than US$2 per day. Poverty generally decreases from the north to the south. Poverty rates in the Volta and Brong Ahafo Regions—areas with mostly transition vegetation—are higher than for the other southern regions but lower than for the three northern regions.

Poverty is relatively more widespread in the northern part of the country compared to the western part. There are more urban settlements and more economic activities in the west than in the north. Moreover, rainfall is greater in the west, supporting the production of tree crops. The forest sector regions of Ashanti, Central, and Western Regions share a poverty bracket. The Eastern and Greater Accra Regions have the lowest percentage of the population living on less than US$2 a day. The socioeconomic activities associated with the capital city in the Greater Accra Region and with the area around Lake Volta in the Eastern Region could account for the relatively lower poverty rate in those two regions.

FIGURE 6.5   Poverty in Ghana, circa 2005 (percent below US$2 per day)

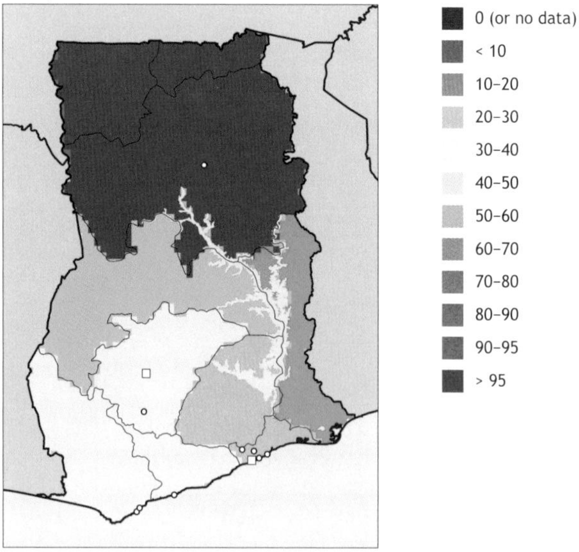

Legend:
- 0 (or no data)
- < 10
- 10–20
- 20–30
- 30–40
- 40–50
- 50–60
- 60–70
- 70–80
- 80–90
- 90–95
- > 95

Source: Wood et al. (2010).
Note: Based on 2005 US$ (US dollars) and on purchasing power parity value.

Review of Land Use and Agriculture

Land Use Overview

Figure 6.6 shows Ghana's land cover and land use as of 2000. The country had lost most of its evergreen forest cover by 2000, except for limited areas of the Western, Ashanti, Brong Ahafo, and Eastern Regions, as well as parts of the Akwapim (Togo ranges along Ghana's eastern borders in the Volta Region). The rate of loss of forest cover is estimated at 1.9 percent per year (Ghana, Forestry Commission 2010). The former forested areas of Western, Ashanti, Central, Brong Ahafo, and Eastern Regions now have mixtures of croplands, trees, and other vegetation types (mosaic terrain). Currently the most extensive vegetation type is open broadleaved deciduous tree cover. The northeastern area of the Upper East Region is the only part of the country that has no vegetative cover and is classified as cultivated and managed area (under permanent cultivation). The cities of Accra-Tema, Sekondi-Takoradi, Obuasi, Kumasi, and Tamale are mapped as artificial surfaces and related areas—an indication that the land covers in those areas have been significantly modified from the original natural cover. The water bodies identified and represented on the map are the Volta Lake system and Lake Bosomtwi; the other known river systems, such as Pra and Ankobrah, are not shown.

Figure 6.7 shows the locations of protected areas, including parks and reserves. Although a substantial number of areas are shown as protected areas, only a few have been classified by the International Union for the Conservation of Nature. The classified areas are in various categories and regions: one is classified as a strict nature reserve (in the Ashanti Region), five as national parks (one each in the Western, Central, Brong Ahafo, Eastern, and Northern Regions), two as habitat or species management areas (in the Ashanti and Brong Ahafo Regions), and two as managed resource protected areas (in the Western and Upper West regions).

Figure 6.8 shows travel times to towns and cities of various sizes as potential markets for agricultural products. The road network is directly related to the population distribution in the country. The best road networks are between the major cities in the southern zone—Accra, Cape Coast, Takoradi, Kumasi, and Sunyani. There are also first-class roads linking the major cities across the country along two main routes: Accra–Kumasi–Wenchi–Wa and Accra–Kumasi–Techiman–Tamale. Well-maintained road networks link most of the district capitals to the major urban towns in the various regions, providing easy delivery of goods and services. Travel times increase for communities

FIGURE 6.6   Land cover and land use in Ghana, 2000

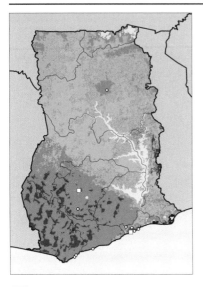

■ Tree cover, broadleaved, evergreen
▦ Tree cover, broadleaved, deciduous, closed
□ Tree cover, broadleaved, deciduous, open
■ Tree cover, broadleaved, needle-leaved, evergreen
▨ Tree cover, broadleaved, needle-leaved, deciduous
▨ Tree cover, broadleaved, mixed leaf type
▨ Tree cover, broadleaved, regularly flooded, fresh water
■ Tree cover, broadleaved, regularly flooded, saline water
▨ Mosaic of tree cover/other natural vegetation
■ Tree cover, burnt
▨ Shrub cover, closed-open, evergreen
▨ Shrub cover, closed-open, deciduous
□ Herbacious cover, closed-open
▨ Sparse herbacious or sparse shrub cover
▨ Regularly flooded shrub or herbacious cover
▨ Cultivated and managed areas
■ Mosaic of cropland/tree cover/other natural vegetation
▨ Mosaic of cropland/shrub/grass cover
▨ Bare areas
▨ Water bodies
□ Snow and ice
■ Artificial surfaces and associated areas
□ No data

Source: GLC2000 (Global Land Cover 2000) (Bartholome and Belward 2005).

FIGURE 6.7   Protected areas in Ghana, 2009

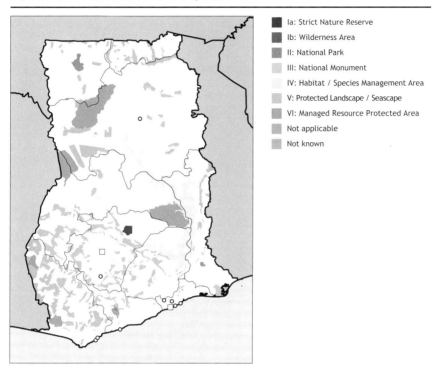

Ia: Strict Nature Reserve
Ib: Wilderness Area
II: National Park
III: National Monument
IV: Habitat / Species Management Area
V: Protected Landscape / Seascape
VI: Managed Resource Protected Area
Not applicable
Not known

Sources: Protected areas are from the World Database on Protected Areas (UNEP and IUCN 2009). Water bodies are from the World Wildlife Fund's Global Lakes and Wetlands Database (Lehner and Döll 2004).

farther from established road networks, without good linking roads. For communities located beyond large water bodies, such as Lake Volta, there are additional travel challenges, because Ghana lacks a well-developed water transport system.

Agriculture Overview

The next three tables show key agricultural commodities in terms of area harvested (Table 6.3), the value of the harvest (Table 6.4), and the provision of food for people (ranked by weight) (Table 6.5). Cocoa remains the single most important cash crop in Ghana, followed by two important food security crops: cassava and maize. The two most important (food and income) crops in the northern sector are groundnuts and sorghum, which rank fourth and fifth in the country, respectively.

Yams and plantains are very important crops in terms of value of production. Although the harvested areas of these crops were lower than for other

FIGURE 6.8   Travel time to urban areas of various sizes in Ghana, circa 2000

To cities of 500,000 or more people

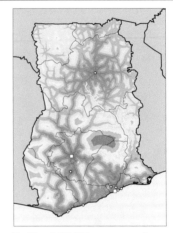

To cities of 100,000 or more people

To towns and cities of 25,000 or more people

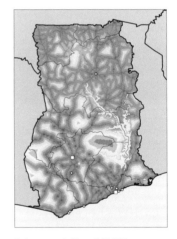

To towns and cities of 10,000 or more people

■ Urban location
■ < 1 hour
■ 1–3 hours
■ 3–5 hours
□ 5–8 hours
  8–11 hours
■ 11–16 hours
■ 16–26 hours
■ > 26 hours

Source: Authors' calculations.

TABLE 6.3 Harvest area of leading agricultural commodities in Ghana, 2006–08 (thousands of hectares)

Rank	Crop	Percent of total	Harvest area
	Total	100.0	6,310
1	Cocoa beans	26.6	1,678
2	Cassava	12.6	797
3	Maize	12.1	764
4	Groundnuts	7.4	470
5	Sorghum	5.3	333
6	Oil palm fruit	4.9	311
7	Plantains	4.8	301
8	Yams	4.7	299
9	Taro cocoyams	4.1	261
10	Millet	3.0	190

Source: FAOSTAT (FAO 2010).
Note: All values are based on the three-year average for 2006–08.

TABLE 6.4 Value of production of leading agricultural commodities in Ghana, 2005–07 (millions of US$)

Rank	Crop	Percent of total	Value of production
	Total	100.0	6,695.6
1	Cassava	17.8	1,189.4
2	Yams	17.2	1,153.1
3	Plantains	15.1	1,014.3
4	Cocoa beans	10.3	689.7
5	Taro cocoyams	7.2	482.1
6	Groundnuts	5.5	368.3
7	Maize	5.2	349.9
8	Chilies and peppers	3.3	219.7
9	Chilies and peppers	2.4	158.9
10	Rice	2.3	155.5

Source: FAOSTAT (FAO 2010).
Note: All values are based on the three-year average for 2005–07. US$ = US dollars.

TABLE 6.5 Consumption of leading food commodities in Ghana, 2003–05 (thousands of metric tons)

Rank	Food	Percent of total	Food consumption
	Total	100.0	15,980
1	Cassava	28.4	4,537
2	Yams	15.2	2,433
3	Plantains	14.1	2,250
4	Other roots and tubers	8.0	1,286
5	Maize	5.6	899
6	Rice	3.2	513
7	Pelagic fish	2.7	426
8	Other vegetables	2.3	363
9	Oranges and mandarins	2.3	363
10	Wheat	2.1	332

Source: FAOSTAT (FAO 2010).
Note: All values are based on the three-year average for 2003–05.

crops, the crops were ranked higher in importance (second and third) because of the value of the products. Cassava is the most widely consumed crop in Ghana. The classification of food commodities by quantities consumed indicates their importance in the diets of Ghanaians: cassava, yams, plantains, maize, and rice rank as the five most important crops produced and consumed in Ghana.

The next four figures show the estimated yield and growing areas of key crops. Figure 6.9 shows that cassava is cultivated in all regions of Ghana—with the exception of the Upper East region—with yields ranging from 7 to more than 10 metric tons per hectare and the main areas of production concentrated in the forest zone.[1] Yam cultivation is carried out across all regions except the Upper East region and is concentrated mainly in the forested and savanna zones as well as a few areas in the transition zone (Figure 6.10).

Rainfed plantain and banana cultivation is concentrated in the forest zone, with yields of 7 tons and above (Figure 6.11). There is some potential for good plantain and banana cultivation in the transition zone but almost none in the savannah zones.

Figure 6.12 shows that rainfed maize is produced in almost all parts of the country, with the major producing areas in the transition and savanna zones. The highest maize yield levels are between 1 and 2 tons per hectare.

---

1 All tons are metric tons.

FIGURE 6.9 Yield (metric tons per hectare) and harvest area density (hectares) for rainfed cassava in Ghana, 2000

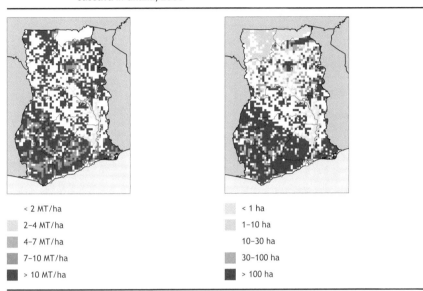

< 2 MT/ha	< 1 ha
2–4 MT/ha	1–10 ha
4–7 MT/ha	10–30 ha
7–10 MT/ha	30–100 ha
> 10 MT/ha	> 100 ha

Sources: SPAM (Spatial Production Allocation Model) (You and Wood 2006; You, Wood, and Wood-Sichra 2006, 2009).
Notes: ha = hectare; MT = metric tons.

FIGURE 6.10 Yield (metric tons per hectare) and harvest area density (hectares) for rainfed yams and sweet potatoes in Ghana, 2000

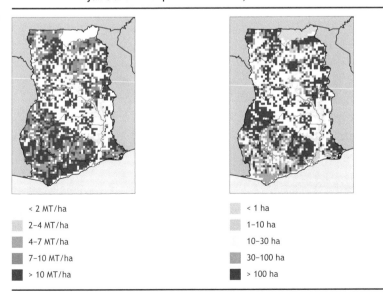

< 2 MT/ha	< 1 ha
2–4 MT/ha	1–10 ha
4–7 MT/ha	10–30 ha
7–10 MT/ha	30–100 ha
> 10 MT/ha	> 100 ha

Sources: SPAM (Spatial Production Allocation Model) (You and Wood 2006; You, Wood, and Wood-Sichra 2006, 2009).
Notes: ha = hectare; MT = metric tons.

FIGURE 6.11   Yield (metric tons per hectare) and harvest area density (hectares) for rainfed plantains and bananas in Ghana, 2000

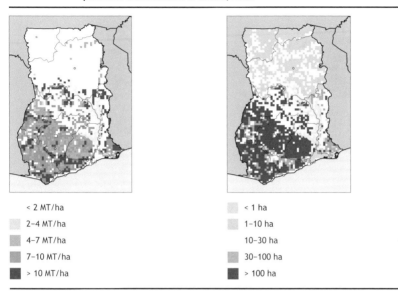

< 2 MT/ha		< 1 ha	
2–4 MT/ha		1–10 ha	
4–7 MT/ha		10–30 ha	
7–10 MT/ha		30–100 ha	
> 10 MT/ha		> 100 ha	

Sources: SPAM (Spatial Production Allocation Model) (You and Wood 2006; You, Wood, and Wood-Sichra 2006, 2009).
Notes: ha = hectare; MT = metric tons.

FIGURE 6.12   Yield (metric tons per hectare) and harvest area density (hectares) for rainfed maize in Ghana, 2000

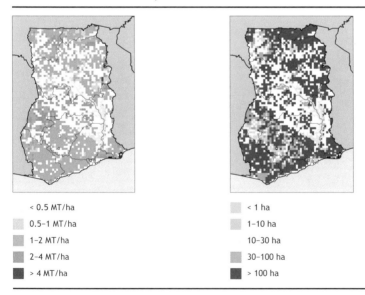

< 0.5 MT/ha		< 1 ha	
0.5–1 MT/ha		1–10 ha	
1–2 MT/ha		10–30 ha	
2–4 MT/ha		30–100 ha	
> 4 MT/ha		> 100 ha	

Sources: SPAM (Spatial Production Allocation Model) (You and Wood 2006; You, Wood, and Wood-Sichra 2006, 2009).
Notes: ha = hectare; MT = metric tons.

Economic and Demographic Scenarios

Population

Figure 6.13 shows population projections for Ghana by the United Nations (UN) population office through 2050. The high variant scenario shows Ghana's population reaching over 50 million by 2050, the medium variant 45 million, and the low variant fewer than 40 million. The low variant and high variant can be viewed as the best-case and worst-case scenarios in terms of population growth. Even in the best-case scenario, Ghana's population is shown as increasing by 50 percent within a 40-year period. The implications of such a population growth rate for overall national development could be significant with regard to the provision of required infrastructure and services.

Income

Figure 6.14 presents three overall scenarios for the gross domestic product (GDP) of Ghana derived by combining three GDP scenarios with the three population scenarios of Figure 6.13 (based on UN population data). The

FIGURE 6.13   Population projections for Ghana, 2010–50

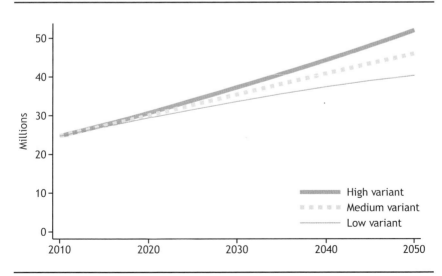

Source: UNPOP (2009).

optimistic scenario combines high GDP with low population scenarios for all countries, the baseline scenario combines the medium GDP projection with the medium population scenario, and the pessimistic scenario combines the low GDP scenario with the high population scenario. The economic modeling in the next section uses these scenarios as well.

The optimistic scenario curve shows the possibility of Ghana's per capita GDP reaching about US$5,000 by 2050, whereas the baseline and pessimistic scenarios show a possible GDP of US$2,800 and US$1,000, respectively. The optimistic scenario is the only one that supports Ghana's vision of attaining middle-income status by 2020, with per capita GDP of US$1,000. Any condition that reduces the economic (GDP) growth rate or increases the population growth rate will effectively limit the achievement of this development goal.

FIGURE 6.14   Gross domestic product (GDP) per capita in Ghana, future scenarios, 2010–50

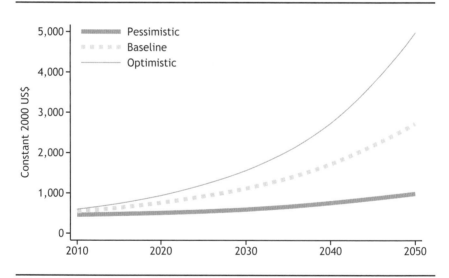

Sources: Computed from GDP data from the World Bank Economic Adaptation to Climate Change project (World Bank 2010), from the Millennium Ecosystem Assessment (2005) reports, and from population data from the United Nations (UNPOP 2009).
Note: US$ = US dollars.

Biophysical Scenarios

Climate Scenarios

Figure 6.15 shows precipitation changes in Ghana in the four downscaled general circulation models (GCMs) using the A1B scenario.[2] The CNRM-CM3 and ECHAM 5 GCMs show that there will be little change in annual precipitation in most regions of the country.[3] CNRM-CM3 shows an increase in the extreme southern part of the country, while ECHAM 5 shows an increase in the southeastern part of the country. According to CSIRO Mark 3, there are possibilities of general reduction in precipitation across the country: –200 to –100 millimeters per year in the middle belt, –100 to –50 millimeters in the northern savanna zone, and –50 to +50 millimeters in the southwestern corner.[4] MIROC 3.2 shows decreased precipitation in the south and increased precipitation in the north.[5] The maps for the latter two GCMs indicate a challenging future for Ghanaian agriculture as long as it remains basically rainfed.

Figure 6.16 shows the change in average daily maximum temperature in the A1B scenario according to various GCMs. The CNRM-CM3 GCM shows a uniform increase in temperature of 2.0°–2.5°C across the country, while the ECHAM 5 GCM shows an increase of 1.5°–2.0°C in most parts of the country but predicts temperatures like those in the CNRM-CM3 GCM for the upper northern part of the country. The CSIRO Mark 3 GCM shows an increase of 1.5°–2.0°C in the north and 1.0°–1.5°C in the south, and the MIROC 3.2 medium-resolution GCM shows a general moderate increase of 1.0°–1.5°C in most parts of the country, with a portion of the southwestern part of the country seeing an increase of 0.5°–1.0°C.

Crop Physiological Response to Climate Change

The effect of climate change on key crops is mapped in the next three figures. The comparison is between the crop yields with 2050 climate and yields with unchanged (2000) climate.

---

2 The A1B scenario is a greenhouse gas emissions scenario that assumes fast economic growth, a population that peaks midcentury, and the development of new and efficient technologies, along with a balanced use of energy sources.

3 CNRM-CM3 is National Meteorological Research Center–Climate Model 3. ECHAM 5 is a fifth-generation climate model developed at the Max Planck Institute for Meteorology in Hamburg.

4 CSIRO Mark 3 is a climate model developed at the Australia Commonwealth Scientific and Industrial Research Organisation.

5 MIROC 3.2 is the Model for Interdisciplinary Research on Climate, developed at the University of Tokyo Center for Climate System Research.

FIGURE 6.15 Changes in mean annual precipitation in Ghana, 2000–2050, A1B scenario (millimeters)

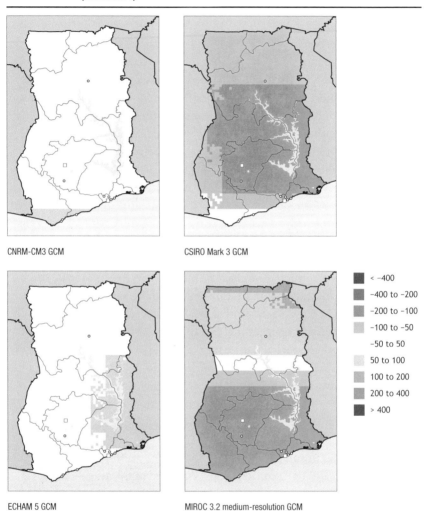

CNRM-CM3 GCM

CSIRO Mark 3 GCM

ECHAM 5 GCM

MIROC 3.2 medium-resolution GCM

< −400

−400 to −200

−200 to −100

−100 to −50

−50 to 50

50 to 100

100 to 200

200 to 400

> 400

Source: Authors' calculations based on Jones, Thornton, and Heinke (2009).

Notes: A1B = greenhouse gas emissions scenario that assumes fast economic growth, a population that peaks midcentury, and the development of new and efficient technologies, along with a balanced use of energy sources; CNRM-CM3 = National Meteorological Research Center–Climate Model 3; CSIRO = climate model developed at the Australia Commonwealth Scientific and Industrial Research Organisation; ECHAM 5 = fifth-generation climate model developed at the Max Planck Institute for Meteorology (Hamburg); GCM = general circulation model; MIROC = Model for Interdisciplinary Research on Climate, developed at the University of Tokyo Center for Climate System Research.

FIGURE 6.16   Change in the monthly mean maximum daily temperature in Ghana for the warmest month, 2000–2050, A1B scenario (°C)

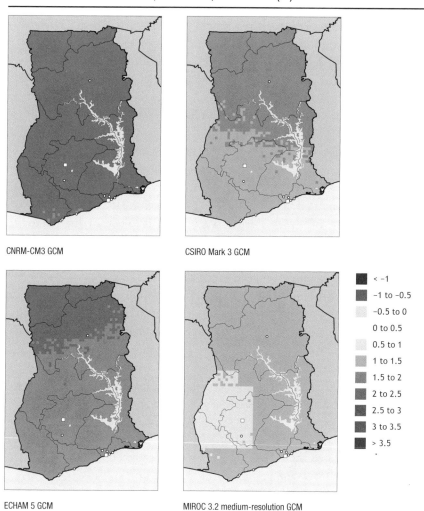

CNRM-CM3 GCM

CSIRO Mark 3 GCM

ECHAM 5 GCM

MIROC 3.2 medium-resolution GCM

Source: Authors' calculations based on Jones, Thornton, and Heinke (2009).

Notes: A1B = greenhouse gas emissions scenario that assumes fast economic growth, a population that peaks midcentury, and the development of new and efficient technologies, along with a balanced use of energy sources; CNRM-CM3 = National Meteorological Research Center–Climate Model 3; CSIRO = climate model developed at the Australia Commonwealth Scientific and Industrial Research Organisation; ECHAM 5 = fifth-generation climate model developed at the Max Planck Institute for Meteorology (Hamburg); GCM = general circulation model; MIROC = Model for Interdisciplinary Research on Climate, developed at the University of Tokyo Center for Climate System Research.

Figure 6.17 shows a general decrease in maize yield across the country. CNRM-CM3 shows relatively less area affected compared to the other three models. The other models also show a yield loss greater than 25 percent in various parts of the country.

The extent and degree of the rice yield loss (Figure 6.18) are relatively less than those for maize, with variation among the models. CNRM-CM3 shows more positive rice yield gain than do the other three models.

All the models show a reduction in rainfed groundnut yields across the country in varying degrees (Figure 6.19). CNRM-CM3 shows relatively less area with a yield loss of 5 to 25 percent and the least area with a yield loss greater than 25 percent. All models show a possible increase in yield in some areas of northern Ghana. ECHAM 5 shows areas with a yield loss greater than 25 percent concentrated in the northern region; both CSIRO Mark 3 and MIROC 3.2 show areas with a yield loss greater than 25 percent limited to the central and lower part of the country.

Agricultural Vulnerability Scenarios (Crop-Specific)

Figure 6.20 shows the impact of future GDP and population scenarios on under-five malnutrition rates in Ghana. The box-and-whisker plots in the figure indicate the range of climate scenario effects. High GDP growth along with low population growth should significantly reduce the number and percentage of malnourished children under age five; a low GDP growth rate with high population growth would have the opposite effect. The vulnerability of the economies of developing countries such as Ghana to shocks from external market fluctuations could be a major constraint to realizing dramatic improvements in nutrition.

Figure 6.21 shows the available kilocalories per capita, illustrating the influence of per capita GDP and population growth rates on availability of calories. The best-case scenario of high GDP growth with low population growth provides for higher availability of calories than the pessimistic scenario, which pegs the availability of calories at 2,000 after year 2020.

Human Vulnerability Scenarios

The next four figures show simulation results associated with key agricultural crops in Ghana. The figure for each featured crop has five graphs: production, yield, area under cultivation, net exports, and world price.

FIGURE 6.17 Yield change under climate change: Rainfed maize in Ghana, 2010–50, A1B scenario

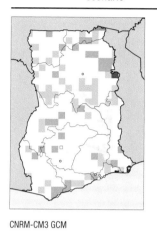

CNRM-CM3 GCM

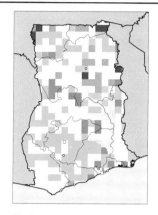

CSIRO Mark 3 GCM

ECHAM 5 GCM

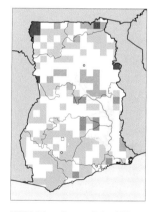

MIROC 3.2 medium-resolution GCM

- ■ 2000 old area lost
- Yield loss > 25% of 2000
- Yield loss 5–25%
- Yield change within 5%
- Yield gain 5–25%
- ■ Yield gain > 25%
- ■ 2050 new area gained

Source: Authors' estimates.

Notes: A1B = greenhouse gas emissions scenario that assumes fast economic growth, a population that peaks midcentury, and the development of new and efficient technologies, along with a balanced use of energy sources; CNRM-CM3 = National Meteorological Research Center–Climate Model 3; CSIRO = climate model developed at the Australia Commonwealth Scientific and Industrial Research Organisation; ECHAM 5 = fifth-generation climate model developed at the Max Planck Institute for Meteorology (Hamburg); GCM = general circulation model; MIROC = Model for Interdisciplinary Research on Climate, developed at the University of Tokyo Center for Climate System Research.

FIGURE 6.18   Yield change under climate change: Rainfed rice in Ghana, 2010–50, A1B
scenario

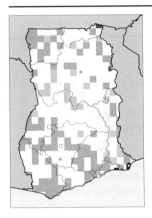

CNRM-CM3 GCM

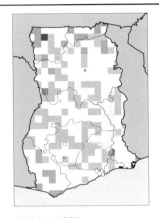

CSIRO Mark 3 GCM

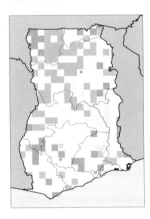

ECHAM 5 GCM

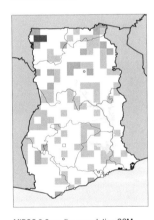

MIROC 3.2 medium-resolution GCM

■ 2000 old area lost

■ Yield loss > 25% of 2000

▢ Yield loss 5–25%

  Yield change within 5%

▢ Yield gain 5–25%

■ Yield gain > 25%

■ 2050 new area gained

Source: Authors' estimates.

Notes: A1B = greenhouse gas emissions scenario that assumes fast economic growth, a population that peaks midcentury, and the development of new and efficient technologies, along with a balanced use of energy sources; CNRM-CM3 = National Meteorological Research Center–Climate Model 3; CSIRO = climate model developed at the Australia Commonwealth Scientific and Industrial Research Organisation; ECHAM 5 = fifth-generation climate model developed at the Max Planck Institute for Meteorology (Hamburg); GCM = general circulation model; MIROC = Model for Interdisciplinary Research on Climate, developed at the University of Tokyo Center for Climate System Research.

FIGURE 6.19   Yield change under climate change: Rainfed groundnuts in Ghana, 2010–50, A1B scenario

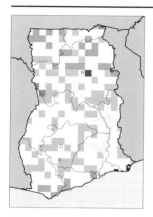

CNRM-CM3 GCM

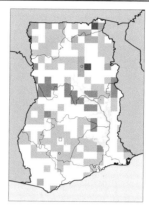

CSIRO Mark 3 GCM

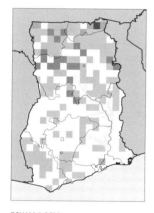

ECHAM 5 GCM

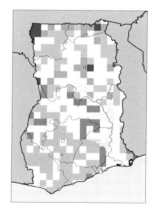

MIROC 3.2 medium-resolution GCM

- 2000 old area lost
- Yield loss > 25% of 2000
- Yield loss 5–25%
- Yield change within 5%
- Yield gain 5–25%
- Yield gain > 25%
- 2050 new area gained

Source: Authors' estimates.

Notes: A1B = greenhouse gas emissions scenario that assumes fast economic growth, a population that peaks midcentury, and the development of new and efficient technologies, along with a balanced use of energy sources; CNRM-CM3 = National Meteorological Research Center–Climate Model 3; CSIRO = climate model developed at the Australia Commonwealth Scientific and Industrial Research Organisation; ECHAM 5 = fifth-generation climate model developed at the Max Planck Institute for Meteorology (Hamburg); GCM = general circulation model; MIROC = Model for Interdisciplinary Research on Climate, developed at the University of Tokyo Center for Climate System Research.

FIGURE 6.20   Number of malnourished children under five years of age in Ghana in
multiple income and climate scenarios, 2010–50

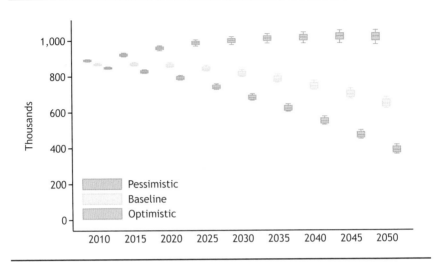

Source: Based on analysis conducted for Nelson et al. (2010).
Note: The box and whiskers plot for each socioeconomic scenario shows the range of effects from the four future climate
scenarios.

FIGURE 6.21   Kilocalories per capita in Ghana in multiple income and climate scenarios,
2010–50

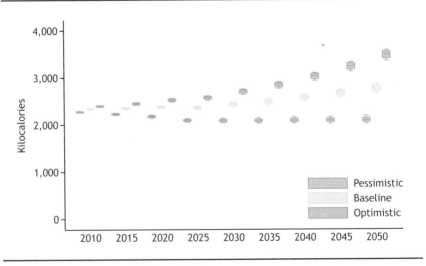

Source: Based on analysis conducted for Nelson et al. (2010).
Note: The box and whiskers plot for each socioeconomic scenario shows the range of effects from the four future climate
scenarios.

Figure 6.22 shows the impact of changes in GDP and population on cassava in Ghana. The production of cassava could increase as a result of an increase in yield, while land area is not expected to change very much. The trend is similar for all the scenarios. The world market price for cassava in 2050 appears higher in the pessimistic scenario than in the optimistic scenario. Cassava imports in all three scenarios could increase minimally until 2025, after which imports may increase in all scenarios. The level of certainty of the export volume diminishes progressively in all the scenarios as the effects of climate change become greater (as shown by increasingly broad percentile spreads).

The production of yams and sweet potatoes increases in all three scenarios until 2050 (Figure 6.23). The yield per hectare is also shown to increase, while the land area will remain virtually constant. The major difference among the three scenarios is that in the optimistic scenario the boxes indicate little or no spread, whereas the spreads for the other two scenarios widen toward 2050, with distributions skewed toward the 75th percentile. Exports are shown to increase starting in 2010, peaking between 2030 and 2035 and then declining until 2050. Greater uncertainty is shown in the baseline scenario than in the pessimistic or the optimistic scenario.

Maize production and yield are projected to increase in Ghana in all scenarios from 2010 to 2050 (Figure 6.24), with slight increases in spreads for all three scenarios. Similar to what is seen in the case of roots and tubers, the increase in total production is predicted to be driven primarily by productivity increases rather than increases in area under production, though we note here an increase in area of more than 10 percent. Maize exports are expected to increase until 2035 or 2040 and decrease thereafter in all scenarios. For all scenarios, the spread of values increases from 2010 to 2050. Values in the pessimistic scenario are higher throughout the period under consideration. It appears that the world market price of maize will rise throughout the period, with slight increases in the range of values. The values of the baseline scenario appear a little higher than those of the other two scenarios for most years.

There is very little difference between scenarios in predictions for the yield of groundnuts (Figure 6.25). We note an across-the-board increase in yield of around 50 percent between 2010 and 2050. All scenarios predict that the area planted in groundnuts will be mostly unchanged through 2025, after which it will fall slightly more rapidly in the optimistic scenario than in the baseline scenario, in which, in turn, it will fall more rapidly than in the pessimistic scenario, which shows virtually no change from 2010, dropping only a small amount. Together, the yield and area changes will result in an increase

FIGURE 6.22   Impact of changes in GDP and population on cassava in Ghana, 2010–50

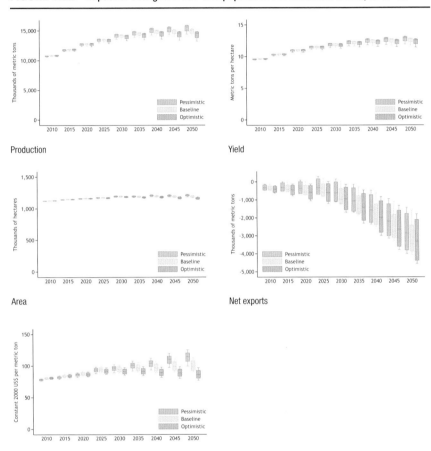

Source: Based on analysis conducted for Nelson et al. (2010).

Notes: The box and whiskers plot for each socioeconomic scenario shows the range of effects from the four future climate scenarios. GDP = gross domestic product; US$ = US dollars.

FIGURE 6.23   Impact of changes in GDP and population on yams and sweet potatoes in Ghana, 2010–50

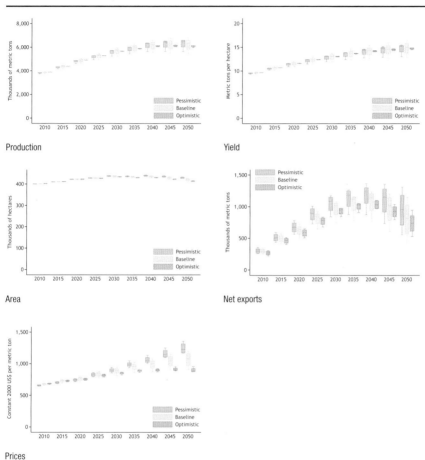

Production

Yield

Area

Net exports

Prices

Source: Based on analysis conducted for Nelson et al. (2010).

Notes: The box and whiskers plot for each socioeconomic scenario shows the range of effects from the four future climate scenarios. GDP = gross domestic product; US$ = US dollars.

FIGURE 6.24   Impact of changes in GDP and population on maize in Ghana, 2010–50

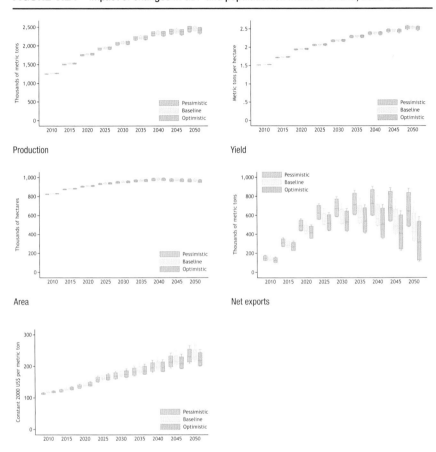

Source: Based on analysis conducted for Nelson et al. (2010).

Notes: The box and whiskers plot for each socioeconomic scenario shows the range of effects from the four future climate scenarios. GDP = gross domestic product; US$ = US dollars.

FIGURE 6.25 Impact of changes in GDP and population on groundnuts in Ghana, 2010–50

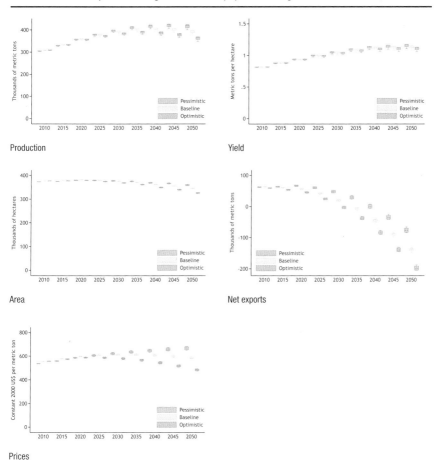

Source: Based on analysis conducted for Nelson et al. (2010).

Notes: The box and whiskers plot for each socioeconomic scenario shows the range of effects from the four future climate scenarios. GDP = gross domestic product; US$ = US dollars.

in production of almost one-third between 2010 and 2050 in the pessimistic scenario, an increase of 25 percent in the baseline scenario, and an increase of around 15 percent in the optimistic scenario. Over the time period, prices rise slightly in the pessimistic scenario, baseline prices will be largely unchanged, and prices in the optimistic scenario will fall slightly. Trade will shift from exports in 2010 to imports in 2050, with the level of imports more than twice as high in the optimistic scenario as in the pessimistic scenario.

Conclusions and Policy Recommendations

The various scenarios have implications for the future development of Ghana, especially in the areas of food security and natural resource management. Ghana's agriculture remains basically rainfed and therefore highly vulnerable to the effects of climatic change. Potentially high temperatures, along with decreased precipitation, could have serious implications for the yield and production of major food security crops like maize, rice, and groundnuts, as shown in this chapter. It is therefore important for food security policies to effectively address anticipated climate change effects.

In two of the four models considered, climate change is anticipated to decrease water availability for rainfed agriculture. The government could consider expanding irrigation infrastructure (thus increasing productivity per unit of water) in order to support the year-long production of a wider range of crops.

Reliable weather and climate information is important in enabling farmers to adapt to current weather events. The government could consider improving collaboration between agricultural and meteorological institutions to provide better and better-focused climatic information to farmers. In addition, research could quicken the development of climate-adaptive technologies for enhancing rainfed agriculture.

High population growth in urban areas results in higher demand for food, requiring increased and timely supply from the rural areas. Reliable transportation can reduce travel times between the cities and the production centers. Therefore, there is a need to improve the road infrastructure and to consider developing alternative transport systems to link rural and urban centers. Additionally, city authorities could consider establishing zoning regulations to create green areas that could support periurban agriculture to help feed the urban populations.

Ghana has great potential in the area of ecotourism; however, this is being eroded by massive degradation of natural resources, which could be exacerbated by climate change effects. Increasing the number of globally recognized protected areas has the potential of increasing the vegetative cover of the country while providing opportunities for ecotourism and thus additional livelihood opportunities for rural communities. However, the road networks leading to most of the protected areas need improvement to facilitate access by tourists.

Although climate change is predicted to have mostly negative consequences for agriculture and although population growth is likely to present additional challenges for food security, housing, and other forms of infrastructure, the projections for economic growth in Ghana suggest that, with wise investment in physical infrastructure and the adoption of sound policies for agricultural adaption to climate change as well as population growth, Ghana can look forward to a bright future. Yet we note that if economic growth takes place at a rate similar to that of the pessimistic scenario, there will be much less room for error, and poor decisions in regard to public investment or public policy could have much more serious consequences.

References

Bartholome, E., and A. S. Belward. 2005. "GLC2000: A New Approach to Global Land Cover Mapping from Earth Observation Data." *International Journal of Remote Sensing* 26 (9): 1959–1977.

Boateng, E. 1998. *Proceedings of Workshop on Land Use Planning.* TCP/GHA/6715/A. FAO Land Use Planning Project. New York: Food and Agriculture Organization of the United Nations.

CIESIN (Center for International Earth Science Information Network, Columbia University), Columbia University, IFPRI (International Food Policy Research Institute), World Bank, and CIAT (Centro Internacional de Agricultura Tropical). 2004. *Global Rural–Urban Mapping Project, Version 1 (GRUMPv1).* Palisades, NY, US: Socioeconomic Data and Applications Center (SEDAC), Columbia University. http://sedac.ciesin.columbia.edu/gpw.

Dickson, K. B., and Benneh, G. 1988. *A New Geography of Ghana.* Burnt Mill, Harlow, Essex, UK: Longman Group UK.

FAO (Food and Agriculture Organization of the United Nations). 2010. *FAOSTAT Database on Agriculture.* Rome.

Ghana, Forestry Commission. 2010. Readiness Preparation Proposal Ghana. Submitted to the Forest Carbon Partnership Facility (World Bank). Final. Accra. www.forestcarbonpartnership.org/fcp/sites/forestcarbonpartnership.org/files/Documents/PDF/Jan2011/Revised_Ghana_R-PP_2_Dec-2010.pdf.

Ghana, GSS (Ghana Statistical Service). 2010. *Ghana's Economic Performance 2009.* Accra.

Ghana, MOFA (Ministry of Food and Agriculture). 2009. *Food and Agriculture Sector Development Policy (FASDEP II)*. Accra.

Jones, P. G., P. K. Thornton, and J. Heinke. 2009. "Generating Characteristic Daily Weather Data Using Downscaled Climate Model Data from the IPCC's Fourth Assessment." Project report for the International Institute for Land Reclamation and Improvement, Wageningen, the Netherlands. Accessed May 7, 2010. www.ccafs-climate.org/pattern_scaling/.

Lehner, B., and P. Döll. 2004. "Development and Validation of a Global Database of Lakes, Reservoirs, and Wetlands." *Journal of Hydrology* 296 (1–4): 1–22.

Millennium Ecosystem Assessment. 2005. *Ecosystems and Human Well-being: Synthesis*. Washington, DC: Island Press. http://www.maweb.org/en/Global.aspx.

Nelson, G. C., M. W. Rosegrant, A. Palazzo, I. Gray, C. Ingersoll, R. Robertson, S. Tokgoz, et al. 2010. *Food Security, Farming, and Climate Change to 2050: Scenarios, Results, Policy Options*. Washington, DC: International Food Policy Research Institute.

UNEP and IUCN (United Nations Environment Programme and International Union for the Conservation of Nature). 2009. *World Database on Protected Areas (WDPA): Annual Release*. Accessed 2009. www.wdpa.org/protectedplanet.aspx.

UNPOP (United Nations Department of Economic and Social Affairs–Population Division). 2009. *World Population Prospects: The 2008 Revision*. New York. http://esa.un.org/unpd/wpp/.

Wood, S., G. Hyman, U. Deichmann, E. Barona, R. Tenorio, Z. Guo, et al. 2010. *Sub-national Poverty Maps for the Developing World Using International Poverty Lines: Preliminary Data Release*. Washington, DC: Harvest Choice and International Food Policy Research Institute. http://labs.harvestchoice.org/2010/08/poverty-maps/.

World Bank. 2009. *World Development Indicators*. Accessed May 2011. http://data.worldbank.org/data-catalog/world-development-indicators.

———. 2010. *Economics of Adaptation to Climate Change: Synthesis Report*. Washington, DC. http://climatechange.worldbank.org/content/economics-adaptation-climate-change-study-homepage.

You, L., and S. Wood. 2006. "An Entropy Approach to Spatial Disaggregation of Agricultural Production." *Agricultural Systems* 90 (1–3): 329–347.

You, L., S. Wood, and U. Wood-Sichra. 2006. "Generating Global Crop Distribution Maps: From Census to Grid." Paper presented at the International Association of Agricultural Economists Conference, Brisbane, Australia, August 11–18.

———. 2009. "Generating Plausible Crop Distribution and Performance Maps for Sub-Saharan Africa Using a Spatially Disaggregated Data Fusion and Optimization Approach." *Agricultural Systems* 99 (2–3): 126–140.

Chapter 7

GUINEA

Sidafa Condé, Abdulai Jalloh, Gerald C. Nelson, and Timothy S. Thomas

The Republic of Guinea covers an area of 245,857 square kilometers divided into seven administrative regions: Kindia, Boké, Mamou, Labé, Faranah, Kankan, and N'Zérékoré. The country consists of four major agroecological regions: coastal (Lower Guinea), middle (Fouta Djallon), upper, and forest Guinea. Guinea has a tropical climate with two alternating seasons, a dry season from November through March and a rainy season from April through October. In general, its rainfall increases from north to south; the mean annual rainfall is 1988 millimeters.

Rice is the staple crop, grown on 80 percent of the farms in the country. Rice is cultivated in the upland as well as various lowland ecologies, including inland valley swamps, mangrove swamps, and flooded plains. Other important foodcrops grown and consumed in Guinea are corn, *fonio* (cultivated grains belonging to the genera *Digitaria exilis* and *Digitaria iburua*), groundnuts, and cassava. Exclusively rainfed agriculture is practiced in Guinea, and crop production is significantly influenced by the weather—a growing challenge for resource-poor farmers. The major constraints faced by rice farmers are drought, weeds, and poor soils.

Review of the Current Situation

Population

The total population of Guinea was over 10.6 million as of the 2009 census. Most of the population is rural, and the agricultural sector is the major employer. Urbanization is a growing phenomenon; the share of the urban population has almost tripled since 1960 (Figure 7.1). Urban migration mainly involved youths fleeing the taxation of agricultural products and political harassment during the years following Guinea's independence in 1958. In recent times the drudgery associated with agriculture and the relatively better social amenities in urban areas are the major driving forces.

FIGURE 7.1   Population trends in Guinea: Total population, rural population, and percent urban, 1960–2008

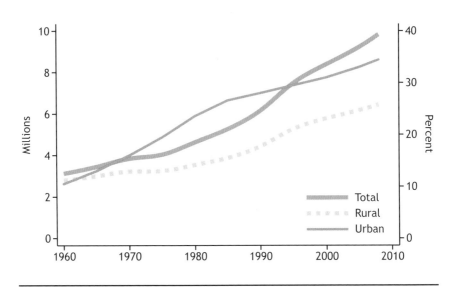

Source: World Development Indicators (World Bank 2009).

The dip in the population growth rate during 1970–79 (Table 7.1) could be accounted for by the mass exodus from Guinea due to the political situation and poor economic conditions. Between 1998 and 2001, almost 500,000 refugees entered the forest region of Guinea from the adjacent areas of Sierra Leone and Liberia due to civil war in those two countries. Between 2000 and 2008, a significant number of refugees from Sierra Leone and Liberia returned to their countries following the end of civil conflicts in both countries. In about the same period, the improving economic situation in Guinea

TABLE 7.1   Population growth rates in Guinea, 1960–2008 (percent)

Decade	Total growth rate	Rural growth rate	Urban growth rate
1960–69	2.2	1.5	6.4
1970–79	1.7	0.8	5.6
1980–89	2.7	2.1	4.5
1990–99	3.3	2.9	4.3
2000–2008	2.0	1.3	3.3

Source: Authors' calculations based on World Development Indicators (World Bank 2009).

encouraged the return of many Guinean exiles from neighboring countries; most of these returnees settled in the urban areas.

The increase in population has shortened the fallow period, when cultivated land is left to regain its fertility, from about 15 years 30 years ago to only 7 years or so now—and even less in certain zones of the country. This decline in the fallow period has had a negative influence on crop yields. Because farmers depend mostly on this fallow period to restore soil fertility, the yields of rice and other major foodcrops have declined over the years.

The population density is higher in the following regions: Boké and Kindia, bordering the Atlantic Ocean; Labé, bordering southern Senegal; Mamou, bordering northern Sierra Leone; and N'Zérékoré, bordering eastern Sierra Leone and upper Liberia (Figure 7.2). Labé is an important trade region linking Guinea with both Senegal and Mali. The least populated regions are Kankan and Faranah, both bordering the Republic of Mali.

Income

Figure 7.3 shows trends in Guine's gross domestic product (GDP) per capita and the proportion of its GDP from agriculture. Agricultural GDP remained at about 20 percent of total GDP from the mid-1980s to 2005, while GDP

FIGURE 7.2 Population distribution in Guinea, 2000 (persons per square kilometer)

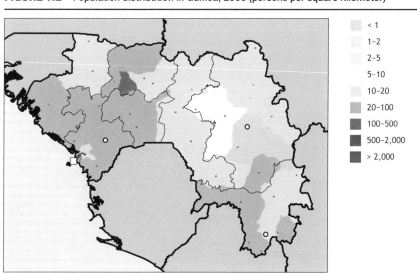

< 1
1–2
2–5
5–10
10–20
20–100
100–500
500–2,000
> 2,000

Source: CIESIN et al. (2004).

FIGURE 7.3   Per capita GDP in Guinea (constant 2000 US$) and share of GDP from
agriculture (percent), 1980–2008

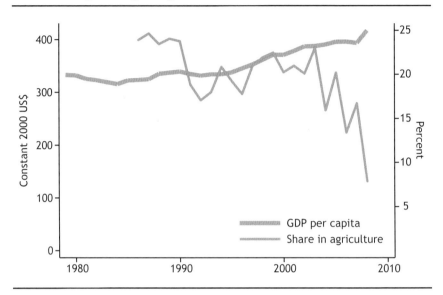

Source: World Development Indicators (World Bank 2009).
Notes: GDP = gross domestic product; US$ = US dollars.

per capita has generally increased since the mid-1980s. By 2009, the share of
GDP from agriculture had declined to less than 10 percent. This more recent
downward trend in the share of Guinea's GDP from agriculture reflects stagnation in agricultural productivity as well as increased development of other sectors of the economy, particularly the mining and service sectors.

Vulnerability to Climate Change

Table 7.2 provides some data on indicators of vulnerability and resiliency to
economic shocks: level of education, literacy, and concentration of labor in
poorer or less dynamic sectors. Guinea's high enrollment rate at the primary
school level contrasts with the very low enrollment in secondary education.
More than half of enrolled children drop out in primary school. Some in both
urban and rural areas leave school to enroll in vocational apprenticeships to
gain employment quickly. In rural areas, parents may keep older children
working on the farm, particularly if they have no means of paying their school
fees. Girls in secondary schools are frequently forced into marriage at the
expense of education.

TABLE 7.2 Education and labor statistics for Guinea, 1990s and 2000s

Indicator	Year	Percent
Primary school enrollment (percent gross, three-year average)	2007	90.8
Secondary school enrollment (percent gross, three-year average)	2007	37.6
Adult literacy rate	2003	29.5
Percent employed in agriculture	1994	76.0
Under-five malnutrition (weight for age)	2005	22.5

Source: Authors' calculations based on World Development Indicators (World Bank 2009).

Figure 7.4 shows two noneconomic correlates of poverty: low life expectancy and a high under-five mortality rate. Since 1960, Guinea has shown improvement in both indicators—a decrease in infant mortality and an increase in life expectancy. Life expectancy was less than 40 years at the country's independence, in 1958, and has increased gradually, reaching almost 60 years in 2008. At the same time, under-five mortality has sharply decreased from more than 300 deaths per 1,000 in 1970 to 150 per 1,000 in 2008. This improvement in well-being indicators could be attributed to the improvement in health conditions, particularly the vaccination of children, as well as the benefits of economic liberalization.

FIGURE 7.4 Well-being indicators in Guinea, 1960–2008

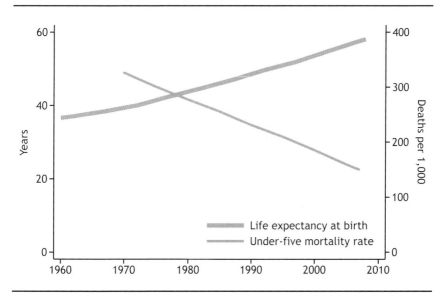

Source: World Development Indicators (World Bank 2009).

Wood et al. (2010) report that 80–90 percent of the Guinean population lives on less than US$2 (US dollars) per day across the country based on the 2005 US dollar and the purchasing power parity measure. Pervasive poverty is related to the inefficient agricultural production system that provides livelihoods for the bulk of the population as well as the high rate of inflation (13.5 percent in December 2008) and the lack of employment opportunities outside the agricultural sector (which consists mainly of subsistence farming).

Review of Land Use and Agriculture

Land Use Overview

Figure 7.5 shows the land cover and land use in Guinea as of 2000. Forest resources, once very important, fall into several distinct types of ecosystems relating to appearance and flora. Most of Guinea is covered with tree cover—broadleaved, deciduous, and open—or with a mosaic terrain of cropland, trees, and other vegetation. The mosaic areas are mainly concentrated in the Kindia, Mamou, lower Faranah, and N'Zérékoré Regions. Almost half of the Kankan Region is covered by shrub cover (closed or open and deciduous). There are a total of 2,039 square kilometers of mangroves in coastal Guinea (UNEP 2007); 700,000 hectares of dense humid forests in forest Guinea, middle Guinea, and coastal Guinea; and 800,000 hectares of dense dry forests and dry woodlands in upper Guinea and middle Guinea (Guinea, MOMGE / UNDP/GEF 2002)

Figure 7.6 shows the locations of protected areas, including parks and reserves. We can compare this map with the land cover map to better understand how well the areas are doing in preventing farm encroachment and preserving the natural ecosystem. Parks can be very important for tourism and also for preserving biodiversity and limiting greenhouse gas emissions from deforestation. We can also compare this map to population density maps and travel time maps for an indication of how much pressure there might be on the protected areas. Finally, the map can give us an idea about whether land that might show new agricultural potential under climate change might be constrained by the parks. This does not imply that an area should no longer be protected if it seems to offer agricultural promise under climate change, but it does help highlight choices policymakers may have to make.

Figure 7.7 shows travel time to urban areas of various sizes as potential markets for agricultural products, as well as centers for providing agricultural

FIGURE 7.5   Land cover and land use in Guinea, 2000

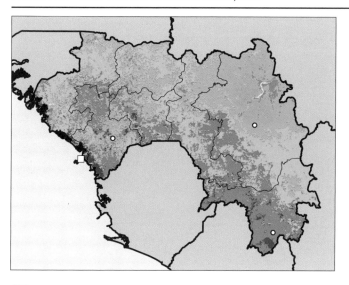

Tree cover, broadleaved, evergreen

Tree cover, broadleaved, deciduous, closed

Tree cover, broadleaved, deciduous, open

Tree cover, broadleaved, needle-leaved, evergreen

Tree cover, broadleaved, needle-leaved, deciduous

Tree cover, broadleaved, mixed leaf type

Tree cover, broadleaved, regularly flooded, fresh water

Tree cover, broadleaved, regularly flooded, saline water

Mosaic of tree cover/other natural vegetation

Tree cover, burnt

Shrub cover, closed-open, evergreen

Shrub cover, closed-open, deciduous

Herbacious cover, closed-open

Sparse herbacious or sparse shrub cover

Regularly flooded shrub or herbacious cover

Cultivated and managed areas

Mosaic of cropland/tree cover/other natural vegetation

Mosaic of cropland/shrub/grass cover

Bare areas

Water bodies

Snow and ice

Artificial surfaces and associated areas

No data

Source: GLC2000 (Global Land Cover 2000) (Bartholome and Belward 2005).

FIGURE 7.6   Protected areas in Guinea, 2009

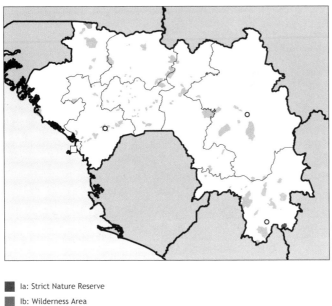

Ia: Strict Nature Reserve
Ib: Wilderness Area
II: National Park
III: National Monument
IV: Habitat / Species Management Area
V: Protected Landscape / Seascape
VI: Managed Resource Protected Area
Not applicable
Not known

Sources: Protected areas are from the World Database on Protected Areas (UNEP and IUCN 2009). Water bodies are from the World Wildlife Fund's Global Lakes and Wetlands Database (Lehner and Döll 2004).

inputs and consumer goods for farm households. The regional headquarters towns are fairly accessible by road; in all the regions, there is adequate access to cities and towns of 10,000 or more. A major trunk road links Conakry in the west to N'Zérékoré in the east. Transport of agricultural inputs and produce between urban and rural areas of Guinea is not much of a problem.

Agriculture Overview

Tables 7.3–7.5 show key agricultural commodities in terms of area harvested, value of harvest, and food consumption (ranked by weight). Rice is the staple crop of Guineans. It is cultivated on 80 percent of farms and provides 65 percent of cereal needs. Other important foodcrops are corn, *fonio,* groundnuts,

FIGURE 7.7   Travel time to urban areas of various sizes in Guinea, circa 2000

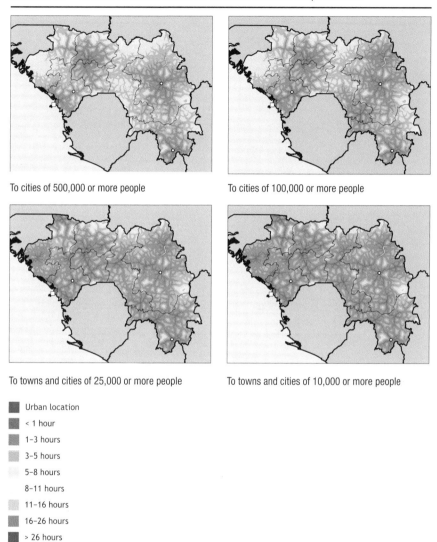

To cities of 500,000 or more people

To cities of 100,000 or more people

To towns and cities of 25,000 or more people

To towns and cities of 10,000 or more people

- Urban location
- < 1 hour
- 1–3 hours
- 3–5 hours
- 5–8 hours
- 8–11 hours
- 11–16 hours
- 16–26 hours
- > 26 hours

Source: Authors' calculations.

and cassava. Rice is grown in various areas, including the upland and several lowland ecologies—inland valley swamps, mangrove swamps, and flooded plains. Major constraints faced by rice farmers are drought, weeds, and poor soils.

TABLE 7.3   Harvest area of leading agricultural commodities in Guinea, 2006–08
(thousands of hectares)

Rank	Crop	Percent of total	Harvest area
	Total	100.0	3,205
1	Rice	24.4	781
2	Maize	12.6	403
3	Millet	11.8	377
4	Oil palm fruit	9.7	310
5	Fonio	6.7	215
6	Groundnuts	6.5	210
7	Cassava	4.3	139
8	Maize (green)	3.5	114
9	Plantains	2.6	84
10	Mangoes, mangosteens, guavas	2.6	82

Source: FAOSTAT (FAO 2010).
Note: All values are based on the three-year average for 2006–08.

TABLE 7.4   Value of production of leading agricultural commodities in Guinea, 2005–07
(millions of US$)

Rank	Crop	Percent of total	Value of production
	Total	100.0	1,495.1
1	Oil palm fruit	23.4	350.0
2	Cassava	14.4	215.5
3	Rice	12.8	191.3
4	Fonio	7.8	115.9
5	Maize (green)	6.6	98.3
6	Groundnuts	5.9	88.2
7	Maize	4.9	73.1
8	Other citrus	3.6	53.1
9	Pineapples	3.5	53.1
10	Millet	3.2	48.1

Source: FAOSTAT (FAO 2010).
Note: All values are based on the three-year average for 2005–07. US$ = US dollars.

TABLE 7.5   Consumption of leading food commodities in Guinea, 2003–05 (thousands of metric tons)

Rank	Crop	Percent of total	Food consumption
	Total	100.0	4,177
1	Cassava	20.8	870
2	Rice	19.4	809
3	Other vegetables	10.8	449
4	Plantains	8.8	366
5	Other fruits	4.0	166
6	Other citrus	3.9	163
7	Sweet potatoes	3.9	162
8	Bananas	2.9	120
9	Wheat	2.8	116
10	Teff and other cereals	2.7	114

Source: FAOSTAT (FAO 2010).
Note: All values are based on the three-year average for 2003–05.

The next five figures show the estimated yield and growing areas of key crops. Rice yields in Guinea tend to average close to 1.8 metric tons per hectare (Figure 7.8).[1] The crop is grown in almost all parts of the country except eastern parts of Labé. The main production areas are along the coast and in the forest region covering N'Zérékoré and lower areas of Kankan and Faranah Regions. There is currently an initiative to support the improved productivity of rice through increased access to improved seeds—particularly NERICA (New Rice for Africa)—as well as pesticides and fertilizers, supplemented with training and monitoring techniques for producers.

The areas of cassava production (Figure 7.9) are similar to those for rice. However, relatively less cassava is produced along the coast compared to rice. The major areas of production are the lower parts of the Kankan and Faranah Regions and, to a lesser extent, the Mamou and Boké Regions. Cassava yields are very low in Guinea (7–10 metric tons per hectare), reflecting the widespread use of unimproved varieties.

Maize is also a major crop grown in all regions where rice and cassava are grown (Figure 7.10). However, unlike rice and cassava, maize is less widely grown along the coast and in the forest region. It is mainly grown in the savannah regions of Mamou, Faranah, and Kankan. Yields range from 1 to 2 metric tons per hectare.

---

1 All tons are metric tons.

FIGURE 7.8   Yield (metric tons per hectare) and harvest area density (hectares) for rainfed rice in Guinea, 2000

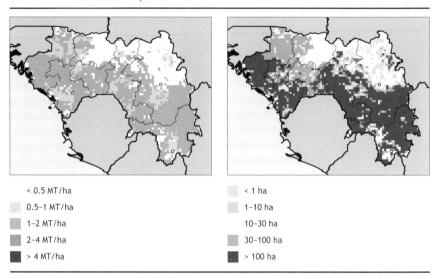

< 0.5 MT/ha	< 1 ha
0.5–1 MT/ha	1–10 ha
1–2 MT/ha	10–30 ha
2–4 MT/ha	30–100 ha
> 4 MT/ha	> 100 ha

Sources: SPAM (Spatial Production Allocation Model) (You and Wood 2006; You, Wood, and Wood-Sichra 2006, 2009).
Notes: ha = hectare; MT = metric tons.

FIGURE 7.9   Yield (metric tons per hectare) and harvest area density (hectares) for rainfed cassava in Guinea, 2000

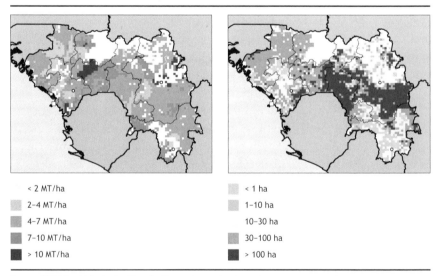

< 2 MT/ha	< 1 ha
2–4 MT/ha	1–10 ha
4–7 MT/ha	10–30 ha
7–10 MT/ha	30–100 ha
> 10 MT/ha	> 100 ha

Sources: SPAM (Spatial Production Allocation Model) (You and Wood 2006; You, Wood, and Wood-Sichra 2006, 2009).
Notes: ha = hectare; MT = metric tons.

FIGURE 7.10   Yield (metric tons per hectare) and harvest area density (hectares) for rainfed maize in Guinea, 2000

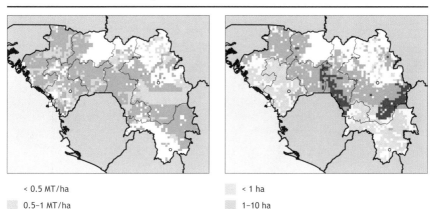

< 0.5 MT/ha	< 1 ha
0.5–1 MT/ha	1–10 ha
1–2 MT/ha	10–30 ha
2–4 MT/ha	30–100 ha
> 4 MT/ha	> 100 ha

Sources: SPAM (Spatial Production Allocation Model) (You and Wood 2006; You, Wood, and Wood-Sichra 2006, 2009).
Notes: ha = hectare; MT = metric tons.

Millet, too, is produced in areas where rice and maize are grown, but the acreage is much less than for rice and maize (Figure 7.11). The average millet yield is about 0.8 metric tons per hectare. Oil palm production in Guinea is concentrated in the regions of Boké and Mamou, the lower part of Faranah, and the forest region of N'Zérékoré, which have sufficient rainfall to support the crop (Figure 7.12). Oil palm production is less common in the savannah regions of upper Kankan, upper Faranah, and Labé.

Economic and Demographic Scenarios

Population

Figure 7.13 shows population projections for Guinea by the United Nations (UN) population office through 2050 (UNPOP 2009). All three scenarios suggest an increase in the population of Guinea over the years. The low variant predicts the doubling of the current population by 2050, whereas both the medium and the high variants predict doubling around 10 or more years earlier than that. Increased population will bring challenges of providing enough food as well as providing much-needed social services like health, education,

FIGURE 7.11   Yield (metric tons per hectare) and harvest area density (hectares) for rainfed millet in Guinea, 2000

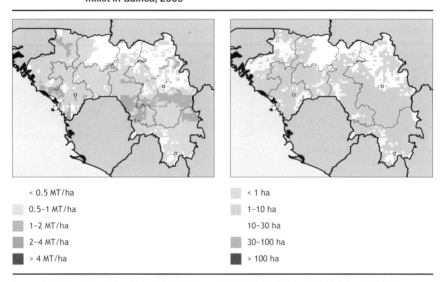

< 0.5 MT/ha	< 1 ha
0.5–1 MT/ha	1–10 ha
1–2 MT/ha	10–30 ha
2–4 MT/ha	30–100 ha
> 4 MT/ha	> 100 ha

Sources: SPAM (Spatial Production Allocation Model) (You and Wood 2006; You, Wood, and Wood-Sichra 2006, 2009).
Notes: ha = hectare; MT = metric tons.

FIGURE 7.12   Yield (metric tons per hectare) and harvest area density (hectares) for rainfed oil palm and other oil crops in Guinea, 2000

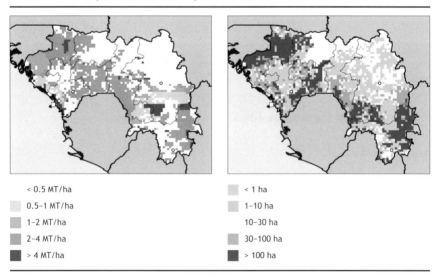

< 0.5 MT/ha	< 1 ha
0.5–1 MT/ha	1–10 ha
1–2 MT/ha	10–30 ha
2–4 MT/ha	30–100 ha
> 4 MT/ha	> 100 ha

Sources: SPAM (Spatial Production Allocation Model) (You and Wood 2006; You, Wood, and Wood-Sichra 2006, 2009).
Notes: ha = hectare; MT = metric tons.

FIGURE 7.13   Population projections for Guinea, 2010–50

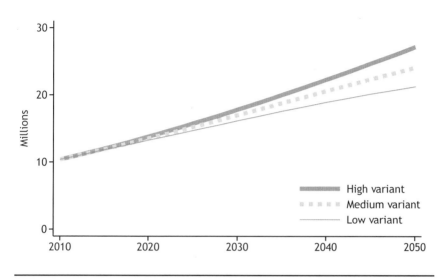

Source: UNPOP (2009).

water supply, electricity, and related infrastructure. There will be increasing pressure on agricultural land, which will result in a further reduction in the fallow period and consequently in decreasing yields unless fertilizers or other nutrient enhancement measures are used.

Income

Figure 7.14 presents three overall scenarios for Guinea's GDP per capita derived by combining three GDP scenarios with the three population scenarios of Figure 7.13 (based on UN population data). The optimistic scenario combines high GDP with low population scenarios for all countries, the baseline scenario combines the medium GDP projection with the medium population scenario, and the pessimistic scenario combines the low GDP scenario with the high population scenario. The agricultural modeling in the next section uses these scenarios.

The baseline scenario shows a gradual increase in GDP per capita, and the pessimistic scenario shows only a minimal increase. The optimistic scenario shows a dramatic increase, to about US$5,000 in 2050. Much planning and commitment will be needed to make progress toward the optimistic scenario,

FIGURE 7.14   Gross domestic product (GDP) per capita in Guinea, future scenarios, 2010–50

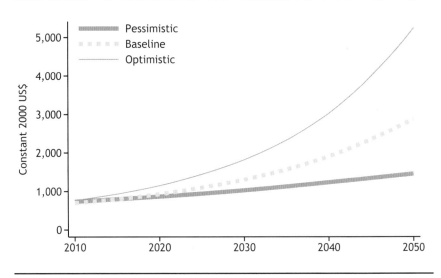

Sources: Computed from GDP data from the World Bank Economic Adaptation to Climate Change project (World Bank 2010), from the Millennium Ecosystem Assessment (2005) reports, and from population data from the United Nations (UNPOP 2009).
Note: US$ = US dollars.

including policies relating to birth control education and increased investments in the economy.

Biophysical Scenarios

Climate Scenarios

Figure 7.15 shows precipitation changes in Guinea in the four downscaled general circulation models (GCMs) in the A1B scenario.[2] All the models show a general deficit in rainfall. However, both the CNRM-CM3 and the MIROC 3.2 GCMs show an increase in precipitation of 50–100 millimeters in the Boké and Kindia Regions.[3] CNRM-CM3 shows relatively wetter areas

---

2 The A1B scenario is a greenhouse gas emissions scenario that assumes fast economic growth, a population that peaks midcentury, and the development of new and efficient technologies, along with a balanced use of energy sources.

3 CNRM-CM3 is National Meteorological Research Center–Climate Model 3. MIROC 3.2 is the Model for Interdisciplinary Research on Climate, developed at the University of Tokyo Center for Climate System Research.

FIGURE 7.15   Changes in mean annual precipitation in Guinea, 2000–2050, A1B scenario (millimeters)

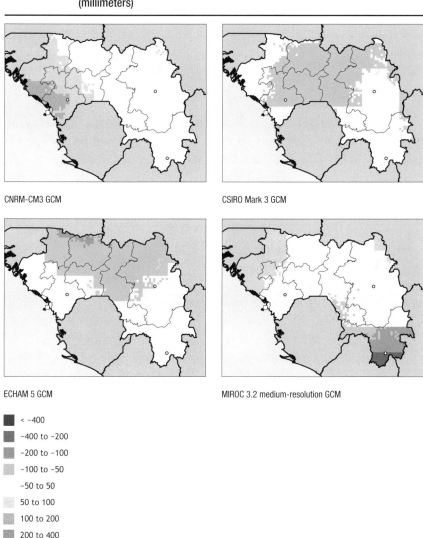

CNRM-CM3 GCM

CSIRO Mark 3 GCM

ECHAM 5 GCM

MIROC 3.2 medium-resolution GCM

■ < −400
■ −400 to −200
■ −200 to −100
□ −100 to −50
  −50 to 50
  50 to 100
  100 to 200
  200 to 400
■ > 400

Source: Authors' calculations based on Jones, Thornton, and Heinke (2009).
Note: A1B = greenhouse gas emissions scenario that assumes fast economic growth, a population that peaks midcentury, and the development of new and efficient technologies, along with a balanced use of energy sources; CNRM-CM3 = National Meteorological Research Center–Climate Model 3; CSIRO = climate model developed at the Australia Commonwealth Scientific and Industrial Research Organisation; ECHAM 5 = fifth-generation climate model developed at the Max Planck Institute for Meteorology (Hamburg); GCM = general circulation model; MIROC = Model for Interdisciplinary Research on Climate, developed by the University of Tokyo Center for Climate System Research.

than does MIROC 3.2. On the other hand, both the CSIRO Mark 3 and the ECHAM 5 CGMs show reductions of −100 to −50 millimeters in large areas of central and upper Guinea.[4] MIROC 3.2 is the only model that shows a substantial decline (−200 to −400 millimeters) in the forest region. In general, except in the CNRM-CM3 GCM, the climate is seen to be getting drier, indicating a water deficit that will have serious consequences for agricultural production in the country as a whole.

Figure 7.16 shows the change in average daily maximum temperature of the warmest month of the year as predicted by the GCMs and assuming the A1B scenario. All the models show an increase of at least 1.0°−1.5°C across the country. However, CNRM-CM3 and ECHAM 5 show relatively higher temperatures (2.0°−2.5°C) than CSIRO Mark 3 or MIROC 3.2 (1.5°−2.0°C), with the ECHAM 5 GCM showing a much warmer section in upper Guinea reaching around 3.0°C warmer than the 2000 climate. An increase in temperature combined with low rainfall would have adverse effects on water availability and thus on agricultural production.

Crop Physiological Response to Climate Change

The effect of climate change on key crops is mapped in the next two figures as a comparison of 2050 crop yields under climate change, with 2050 yields assuming an unchanged (2000) climate. Two models, ECHAM 5 and MIROC 3.2, show a large area with a possible yield *reduction* of 5–25 percent for rice (Figure 7.17). The other two models, CNRM-CM3 and CSIRO Mark 3, show a significant area with a possible yield *gain* of 5–25 percent of the baseline.

For maize, all the models have large areas of yield reduction (Figure 7.18). Both ECHAM 5 and MIROC 3.2 show a yield reduction greater than 25 percent in the southern border areas of N'Zérékoré and Kankan. Yet the ECHAM 5 model, in particular, shows areas of potential gains in yield under climate change.

Agriculture Vulnerability Scenarios (Crop-Specific)

Figure 7.19 shows the impact of future GDP and population scenarios on under-five malnutrition rates. The box-and-whisker plots in the figure indicate the range of climate scenario effects. The number of malnourished

---

4 CSIRO Mark 3 is a climate model developed at the Australia Commonwealth Scientific and Industrial Research Organisation. ECHAM 5 is a fifth-generation climate model developed at the Max Planck Institute for Meteorology in Hamburg.

FIGURE 7.16 Change in the normal daily maximum temperature in Guinea for the warmest month, 2000–2050, A1B scenario (°C)

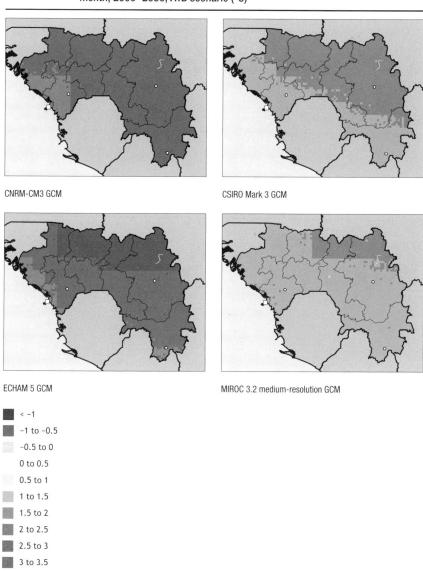

CNRM-CM3 GCM

CSIRO Mark 3 GCM

ECHAM 5 GCM

MIROC 3.2 medium-resolution GCM

■ < −1
■ −1 to −0.5
□ −0.5 to 0
□ 0 to 0.5
□ 0.5 to 1
□ 1 to 1.5
■ 1.5 to 2
■ 2 to 2.5
■ 2.5 to 3
■ 3 to 3.5
■ > 3.5

Source: Authors' calculations based on Jones, Thornton, and Heinke (2009).

Note: A1B = greenhouse gas emissions scenario that assumes fast economic growth, a population that peaks midcentury, and the development of new and efficient technologies, along with a balanced use of energy sources; CNRM-CM3 = National Meteorological Research Center–Climate Model 3; CSIRO = climate model developed at the Australia Commonwealth Scientific and Industrial Research Organisation; ECHAM 5 = fifth-generation climate model developed at the Max Planck Institute for Meteorology (Hamburg); GCM = general circulation model; MIROC = Model for Interdisciplinary Research on Climate, developed by the University of Tokyo Center for Climate System Research.

FIGURE 7.17   Yield change under climate change: Rainfed rice in Guinea, 2000–2050, A1B
scenario

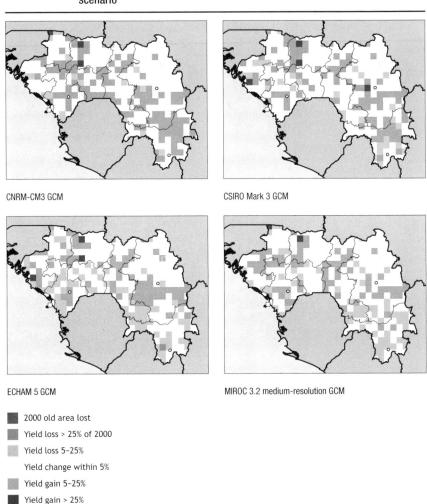

CNRM-CM3 GCM

CSIRO Mark 3 GCM

ECHAM 5 GCM

MIROC 3.2 medium-resolution GCM

■ 2000 old area lost

■ Yield loss > 25% of 2000

▫ Yield loss 5–25%

   Yield change within 5%

▪ Yield gain 5–25%

■ Yield gain > 25%

■ 2050 new area gained

Source: Authors' estimates.

Notes: A1B = greenhouse gas emissions scenario that assumes fast economic growth, a population that peaks midcentury,
and the development of new and efficient technologies, along with a balanced use of energy sources; CNRM-CM3 = National
Meteorological Research Center–Climate Model 3; CSIRO = climate model developed at the Australia Commonwealth Scientific and Industrial Research Organisation; ECHAM 5 = fifth-generation climate model developed at the Max Planck Institute
for Meteorology (Hamburg); GCM = general circulation model; MIROC = Model for Interdisciplinary Research on Climate,
developed at the University of Tokyo Center for Climate System Research.

FIGURE 7.18   Yield change under climate change: Rainfed maize in Guinea, 2000–2050, A1B scenario

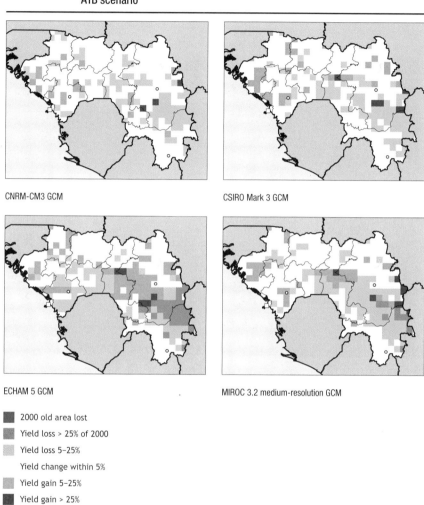

CNRM-CM3 GCM

CSIRO Mark 3 GCM

ECHAM 5 GCM

MIROC 3.2 medium-resolution GCM

■ 2000 old area lost
▨ Yield loss > 25% of 2000
▤ Yield loss 5–25%
   Yield change within 5%
▨ Yield gain 5–25%
■ Yield gain > 25%
■ 2050 new area gained

Source: Authors' estimates.

Notes: A1B = greenhouse gas emissions scenario that assumes fast economic growth, a population that peaks midcentury, and the development of new and efficient technologies, along with a balanced use of energy sources; CNRM-CM3 = National Meteorological Research Center–Climate Model 3; CSIRO = climate model developed at the Australia Commonwealth Scientific and Industrial Research Organisation; ECHAM 5 = fifth-generation climate model developed at the Max Planck Institute for Meteorology (Hamburg); GCM = general circulation model; MIROC = Model for Interdisciplinary Research on Climate, developed at the University of Tokyo Center for Climate System Research.

FIGURE 7.19 Number of malnourished children under five years of age in Guinea in multiple income and climate scenarios, 2010–50

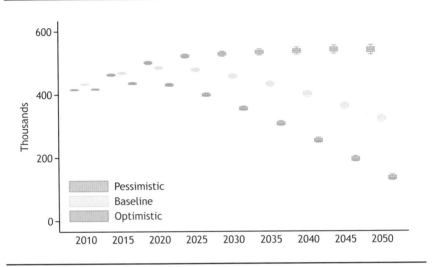

Source: Based on analysis conducted for Nelson et al. (2010).
Note: The box and whiskers plot for each socioeconomic scenario shows the range of effects from the four future climate scenarios.

children under five years of age is shown as decreasing after 2020 in the baseline and optimistic scenarios. In the pessimistic scenario, however, that number is shown to be increasing through 2035 and then remaining level through 2050. Although this scenario shows an increase in the absolute number of malnourished children, because of population growth the proportion of malnourished children should decline in all scenarios.

The availability of kilocalories increases in either the baseline or the optimistic scenario and decreases in the pessimistic scenario (Figure 7.20). The trend in availability of kilocalories is consistent with that for the number of malnourished children under age five.

Human Vulnerability Scenarios

The next four figures show simulation results associated with key agricultural crops in Guinea. The figure for each featured crop has five graphs: production, yield, area, net exports, and world price.

The rice yield in Guinea is shown to increase in all scenarios, from about 0.8 metric tons per hectare to 1.3 metric tons per hectare, due to improved productivity; the area planted with the crop is shown virtually unchanged (Figure 7.21). Productivity improvement is likely to entail improved

FIGURE 7.20   Kilocalories per capita in Guinea in multiple income and climate scenarios, 2010–50

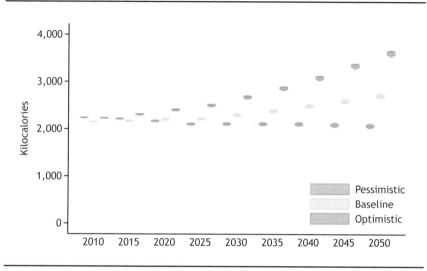

Source: Based on analysis conducted for Nelson et al. (2010).
Note: The box and whiskers plot for each socioeconomic scenario shows the range of effects from the four future climate scenarios.

management because local and improved varieties already have a higher yield potential, 2–5 metric tons per hectare. Net exports will continue to decrease in all the scenarios, reflecting an increase in population (and hence demand) without a sufficiently corresponding increase in rice production.

Unlike in the case of rice, the area planted with cassava and other tubers increases slightly over the years; nevertheless, here too the increase in total production will be influenced more by increased productivity than by the increase in area (Figure 7.22). Similar to the case of rice, the improved productivity of cassava depends more on efficient management than on genetic enhancement because most currently available local and improved cassava varieties have a yield potential higher than the 2050 figure. In the optimistic scenario, the world price of cassava does not increase after 2030; net exports of cassava will decline steadily due to an increase in population, causing Guinea to shift from a net exporter to a net importer.

Similar to the cases of both rice and cassava, maize production in Guinea increases as a result of higher productivity, mainly due to improved management (Figure 7.23). The world price of maize is expected to increase. Unlike in the cases of rice and cassava, exports of maize will increase.

FIGURE 7.21   Impact of changes in GDP and population on rice in Guinea, 2010–50

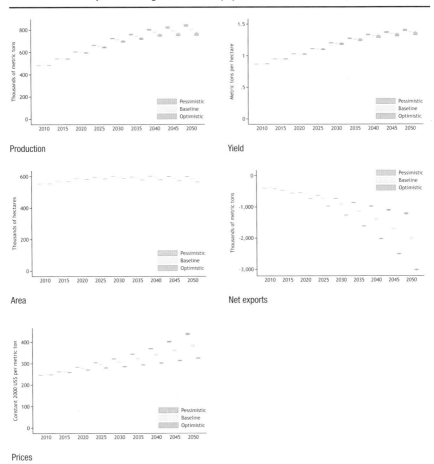

Source: Based on analysis conducted for Nelson et al. (2010).

Notes: The box and whiskers plot for each socioeconomic scenario shows the range of effects from the four future climate scenarios. GDP = gross domestic product; US$ = US dollars.

FIGURE 7.22 Impact of changes in GDP and population on cassava in Guinea, 2010–50

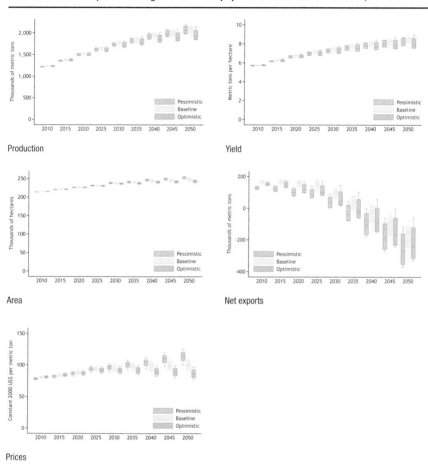

Source: Based on analysis conducted for Nelson et al. (2010).

Notes: The box and whiskers plot for each socioeconomic scenario shows the range of effects from the four future climate scenarios. GDP = gross domestic product; US$ = US dollars.

FIGURE 7.23 Impact of changes in GDP and population on maize in Guinea, 2010–50

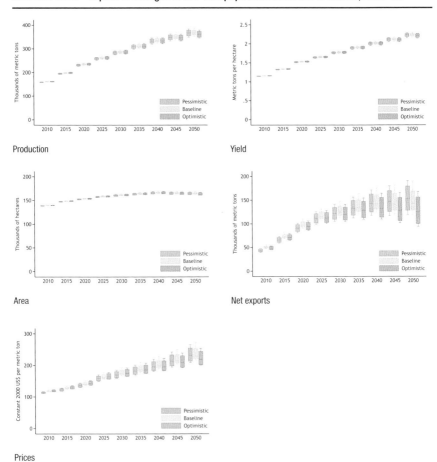

Production

Yield

Area

Net exports

Prices

Source: Based on analysis conducted for Nelson et al. (2010).

Notes: The box and whiskers plot for each socioeconomic scenario shows the range of effects from the four future climate scenarios. GDP = gross domestic product; US$ = US dollars.

FIGURE 7.24 Impact of changes in GDP and population on millet in Guinea, 2010–50

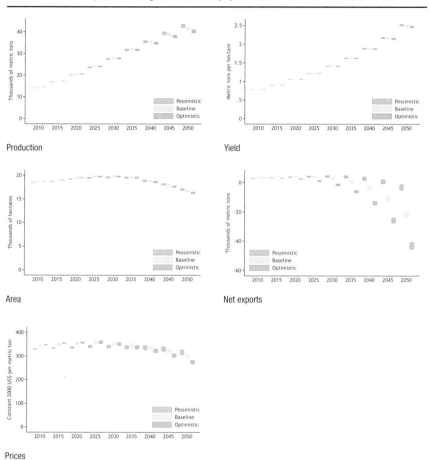

Source: Based on analysis conducted for Nelson et al. (2010).

Notes: The box and whiskers plot for each socioeconomic scenario shows the range of effects from the four future climate scenarios. GDP = gross domestic product; US$ = US dollars.

The production of millet increases in all scenarios, showing strong links between production and yield, although the area planted with the crop is shown to decrease after 2030 (Figure 7.24). Net exports of millet appear to be strongly linked with price, declining after 2030—though much less in the pessimistic scenario than in the optimistic scenario. Based on both the baseline and optimistic scenarios, net exports appear negative after 2030; in the pessimistic scenario, net exports become negative after 2040.

Conclusions and Policy Recommendations

Climate change is expected to affect the productivity of crops and consequently food production in Guinea. Most of the impact is anticipated to be negative, and yet in certain climate models there are areas in which the impact of climate change could be positive. Policies should be implemented to help farmers adapt to climate-related challenges to agricultural production. In this regard it would be useful for the Government of Guinea to consider the following in designing policies related to climate change and its effect on agriculture:

- Improving the capacity of the meteorological department to adequately monitor climate elements so as to be able to predict the weather and provide relevant information for farmers as well as the government to take necessary actions.

- Supporting the agricultural research and extension system to develop appropriate crop varieties for resilience to climate change—particularly rice, maize, and groundnuts, which have been shown by this chapter to be adversely affected by climate—and to improve yields and farm income in general. In addition, the research system should determine appropriate management practices related to such things as the time of planting, crop densities, intercropping, and crop rotations for improved productivity. A more profitable and dynamic agricultural sector would likely serve to stem the flow of young people from rural areas to urban areas.

- Designing adequate regulations and measures as well as a related legal framework to ensure the protection of forests, parks, watersheds, and marine ecosystems so that they will not be degraded through the expansion of agricultural areas as a result of population growth and climate change.

- Designing strategies to manage food crises when weather-related shocks such as droughts, storms, and floods occur.

With proper investment and policy adjustment, Guinea can minimize the likely negative impact of climate change on agriculture, helping farmers learn to increase their yields and profits despite a harsher environment than exists at present.

References

Bartholome, E., and A. S. Belward. 2005. "GLC2000: A New Approach to Global Land Cover Mapping from Earth Observation Data." *International Journal of Remote Sensing* 26 (9): 1959–1977.

CIESIN (Center for International Earth Science Information Network, Columbia University), Columbia University, IFPRI (International Food Policy Research Institute), World Bank, and CIAT (Centro Internacional de Agricultura Tropical). 2004. *Global Rural–Urban Mapping Project, Version 1 (GRUMPv1)*. Palisades, NY, US: Socioeconomic Data and Applications Center (SEDAC), Columbia University. http://sedac.ciesin.columbia.edu/gpw.

FAO (Food and Agriculture Organization of the United Nations). 2010. *FAOSTAT Database on Agriculture*. Rome.

Guinea, MOMGE /UNDP/GEF (Ministry of Mines, Geology, and the Environment / United Nations Development Programme/Global Environment Facility). 2002. *National Strategy and Action Plan for Biological Diversity*. Vol. 1, *National Strategy for Conservation Regarding Biological Diversity and the Sustainable Use of These Resources*. Conakry. www.cbd.int/doc/world/gn/gn-nbsap-01-p1-en.pdf.

Jones, P. G., P. K. Thornton, and J. Heinke. 2009. "Generating Characteristic Daily Weather Data Using Downscaled Climate Model Data from the IPCC's Fourth Assessment." Project report for the International Institute for Land Reclamation and Improvement, Wageningen, the Netherlands. Accessed May 7, 2010. www.ccafs-climate.org/pattern_scaling/.

Lehner, B., and P. Döll. 2004. "Development and Validation of a Global Database of Lakes, Reservoirs, and Wetlands." *Journal of Hydrology* 296 (1–4): 1–22.

Millennium Ecosystem Assessment. 2005. *Ecosystems and Human Well-being: Synthesis*. Washington, DC: Island Press. http://www.maweb.org/en/Global.aspx.

Nelson, G. C., M. W. Rosegrant, A. Palazzo, I. Gray, C. Ingersoll, R. Robertson, S. Tokgoz, et al. 2010. *Food Security, Farming, and Climate Change to 2050: Scenarios, Results, Policy Options*. Washington, DC: International Food Policy Research Institute.

UNEP (United Nations Environment Programme). 2007. *Mangroves of Western and Central Africa.* Cambridge, UK: UNEP–Regional Seas Programme / UNEP–WCMC (World Conservation Monitoring Centre).

UNEP and IUCN (United Nations Environment Programme and International Union for the Conservation of Nature). 2009. *World Database on Protected Areas (WDPA): Annual Release.* Accessed 2009. www.wdpa.org/protectedplanet.aspx.

UNPOP (United Nations Department of Economic and Social Affairs–Population Division). 2009. *World Population Prospects: The 2008 Revision.* New York. http://esa.un.org/unpd/wpp/.

Wood, S., G. Hyman, U. Deichmann, E. Barona, R. Tenorio, Z. Guo, et al. 2010. *Sub-national Poverty Maps for the Developing World Using International Poverty Lines: Preliminary Data Release.* Washington, DC: Harvest Choice and International Food Policy Research Institute. http://labs.harvestchoice.org/2010/08/poverty-maps/.

World Bank. 2009. *World Development Indicators.* Accessed May 2011. http://data.worldbank.org/data-catalog/world-development-indicators.

———. 2010. *Economics of Adaptation to Climate Change: Synthesis Report.* Washington, DC. http://climatechange.worldbank.org/content/economics-adaptation-climate-change-study-homepage.

You, L., and S. Wood. 2006. "An Entropy Approach to Spatial Disaggregation of Agricultural Production." *Agricultural Systems* 90 (1–3): 329–347.

You, L., S. Wood, and U. Wood-Sichra. 2006. "Generating Global Crop Distribution Maps: From Census to Grid." Paper presented at the International Association of Agricultural Economists Conference, Brisbane, Australia, August 11–18.

———. 2009. "Generating Plausible Crop Distribution and Performance Maps for Sub-Saharan Africa Using a Spatially Disaggregated Data Fusion and Optimization Approach." *Agricultural Systems* 99 (2–3): 126–140.

Chapter 8

LIBERIA

Benjamin S. Karmorh Jr., Abdulai Jalloh, Gerald C. Nelson, and
Timothy S. Thomas

L iberia is situated at the southwest corner of the West Coast of Africa. It
lies between the longitudes of 7°30′ and 11°30′ west and latitudes 4°18′
and 8°30′ north. It covers a surface area of about 111,370 square kilometers (about 43,506 square miles). The extent of its dry land is 96,160 square
kilometers or 37,570 square miles (UNDP Liberia 2006). Liberia is bordered
on the west by Sierra Leone, on the north by Guinea, on the east by Côte
d'Ivoire, and on the south by the Atlantic Ocean. The country has two seasons: rainy and dry. The rainy season lasts from May to October, and the dry
season runs from November to April. The farming system is characterized by
shifting cultivation, which has led to the conversion of extensive areas of forest
into farmland and grassland in many parts of the country.

Rice is the staple food of Liberians, while cassava is the second major foodcrop. Overall, Liberian farmers are resource poor and invariably produce at
a subsistence level. Against the background of limited resources, the typical
Liberian farmer is faced with numerous biophysical constraints, including low-
yielding crop varieties, pests, and diseases, as well as poor soil conditions.
Heavy reliance on rainfall exposes farmers to the vagaries of the weather. There
are 700 kilometers of paved roads in Liberia, extending from Monrovia to Bo
Waterside (on the Sierra Leone border), Ganta, and Buchanan Counties, making these areas easily accessible; they are very different from the 1,600 kilometers of unpaved roads, mostly in need of repair, that make it difficult to
transport agricultural products from the southeastern counties to Monrovia.

According to the high-variant scenario, Liberia's population would double by
2040. Major challenges associated with population growth include the country's
dilapidated infrastructure, weak health system, malnutrition, lack of clean drinking water, bad road conditions, and high level of unemployment. As the population increases, there will be a high demand for not only the currently limited
basic social services but also for natural resources.

The purpose of the chapter is to help Liberian policymakers and researchers better understand and anticipate the likely impacts of climate change on

agriculture and on vulnerable households. The chapter reviews current data on agriculture and economic development, models anticipated changes in climate between now and 2050, applies crop models to assess the impact of climate change on agricultural production, and models global supply and demand for food to predict relevant food price trends. The findings of this chapter have several significant policy implications, especially because the Government of Liberia, through the Ministry of Agriculture, has made it a priority to monitor the actual and potential impacts of climate change on the agricultural sector.

Review of the Current Situation

Population

The total population of Liberia increased from about 1 million in 1960 to just over 2 million in the mid-1980s (Figure 8.1). The population declined markedly during 1987–94 due to the civil war in the country (especially in the rural areas,

FIGURE 8.1   Population trends in Liberia: Total population, rural population, and percent urban, 1960–2008

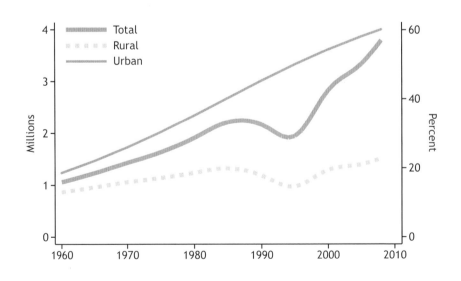

Source: World Development Indicators (World Bank 2009).

where the fighting took place). There was also a steady increase in the percentage of the urban population due to the mass migration from rural areas to urban areas in search of safety and food. Table 8.1 shows that the urban growth rate is higher than the rural growth rate, possibly reflecting the relatively better health facilities in the urban areas, as well as employment opportunities, more social amenities, better communication and transport connections, and commercial activities that serve as driving forces of urban migration.

Figure 8.2 shows the geographic distribution of the population in Liberia based on census data and other sources. The population density is relatively lower in the southeastern region, particularly in Grand Gedeh, Sinoe, and River Gee Counties, as well as Gbarpolu in the western part of the country; these areas are characterized by heavy forest cover, poor communications and transport systems, and underdeveloped physical infrastructure and social amenities, coupled with generally fewer employment opportunities (Liberia, ISGS 2009). The counties with relatively high population densities are Montserrado, Nimba, Margibi, and Maryland Counties (Maryland County, bordering Côte d'Ivoire, is highly populated compared to other southeastern counties). These areas have better transport and communication systems, fertile agricultural lands, local alluvial mining activities, and international commercial mining and agricultural operations, as well as opportunities for employment and trade with neighboring countries. The capital city, Monrovia, is densely populated, with relatively superior socioeconomic conditions, including better infrastructure; better health, transport, and communication systems; and its status as a major hub for employment opportunities, including those at its seaport.

Income

The share of income earned in agriculture in Liberia shows the importance of agriculture as a sector of the economy. Figure 8.3 shows trends in gross

TABLE 8.1   Population growth rates in Liberia, 1960–2008 (percent)

Decade	Total growth rate	Rural growth rate	Urban growth rate
1960–69	3.0	2.1	6.4
1970–79	2.8	1.5	5.9
1980–89	1.7	0.0	4.3
1990–99	2.1	0.3	4.0
2000–2008	3.5	1.8	4.8

Source: Authors' calculations based on World Development Indicators (World Bank 2009).

FIGURE 8.2   Population distribution in Liberia, 2000 (persons per square kilometer)

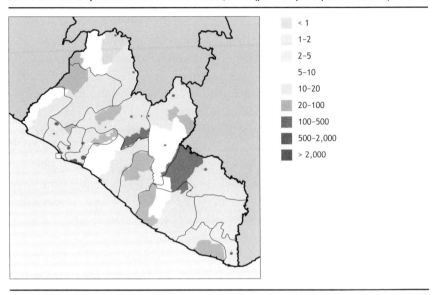

Source: CIESIN et al. (2004).

FIGURE 8.3   Per capita GDP in Liberia (constant 2000 US$) and share of GDP from agriculture (percent), 1960–2008

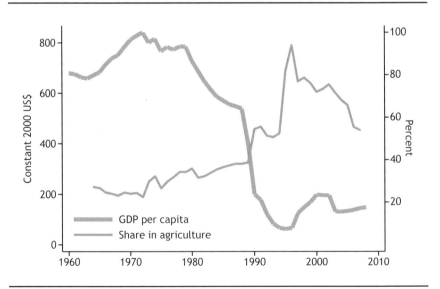

Source: World Development Indicators (World Bank 2009).
Note: GDP = gross domestic product; US$ = US dollars.

domestic product (GDP) per capita and the proportion of GDP from agriculture—a sector that is vulnerable to the impacts of climate change.

Liberia's GDP per capita increased from about US$700 (US dollars) in 1960 to just above US$800 in 1970 and then dropped throughout the 1980s to its lowest level, less than US$100, during the civil war of the mid-1990s. The decrease from 1970 to 1990 reflected the downward shift in the global economy. From 1995 onward, Liberia's GDP started improving. The share of its GDP from agriculture increased slowly, from about 30 to 40 percent between the mid-1960s and 1990. During the civil war, the share of its agricultural GDP increased sharply because other sectors of the economy were disrupted and most became nonfunctional. Agricultural companies such as Firestone were still in operation, with intermittent interruptions during the civil war. Later, during the civil crisis (1999–2003), agricultural production started to drop as people fled their farms and the supporting infrastructure collapsed. After the 2005 general election and presidential election, other sectors of the economy revived, including forestry, mining, and international trade, leading to a gradual rise in GDP.

Vulnerability to Climate Change

Vulnerability is the lack of ability to recover from a stress. Poor people are vulnerable to many different kinds of stresses because they lack the financial resources to respond. In agriculture, poor people are particularly vulnerable to the stresses of an uncertain climate. At the national level, vulnerability arises in the interactions among population and income growth and the availability of natural and manufactured resources. Vulnerability has many dimensions; in this chapter, the focus is on income level and income sources.

Table 8.2 provides data on Liberia's performance on additional indicators of a country's vulnerability and resiliency to economic shocks: level of education, literacy, and concentration of labor in poorer or less dynamic sectors. As

TABLE 8.2   Education and labor statistics for Liberia, 2000s

Indicator	Year	Percent
Primary school enrollment (percent gross, three-year average)	2008	83.4
Secondary school enrollment (percent gross, three-year average)	2000	32.3
Adult literacy rate	2007	55.5
Percent employed in agriculture	2008	70.0
Under-five malnutrition (weight for age)	2007	20.4

Source: Authors' calculations based on World Development Indicators (World Bank 2009).

in most countries in West Africa, secondary school enrollment in Liberia is significantly lower than primary school enrollment. The low literacy rate, poverty, and associated sociocultural circumstances—including the need for farm labor as well as early marriages—account for the high dropout rate in secondary schools. Table 8.2 also shows that the bulk of the Liberian population is engaged in agriculture and that under-five malnutrition is still high in the country, at 20.4 percent.

Figure 8.4 shows Liberia's performance on two noneconomic correlates of poverty—life expectancy and under-five mortality. Life expectancy increased slightly from 1960 to 1979 and stabilized at about 48 years through the late 1980s. Since then, life expectancy has been increasing, to about 60 years in 2008. Under-five mortality has been falling steadily. According to the Liberian Poverty Reduction Strategy Paper (PSRP) (Liberia 2008), between 1999–2000 and 2006–07, the infant mortality rate fell from 117 to 72 deaths per 1,000 live births, while under-five mortality fell from 194 to 111 deaths per 1,000 births. This steady decline is attributable to the cessation of conflict, the restoration of basic services in some areas, and increased immunization.

FIGURE 8.4   Well-being indicators in Liberia, 1960–2008

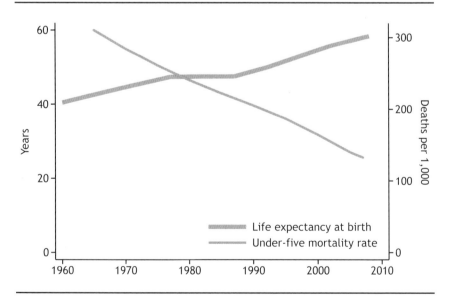

Source: World Development Indicators (World Bank 2009).

According to Wood et al. (2010), the proportion of the population living on less than US$2 per day is 90–95 percent of the population of Liberia based on the 2005 US dollar and the purchasing power parity measure. According to the 2010 Millennium Development Goals report (Liberia, MPEA 2010), 63.8 percent of the population lives in extreme poverty, living on less than US$1 per day, a situation that needs significant improvement. The Government of Liberia developed the Poverty Reduction Strategy Paper to address this issue (Liberia 2008).

Review of Land Use and Agriculture

Land Use Overview

Figure 8.5 shows Liberia's land cover and land use as of 2000. Agricultural production in Liberia is based on subsistence farming largely using shifting cultivation, which has led to the cutting down of extensive areas of forest. A significant portion of the forested areas of the country has been converted to farmland, bush, and grasslands. Tree cover and broad-leaved evergreen vegetation are now present in only about one-fourth of the country. Other human activities, such as charcoal production and alluvial mining, have contributed immensely to land cover change. Recently the government has ratified oil palm concessions that will entail massive felling of old rubber trees in the northwestern and southeastern parts of the country, exposing the land to erosion for extensive periods before a full canopy can form. Patches of rubber plantations remain in the central region of the country (in Margibi, Bassa, Bong, and Nimba Counties).

Figure 8.6 shows the locations of protected areas, including parks and reserves. These locations provide important protection for fragile environmental areas, which may also be important for the tourism industry. In Liberia there are two gazetted protected areas: Sapo National Park is located in the southeastern part of the country, bordering the Sinoe River in the south and the Putu Range in the north; the Mount Nimba Nature Reserve is located in the north, sharing a massif with Côte d'Ivoire and Guinea. Sapo National Park has an area of 180,363 hectares of lowland rainforest, including swampy areas, drylands, and riparian forests; it represents one of the most intact forest ecosystems in Liberia, located in the only remaining evergreen block of forest in the Upper Guinea Forest Ecosystem. Mount Nimba Nature Reserve covers an area of 11,723 hectares. In addition, there are five proposed protected areas: Lake Piso Nature Reserve (estimated area 30,766 hectares), Cestos Senkwen National Park (estimated area 91,698 hectares), Wologezi National

FIGURE 8.5   Land cover and land use in Liberia, 2000

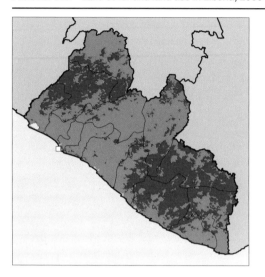

■ Tree cover, broadleaved, evergreen

☐ Tree cover, broadleaved, deciduous, closed

☐ Tree cover, broadleaved, deciduous, open

■ Tree cover, broadleaved, needle–leaved, evergreen

☐ Tree cover, broadleaved, needle–leaved, deciduous

☐ Tree cover, broadleaved, mixed leaf type

☐ Tree cover, broadleaved, regularly flooded, fresh water

■ Tree cover, broadleaved, regularly flooded, saline water

☐ Mosaic of tree cover/other natural vegetation

■ Tree cover, burnt

☐ Shrub cover, closed–open, evergreen

☐ Shrub cover, closed–open, deciduous

☐ Herbacious cover, closed–open

☐ Sparse herbacious or sparse shrub cover

☐ Regularly flooded shrub or herbacious cover

☐ Cultivated and managed areas

☐ Mosaic of cropland/tree cover/other natural vegetation

☐ Mosaic of cropland/shrub/grass cover

☐ Bare areas

☐ Water bodies

☐ Snow and ice

■ Artificial surfaces and associated areas

☐ No data

Source: GLC2000 (Global Land Cover 2000) (Bartholome and Belward 2005).

FIGURE 8.6   Protected areas in Liberia, 2009

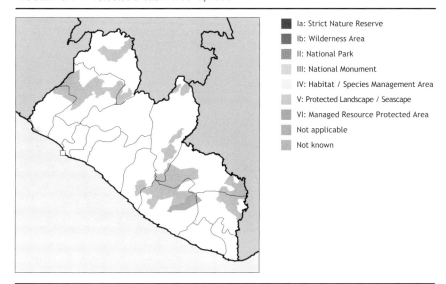

Ia: Strict Nature Reserve
Ib: Wilderness Area
II: National Park
III: National Monument
IV: Habitat / Species Management Area
V: Protected Landscape / Seascape
VI: Managed Resource Protected Area
Not applicable
Not known

Source: Protected areas are from the World Database on Protected Areas (UNEP and IUCN 2009). Water bodies are from the World Wildlife Fund's Global Lakes and Wetlands Database (Lehner and Döll 2004).

Park (estimated area 80,001 hectares), Wenegizi National Park (estimated area 71,422 hectares), and Grebo National Park (estimated area 260,326 hectares) (UNDP Liberia 2006; UNEP-WCMC 2006).

Figure 8.7 shows travel time to urban areas as potential markets for agricultural products and as sources of consumption items and agricultural inputs. There are 700 kilometers of paved roads in Liberia, extending from Monrovia to Bo Waterside (at the Sierra Leone border), Ganta, and Buchanan. These areas are easily accessible, unlike the 1,600 kilometers of unpaved roads, which are mostly in need of repair. Traveling from the southeastern part of the country to Monrovia requires more time due to road conditions, and it is very difficult to transport agricultural products from the southeastern counties to Monrovia.

Agriculture Overview

Tables 8.3 and 8.4 show key agricultural commodities of Liberia in terms of area harvested and food for human consumption (as ranked by weight). Rice occupies the largest cultivated area, followed by rubber and cassava. Rice and cassava are the first- and second-ranked staple foodcrops. Rice production

FIGURE 8.7   Travel time to urban areas of various sizes in Liberia, circa 2000

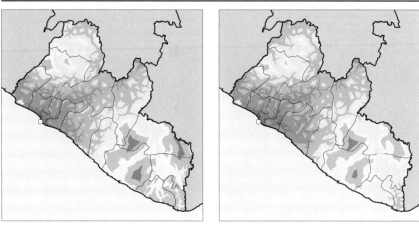

To cities of 500,000 or more people   To cities of 100,000 or more people

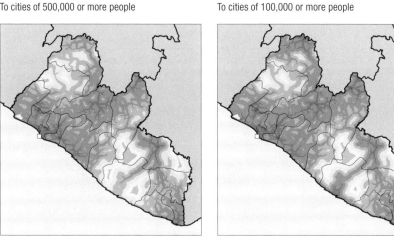

To towns and cities of 25,000 or more people   To towns and cities of 10,000 or more people

Urban location
< 1 hour
1–3 hours
3–5 hours
5–8 hours
8–11 hours
11–16 hours
16–26 hours
> 26 hours

Source: Authors' calculations.

TABLE 8.3   Harvest area of leading agricultural commodities in Liberia, 2006–08 (thousands of hectares)

Rank	Crop	Percent of total	Harvest area
	Total	100.0	536
1	Rice	29.9	160
2	Rubber	23.4	125
3	Cassava	15.9	85
4	Sugarcane	4.8	26
5	Plantains	3.6	19
6	Coffee	3.2	17
7	Oil palm fruit	3.2	17
8	Cocoa beans	3.1	17
9	Other fresh vegetables	2.5	13
10	Bananas	2.0	11

Source: FAOSTAT (FAO 2010).
Note: All values are based on the three-year average for 2006–08.

TABLE 8.4   Consumption of leading food commodities in Liberia, 2003–05 (thousands of metric tons)

Rank	Crop	Percent of total	Food consumption
	Total	100.0	1,261
1	Cassava	38.8	490
2	Rice	13.5	170
3	Bananas	8.0	101
4	Wheat	8.0	101
5	Other vegetables	5.4	68
6	Palm oil	3.4	43
7	Plantains	3.1	39
8	Sugarcane	2.9	36
9	Other roots and tubers	1.8	23
10	Yams	1.4	18

Source: FAOSTAT (FAO 2010).
Note: All values are based on the three-year average for 2003–05.

FIGURE 8.8   Yield (metric tons per hectare) and harvest area density (hectares) for rainfed rice in Liberia, 2000

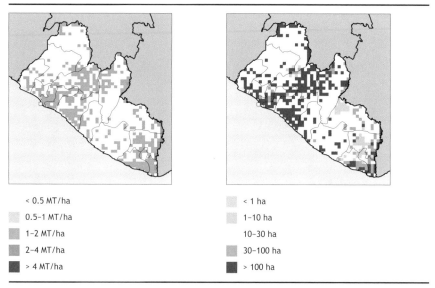

< 0.5 MT/ha		< 1 ha
0.5–1 MT/ha		1–10 ha
1–2 MT/ha		10–30 ha
2–4 MT/ha		30–100 ha
> 4 MT/ha		> 100 ha

Sources: SPAM (Spatial Production Allocation Model) (You and Wood 2006; You, Wood, and Wood-Sichra 2006, 2009).
Notes: ha = hectare; MT = metric tons.

was estimated at 693,770 metric tons in 2007 (Liberia, MOA 2008).[1] Approximately 63 percent of subsistence households produce rice, mainly on the uplands. Rubber, a major export crop, contributes 26 percent of the country's GDP (Liberia 2008).

The next four figures show the estimated yield and growing areas of key crops. Rice (Figure 8.8) and cassava (Figure 8.9) are widely cultivated in the middle part of Liberia (Nimba, Bong, Bassa, and Margibi Counties) and some parts of Maryland and River Gee.[2] Yields range from 1 to 2 tons per hectare for rice and from 4 to 7 metric tons per hectare for cassava. Sugarcane (Figure 8.10) and plantains and bananas (Figure 8.11) are mainly cultivated in counties bordering the coast, as well as River Gee and Grand Gedeh Counties. Sugarcane yields an average of 10 metric tons per hectare, whereas plantains yield 2–4 metric tons per hectare.

---

1   All tons are metric tons.

2   Because of the civil war, Lofa County, formerly known as one of the bread baskets of rice production in Liberia, had a low yield in 2000.

FIGURE 8.9   Yield (metric tons per hectare) and harvest area density (hectares) for rainfed cassava in Liberia, 2000

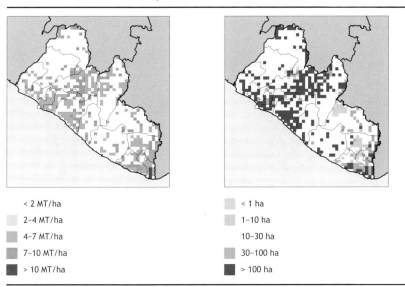

< 2 MT/ha		< 1 ha
2–4 MT/ha		1–10 ha
4–7 MT/ha		10–30 ha
7–10 MT/ha		30–100 ha
> 10 MT/ha		> 100 ha

Sources: SPAM (Spatial Production Allocation Model) (You and Wood 2006; You, Wood, and Wood-Sichra 2006, 2009).
Notes: ha = hectare; MT = metric tons.

FIGURE 8.10   Yield (metric tons per hectare) and harvest area density (hectares) for rainfed sugarcane in Liberia, 2000

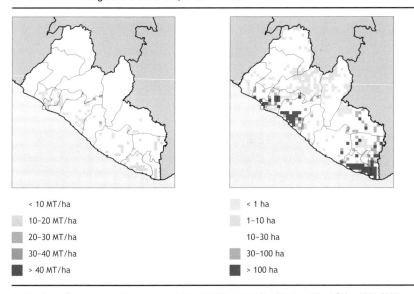

< 10 MT/ha		< 1 ha
10–20 MT/ha		1–10 ha
20–30 MT/ha		10–30 ha
30–40 MT/ha		30–100 ha
> 40 MT/ha		> 100 ha

Sources: SPAM (Spatial Production Allocation Model) (You and Wood 2006; You, Wood, and Wood-Sichra 2006, 2009).
Notes: ha = hectare; MT = metric tons.

FIGURE 8.11   Yield (metric tons per hectare) and harvest area density (hectares) for rainfed plantains and bananas in Liberia, 2000

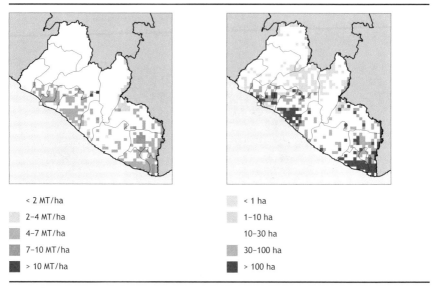

< 2 MT/ha	< 1 ha
2–4 MT/ha	1–10 ha
4–7 MT/ha	10–30 ha
7–10 MT/ha	30–100 ha
> 10 MT/ha	> 100 ha

Sources: SPAM (Spatial Production Allocation Model) (You and Wood 2006; You, Wood, and Wood-Sichra 2006, 2009).
Notes: ha = hectare; MT = metric tons.

Economic and Demographic Scenarios

Population

Figure 8.12 shows population projections for Liberia by the United Nations (UN) population office through 2050 (UNPOP 2009). As the population increases, there will be a high demand for the limited basic social services. Liberia has abundant natural resources, but they are largely untapped. The high-variant scenario predicts a doubling of the population before 2040. Major challenges associated with an increase in population include the country's dilapidated infrastructure, weak health system, malnutrition, lack of clean drinking water, poor road conditions, and high level of unemployment.

Income

Figure 8.13 presents three overall scenarios for Liberia's future GDP per capita derived by combining three GDP scenarios with the three population scenarios of Figure 8.12 (based on UN population data). The optimistic scenario combines high GDP with low population scenarios for all countries, the baseline scenario combines the medium GDP projection with the medium

FIGURE 8.12 Population projections for Liberia, 2010–50

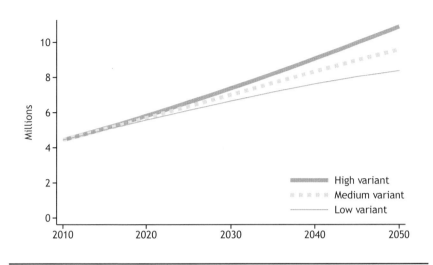

Source: UNPOP (2009).

FIGURE 8.13 Gross domestic product (GDP) per capita in Liberia, future scenarios, 2010–50

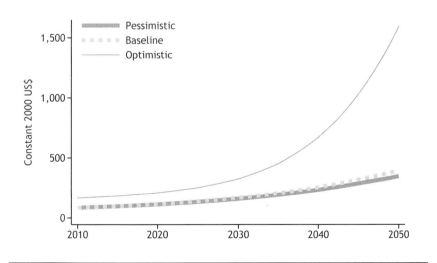

Sources: Computed from GDP data from the World Bank Economic Adaptation to Climate Change project (World Bank 2010), from the Millennium Ecosystem Assessment (2005) reports, and from population data from the United Nations (UNPOP 2009).
Note: US$ = US dollars.

population scenario, and the pessimistic scenario combines the low GDP scenario with the high population scenario. The agricultural modeling in the next section uses these scenarios.

The pessimistic scenario for per capita GDP is similar to the baseline scenario, with GDP per capita less than US$200 in 2030 and no higher than US$400 in 2050. GDP per capita in the optimistic scenario is at least double these levels. The optimistic scenario shows a sharp increase after 2030 in GDP per capita, which will reach US$600 before 2040 and over US$1,500 by 2050. Crucial policy approaches will be needed to address population growth and allow for the adoption of prudent economic policies, including policies related to agriculture.

Biophysical Scenarios

Climate Scenarios

Figure 8.14 shows precipitation changes in Liberia in the four downscaled general circulation models (GCMs) using the A1B climate scenario.[3] The CSIRO Mark 3 GCM shows a wetter situation than does CNRM-CM3.[4] The ECHAM 5 GCM also shows wet conditions in central Liberia but a reduction in rainfall (−100 to −50 millimeters) in Grand Kru, River Geo, and Maryland Counties.[5] The MIROC 3.2 medium-resolution GCM predicts very dry conditions all over the country, with decreases in rainfall of up to −400 millimeters.[6]

Figure 8.15 shows how the average daily maximum temperature of the warmest month of the year will change in the A1B scenario according to various GCMs. All the models show a relatively uniform increase in temperature across the country, with variation among the models in the level of increase in temperature. The CNRM-CM3 GCM predicts an increase of 2.0°–2.5°C; both CSIRO Mark 3 and the MIROC 3.2 medium-resolution GCM predict

---

3 The A1B scenario is a greenhouse gas emissions scenario that assumes fast economic growth, a population that peaks midcentury, and the development of new and efficient technologies, along with a balanced use of energy sources.

4 CSIRO Mark 3 is a climate model developed at the Australia Commonwealth Scientific and Industrial Research Organisation. CNRM-CM3 is National Meteorological Research Center–Climate Model 3.

5 ECHAM 5 is a fifth-generation climate model developed at the Max Planck Institute for Meteorology in Hamburg.

6 MIROC is the Model for Interdisciplinary Research on Climate, developed at the University of Tokyo Center for Climate System Research.

FIGURE 8.14   Changes in mean annual precipitation in Liberia, 2000–2050, A1B scenario (millimeters)

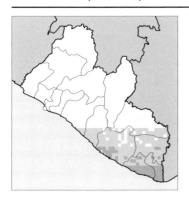

CNRM-CM3 GCM

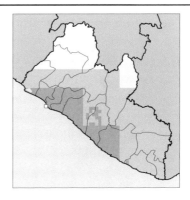

CSIRO Mark 3 GCM

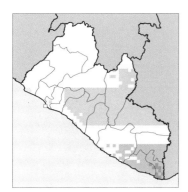

ECHAM 5 GCM

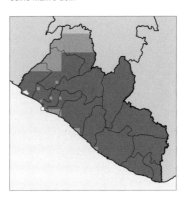

MIROC 3.2 medium-resolution GCM

- < –400
- –400 to –200
- –200 to –100
- –100 to –50
- –50 to 50
- 50 to 100
- 100 to 200
- 200 to 400
- > 400

Source: Authors' calculations based on Jones, Thornton, and Heinke (2009).

Notes: A1B = greenhouse gas emissions scenario that assumes fast economic growth, a population that peaks midcentury, and the development of new and efficient technologies, along with a balanced use of energy sources; CNRM-CM3 = National Meteorological Research Center–Climate Model 3; CSIRO = climate model developed at the Australia Commonwealth Scientific and Industrial Research Organisation; ECHAM 5 = fifth-generation climate model developed at the Max Planck Institute for Meteorology (Hamburg); GCM = general circulation model; MIROC = Model for Interdisciplinary Research on Climate, developed at the University of Tokyo Center for Climate System Research.

FIGURE 8.15   Change in normal daily maximum temperature in Liberia for the warmest month, 2000–2050, A1B scenario (°C)

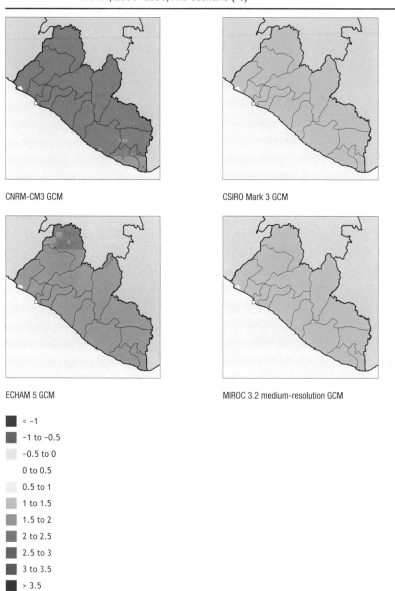

CNRM-CM3 GCM

CSIRO Mark 3 GCM

ECHAM 5 GCM

MIROC 3.2 medium-resolution GCM

■ < –1
■ –1 to –0.5
   –0.5 to 0
   0 to 0.5
   0.5 to 1
   1 to 1.5
■ 1.5 to 2
■ 2 to 2.5
■ 2.5 to 3
■ 3 to 3.5
■ > 3.5

Source: Authors' calculations based on Jones, Thornton, and Heinke (2009).
Notes: A1B = greenhouse gas emissions scenario that assumes fast economic growth, a population that peaks midcentury, and the development of new and efficient technologies, along with a balanced use of energy sources; CNRM-CM3 = National Meteorological Research Center–Climate Model 3; CSIRO = climate model developed at the Australia Commonwealth Scientific and Industrial Research Organisation; ECHAM 5 = fifth-generation climate model developed at the Max Planck Institute for Meteorology (Hamburg); GCM = general circulation model; MIROC = Model for Interdisciplinary Research on Climate, developed at the University of Tokyo Center for Climate System Research.

an increase of 1. 0°–1.5°C. The ECHAM 5 GCM predicts an increase of 1.5°–2.0°C.

Crop Physiological Response to Climate Change

The output for rainfed rice is mapped in Figure 8.16, which compares the potential crop yields in Liberia for 2050 assuming climate change with the potential yields assuming an unchanged (2000) climate. All the GCMs predict more areas of yield increase than yield decrease, and for the most part the changes are less than 25 percent of the baseline yields for 2000. Although the GCMs have very similar results, it seems that the CNRM-CM3 GCM has a slightly higher ratio of gains to losses, and it even has two areas for which yield increases are predicted to exceed 25 percent. The MIROC 3.2 GCM has probably the lowest ratio of gains to losses ratio, with most of the losses concentrated in the northern portion of the country. These results are encouraging because they suggest that climate change will bring more benefits than costs, at least for rainfed rice. It is not entirely clear why the projected drop in annual rainfall in MIROC did not result in more yield reduction, but it could be that the rainfall was not too adversely affected during the growing season, which is all the crop models in the DSSAT software focus on.

Agricultural Vulnerability Scenarios (Crop-Specific)

The next three figures show simulation results from the International Model for Policy Analysis of Agricultural Commodities and Trade (IMPACT) for key agricultural crops in Liberia. The figure for each featured crop has five graphs showing production, yield, area, net exports, and world price. Rice production is shown to increase, reflecting productivity increases. All scenarios show very little change in the area planted with rice (Figure 8.17). Any projected increase in rice production will be the result of improved management, because there are already rice varieties with a yield potential of up to 4 tons. Liberia is not self-sufficient in rice, and the scenarios show an increasing deficit based on an increase in population without a sufficiently large corresponding increase in rice production. An increasing world price for rice would therefore increase the burden on the country's economy.

Unlike rice production, cassava production is predicted to increase only until 2030 and then to be relatively flat (with some small increases and some small decreases) thereafter. Similar to the case of rice, improved management practices rather than improved varieties will be responsible for any increase in production (Figure 8.18). The area planted with cassava will decrease more

FIGURE 8.16   Yield change under climate change: Rainfed rice in Liberia, 2000–2050, A1B scenario

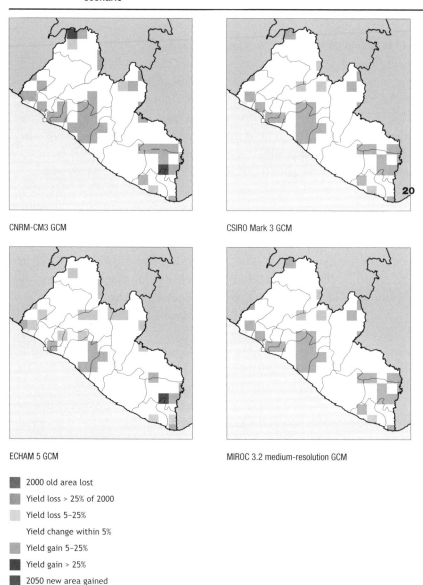

CNRM-CM3 GCM

CSIRO Mark 3 GCM

ECHAM 5 GCM

MIROC 3.2 medium-resolution GCM

- 2000 old area lost
- Yield loss > 25% of 2000
- Yield loss 5–25%
- Yield change within 5%
- Yield gain 5–25%
- Yield gain > 25%
- 2050 new area gained

Source: Authors' calculations based on Jones, Thornton, and Heinke (2009).
Notes: A1B = greenhouse gas emissions scenario that assumes fast economic growth, a population that peaks midcentury, and the development of new and efficient technologies, along with a balanced use of energy sources; CNRM-CM3 = National Meteorological Research Center–Climate Model 3; CSIRO = climate model developed at the Australia Commonwealth Scientific and Industrial Research Organisation; ECHAM 5 = fifth-generation climate model developed at the Max Planck Institute for Meteorology (Hamburg); GCM = general circulation model; MIROC = Model for Interdisciplinary Research on Climate, developed at the University of Tokyo Center for Climate System Research.

FIGURE 8.17   Impact of changes in GDP and population on rice in Liberia, 2010–50

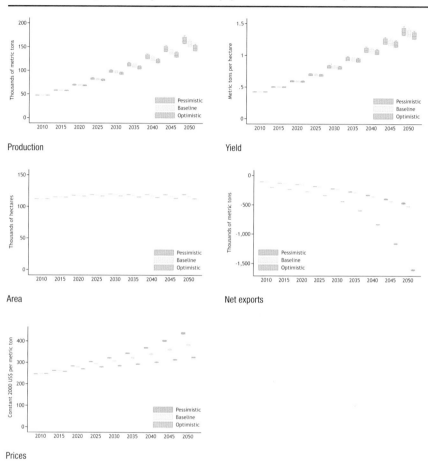

Production

Yield

Area

Net exports

Prices

Source: Based on analysis conducted for Nelson et al. (2010).

Notes: The box and whiskers plot for each socioeconomic scenario shows the range of effects from the four future climate scenarios. GDP = gross domestic product; US$ = US dollars.

FIGURE 8.18   Impact of changes in GDP and population on cassava in Liberia, 2010–50

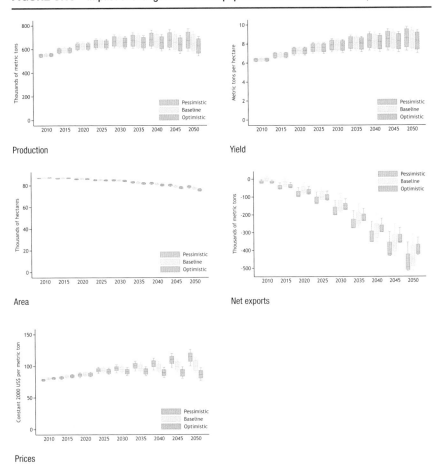

Source: Based on analysis conducted for Nelson et al. (2010).

Notes: The box and whiskers plot for each socioeconomic scenario shows the range of effects from the four future climate scenarios. GDP = gross domestic product; US$ = US dollars.

than the area planted with rice. The decrease in the area planted and the possible increase in population will cause the country to become an increasingly larger importer of cassava. After 2025, the world price for cassava will tend to be higher in the pessimistic scenario than in the optimistic scenario.

Unlike the production of rice and cassava, the production of sugarcane will be significantly influenced by the area under cultivation. Figure 8.19 shows the area planted with sugarcane increasing in line with production increases, while productivity appears to be unchanged. However, similar to the cases of both rice and cassava, the net export of sugarcane would decrease despite the increase in world price. The increase in imports is a consequence of increased consumption in the country as a result of population increase.

Human Vulnerability Scenarios

In addition to agricultural outcomes, IMPACT also predicts the number of malnourished children under the age of five and the number of available kilocalories per capita. Figure 8.20 shows the impact of future GDP and population scenarios on under-five malnutrition rates. The box-and-whisker plots in the figure indicate the range of climate scenario effects. Low GDP per capita and a larger population will result in an increase in the number of children under age five who suffer from malnutrition until 2030 in the baseline scenario and until 2035 in the pessimistic scenario, though the malnutrition rates might fall slightly during those years because the population is projected to grow at a faster rate than the number of malnourished children.

We also note that the kilocalories available to each person will eventually increase with the increase in GDP per capita (Figure 8.21), though they will be fairly constant between 2010 and 2025. There is a correlation between the availability of kilocalories and the reduction of under-five malnutrition.

Conclusions and Policy Recommendations

Liberia has experienced a relatively high rate of urban population growth promoted by better transport and communication systems, fertile agricultural lands, local alluvial mining activities, and the presence of international mining and agricultural companies, as well as opportunities for employment and trade with contiguous West African countries. Monrovia is the most densely populated city due to its relatively superior socioeconomic conditions. Major challenges associated with population growth include dilapidated infrastructure,

FIGURE 8.19   Impact of changes in GDP and population on sugarcane in Liberia, 2010–50

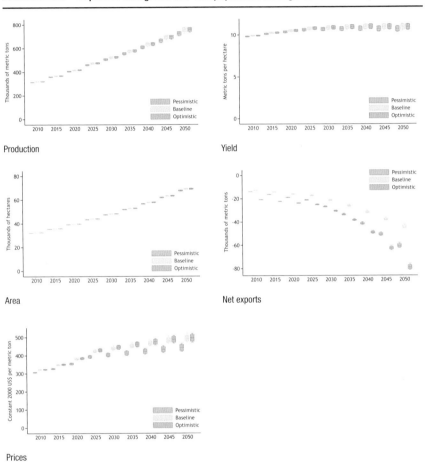

Source: Based on analysis conducted for Nelson et al. (2010).

Notes: The box and whiskers plot for each socioeconomic scenario shows the range of effects from the four future climate scenarios. GDP = gross domestic product; US$ = US dollars.

FIGURE 8.20 Number of malnourished children under five years of age in Liberia in multiple income and climate scenarios, 2010–50

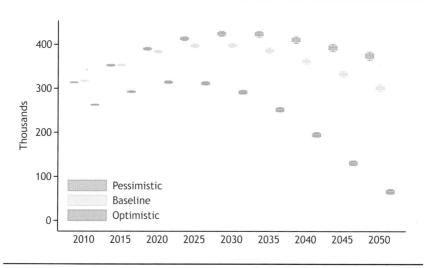

Source: Based on analysis conducted for Nelson et al. (2010).

Note: The box and whiskers plot for each socioeconomic scenario shows the range of effects from the four future climate scenarios.

FIGURE 8.21 Kilocalories per capita in Liberia in multiple income and climate scenarios, 2010–50

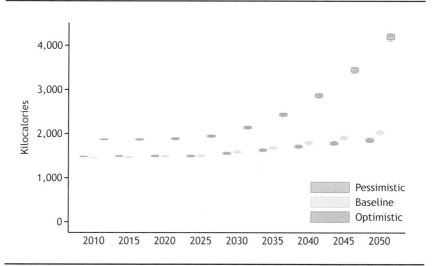

Source: Based on analysis conducted for Nelson et al. (2010).

Note: The box and whiskers plot for each socioeconomic scenario shows the range of effects from the four future climate scenarios.

a weak health system, malnutrition, a lack of clean drinking water, bad road conditions, and high levels of unemployment. As the population increases, there will be a high demand not only for the limited basic social services but also for the untapped natural resources. Transportation is very important for agricultural development. In Liberia, the poor road conditions make it very difficult to transport agricultural products from the southeastern counties to Monrovia.

During the civil war, the share of agricultural GDP increased sharply because most other sectors of the economy became disrupted and nonfunctional. The majority of the population is engaged in agriculture. However, 90–95 percent of the population of Liberia lives on less than US$2 per day. This is certainly a situation that needs significant improvement. To address this issue of extreme poverty, the Government of Liberia has developed a Poverty Reduction Strategy.

Although our analysis shows an increase in the importation of staple commodities, it does not appear that this will adversely affect the nation's food security, because the IMPACT model predicts that in the latter half of the period under study, the malnutrition rates of children will decline and the number of calories consumed per capita will increase.

There has been considerable variation in the predictions for temperature and precipitation changes due to climate change, which has resulted in different projected outcomes regarding the production of rice, with some models showing most areas actually increasing in yield due to favorable changes in climate and other models showing losses in yield due to unfavorable changes in climate. These results point to a need for flexibility and responsiveness in the agricultural sector in regard to adapting to climate change.

Based on the results of our study, we recommend the following:

- Liberia's Ministry of Agriculture (MOA) should improve its policy on monitoring climate change, incorporating guidance on adaptation measures to reduced rainfall and higher temperatures.

- The MOA should strengthen its policies on nationwide awareness of environmental considerations in all agricultural activities by providing farmers with climate change–related information.

- The government should develop policies to address the challenges associated with population growth.

- The government should improve the implementation of its policy on rehabilitated, reconstructed, and recommissioned rural infrastructure to facilitate transporting agricultural products from rural to urban areas.

- The MOA should incorporate policies to support the development of suitable varieties of major crops as well as associated management practices to enhance the productivity of these crops, particularly staple foods and rice.

- The government should strengthen its policy on food and nutrition security for vulnerable groups—especially those who depend on agricultural activities for their livelihoods—including the provision of safety nets.

As Liberia continues to rebuild after decades of civil unrest, there are many competing demands for limited funds. The good news about adaptation to climate change is that many of the same policies and investments needed to make agriculture more productive now will also help farmers adapt in the future. It is encouraging that the government has taken steps to increase funding to agriculture since 2005, and agriculture as a sector is receiving substantially more money than before. Continued commitment to the sector by the government will likely result in much enhanced performance, both in the short run and in the longer run, when the more serious impacts of climate change will be felt.

References

Bartholome, E., and A. S. Belward. 2005. "GLC2000: A New Approach to Global Land Cover Mapping from Earth Observation Data." *International Journal of Remote Sensing* 26 (9): 1959–1977.

CIESIN (Center for International Earth Science Information Network, Columbia University), Columbia University, IFPRI (International Food Policy Research Institute), World Bank, and CIAT (Centro Internacional de Agricultura Tropical). 2004. *Global Rural–Urban Mapping Project, Version 1 (GRUMPv1)*. Palisades, NY, US: Socioeconomic Data and Applications Center (SEDAC), Columbia University. http://sedac.ciesin.columbia.edu/gpw.

FAO (Food and Agriculture Organization of the United Nations). 2010. *FAOSTAT Database on Agriculture*. Rome.

Jones, P. G., P. K. Thornton, and J. Heinke. 2009. "Generating Characteristic Daily Weather Data Using Downscaled Climate Model Data from the IPCC's Fourth Assessment." Project report for the International Institute for Land Reclamation and Improvement, Wageningen, the Netherlands. Accessed May 7, 2010. www.ccafs-climate.org/pattern_scaling/.

Lehner, B., and P. Döll. 2004. "Development and Validation of a Global Database of Lakes, Reservoirs, and Wetlands." *Journal of Hydrology* 296 (1–4): 1–22.

Liberia. 2008. *Poverty Reduction Strategy Paper (PRSP).* Monrovia.

Liberia, ISGS (Institute of Statistics and Geo-information Services). 2009. *2008 National Population and Housing Census.* Monrovia.

Liberia, MOA (Ministry of Agriculture). 2008. *Food and Agriculture Policy Strategy.* Monrovia.

Liberia, MPEA (Ministry of Planning and Economic Affairs) and UNDP (United Nations Development Programme). 2010. *Republic of Liberia Millennium Development Goals 2010 Report: Progress, Prospects and Challenges Towards Achieving the MDGs.* Monrovia.

Millennium Ecosystem Assessment. 2005. *Ecosystems and Human Well-being: Synthesis.* Washington, DC: Island Press. http://www.maweb.org/en/Global.aspx.

Nelson, G. C., M. W. Rosegrant, A. Palazzo, I. Gray, C. Ingersoll, R. Robertson, S. Tokgoz, et al. 2010. *Food Security, Farming, and Climate Change to 2050: Scenarios, Results, Policy Options.* Washington, DC: International Food Policy Research Institute.

UNDP (United Nations Development Programme) Liberia. 2006. *First State of the Environment Report for Liberia.* Monrovia.

UNEP and IUCN (United Nations Environment Programme and International Union for the Conservation of Nature). 2009. *World Database on Protected Areas (WDPA): Annual Release.* Accessed 2009. www.wdpa.org/protectedplanet.aspx.

UNEP-WCMC (World Conservation Monitoring Centre). 2006. *World Database on Protected Areas.* Accessed September 2012. www.unep-wcmc.org/wdpa.

UNPOP (United Nations Department of Economic and Social Affairs–Population Division). 2009. *World Population Prospects: The 2008 Revision.* New York. http://esa.un.org/unpd/wpp/.

Wood, S., G. Hyman, U. Deichmann, E. Barona, R. Tenorio, Z. Guo, et al. 2010. *Sub-national Poverty Maps for the Developing World Using International Poverty Lines: Preliminary Data Release.* Washington, DC: Harvest Choice and International Food Policy Research Institute. http://labs.harvestchoice.org/2010/08/poverty-maps/.

World Bank. 2009. *World Development Indicators.* Accessed May 2011. http://data.worldbank.org/data-catalog/world-development-indicators.

———. 2010. *Economics of Adaptation to Climate Change: Synthesis Report.* Washington, DC. http://climatechange.worldbank.org/content/economics-adaptation-climate-change-study-homepage.

You, L., and S. Wood. 2006. "An Entropy Approach to Spatial Disaggregation of Agricultural Production." *Agricultural Systems* 90 (1–3): 329–347.

You, L., S. Wood, and U. Wood-Sichra. 2006. "Generating Global Crop Distribution Maps: From Census to Grid." Paper presented at the International Association of Agricultural Economists Conference, Brisbane, Australia, August 11–18.

———. 2009. "Generating Plausible Crop Distribution and Performance Maps for Sub-Saharan Africa Using a Spatially Disaggregated Data Fusion and Optimization Approach." *Agricultural Systems* 99 (2–3): 126–140.

Chapter 9

NIGER

Hassane Yayé, Adamou Danguioua, Abdulai Jalloh, Robert Zougmoré,
Gerald C. Nelson, and Timothy S. Thomas

Niger is a landlocked country in West Africa located between 11°37′ and 23°23′ north latitude and between 00°10′ and 16°00′ east longitude, with an area of 1,267,000 square kilometers. Niger shares borders with Algeria and Libya in the north, Chad in the east, Nigeria and Benin in the south, and Burkina Faso and Mali in the west. Three-fourths of Niger is covered by the Sahara Desert. The southern part of the country is in the Sahelian climate zone, with Sudan savannah vegetation. The rainy season lasts for only three months, with total rainfall ranging from 150 to 600 millimeters per year in the Sudan savannah; maximum temperatures are high (45°C in the shade in April–May). The vegetation cover is sparse, and nomadic agriculture is dominant.

Review of the Current Situation

Population

Figure 9.1 shows trends in the size of the total population and the rural population (left axis), along with the share of the urban population (right axis). The population of Niger grew from 3.1 million in 1960 to 14.7 million in 2008. Based on the 2010 population census, the growth rate of the population was 3.3 percent between 1975 and 2010; a full 83 percent live in rural areas. The high fertility rate (7.1 children per woman) contributes significantly to the country's rapid population growth. In the 1960s and 1970s, the urban population grew much faster than the rural population (Table 9.1). Since the 1970s, the growth rate in the urban areas has declined, possibly due to sensitization campaigns as well as economic conditions. The capital city houses the bulk of the urban population (39.3 percent).

Figure 9.2 shows the (estimated) geographic distribution of the population. The population of Niger is concentrated in the southern part of the country, largely due to the pattern of increasing aridity from south to north.

FIGURE 9.1   Population trends in Niger: Total population, rural population, and percent urban, 1960–2008

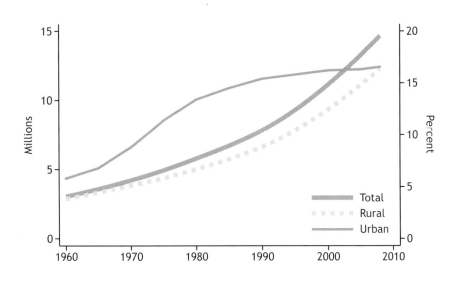

Source: World Development Indicators (World Bank 2009).

TABLE 9.1   Population growth rates in Niger, 1960–2008 (percent)

Decade	Total growth rate	Rural growth rate	Urban growth rate
1960–69	3.2	2.9	7.3
1970–79	3.2	2.6	7.5
1980–89	3.0	2.7	4.4
1990–99	3.5	3.4	4.0
2000–2008	3.5	3.4	3.7

Source: Authors' calculations based on World Development Indicators (World Bank 2009).

In addition to the capital city—Niamey, in the Tillabéri Region—the Dosso, Tahoua, Maradi, Zinder, and Diffa Regions are also highly populated. The unequal population distribution imposes considerable pressure on the arable land in the southwestern part of the country. In areas such as Madarounfa, Guidan-Roumdji, Matameye, Mirriah, and Magaria, the density is 100 inhabitants per square kilometer compared to the national average of 8 inhabitants per square kilometer.

FIGURE 9.2   Population distribution in Niger, 2000 (persons per square kilometer)

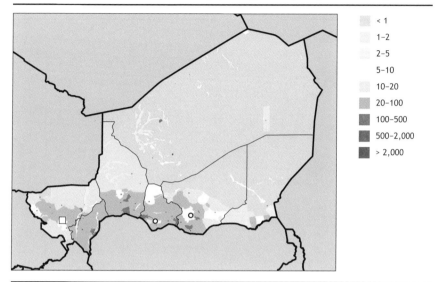

Legend:
< 1
1–2
2–5
5–10
10–20
20–100
100–500
500–2,000
> 2,000

Source: CIESIN et al. (2004).

Income

The share of income earned in agriculture shows the importance of agriculture as a sector for the economy. Figure 9.3 shows trends in gross domestic product (GDP) per capita, as well as the proportion of GDP from agriculture.

In Niger the rural sector accounted for 41 percent of GDP in 2007 and 49 percent in 2009, and it contributes significantly to export earnings. However, because the majority of the population lives in rural areas, the creation of wealth per capita in the rural zone is significantly lower than in the urban areas.

Climate change has had significant effects on the development of the country. Since 1967 there have been several food crises (one every three years on average) due mainly to unfavorable climatic conditions, resulting in a drastic reduction in living standards. The situation worsened when the CFA franc was devaluated in January 1994. The country entered a turbulent political era in the 1990s, with two military coups (in January 1996 and April 1999). This situation culminated in major donors suspending aid to the country, with severe consequences for the national economy and the living standards of the people.

Figure 9.3 clearly shows that since the 1960s the contribution of the agricultural sector to GDP has been declining, from more than 70 percent to about 40 percent in the 1980s and then leveling out onward. Increasing

FIGURE 9.3   Per capita GDP in Niger (constant 2000 US$) and share of GDP from
agriculture (percent), 1960–2008

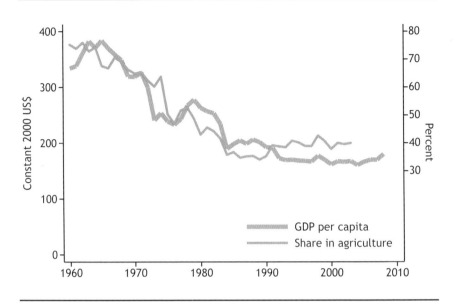

Source: World Development Indicators (World Bank 2009).
Note: GDP = gross domestic product; US$ = US dollars.

urbanization along with the development of the service industry has resulted
in this decline in the contribution of the agricultural sector to GDP.

Vulnerability to Climate Change

Table 9.2 provides some data on Niger's performance on several indicators of a
population's vulnerability and resiliency to economic shocks beyond the factor
of income level: level of education, literacy, and concentration of labor in poorer
or less dynamic sectors. These social indicators show Niger among the most vulnerable countries in the region. Its primary school enrolment is about 50 percent, while its enrolment in secondary school is below 15 percent. The dropout
rate after primary school is drastic. In addition, the adult literacy rate is very low
(29 percent). Niger has a Muslim majority, and many families prefer Islamic education, sending their children to Koranic schools rather than the formal schools.
The popularity of Koranic schools may help to account for the low enrolment in
primary schools. The drastic fall in secondary school education could be due to
poverty, early marriages for girls, and the need for family labor on farms.

TABLE 9.2 Education and labor statistics for Niger, 2000s

Indicator	Year	Percent
Primary school enrollment (percent gross, three-year average)	2007	53.3
Secondary school enrollment (percent gross, three-year average)	2007	10.6
Adult literacy rate	2005	28.7
Percent employed in agriculture	2008	80.0
Under-five malnutrition (weight for age)	2006	39.9

Source: Authors' calculations based on World Development Indicators (World Bank 2009).

Figure 9.4 shows two noneconomic correlates of poverty: life expectancy and under-five mortality. Life expectancy in Niger stagnated at about 40 years during the 1960s–1980s but gradually increased to 50 in the 1990s and to about 55 years after 2000. The increase in life expectancy after the mid-1980s slightly preceded the decrease in infant mortality, which fell from over 300 deaths per 1,000 to below 200 in 2008. The improvement in life expectancy and the decline in under-five mortality could be accounted for by the gradual improvement in heath conditions, including vaccinations, as well as by the increase in the world price of uranium, a resource abundant in Niger, in the 1990s.

FIGURE 9.4 Well-being indicators in Niger, 1960–2008

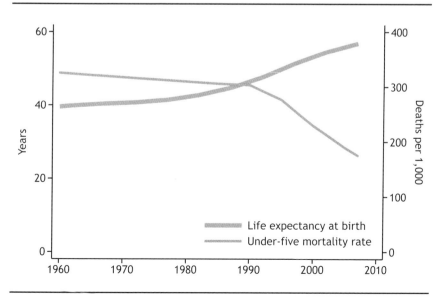

Source: World Development Indicators (World Bank 2009).

Figure 9.5 shows the proportion of the population living on less than US$2 (US dollars) per day. In general, the incidence of poverty in Niger is higher in the densely populated areas. More than 95 percent of the population lives on less than US$2 (800 CFA francs) per day in the regions of Dosso, Maradi, and Zinder; the number is 80–90 percent in Diffa. Agadez and Tahoua have 60–70 percent of their populations living on less than US$2 per day. The Tillabéri Region, which hosts the capital city Niamey, has the lowest poverty rate, at 20–30 percent. This may reflect the relatively greater and more diversified employment opportunities in and around the capital city.

Review of Land Use and Agriculture

Land Use Overview

Figure 9.6 shows land cover and land use in Niger as of 2000. Three-fourths of the area of Niger is covered by the Sahara Desert, and the Sudan savanna covers the southern quarter of the country. The vegetation cover is sparse, and nomadic agriculture is dominant. Most grasses are annuals because of drought stress in the

FIGURE 9.5   Poverty in Niger, 1960–2008 (percentage of population living on less than US$2 per day)

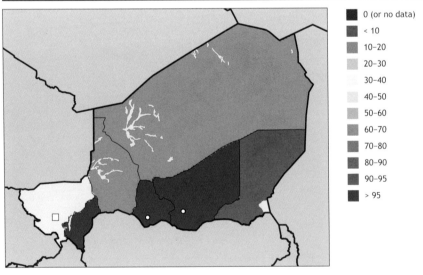

Source: Wood et al. (2010).
Note: Based on 2005 US$ (US dollars) and on purchasing power parity value.

FIGURE 9.6 Land cover and land use in Niger, 2000

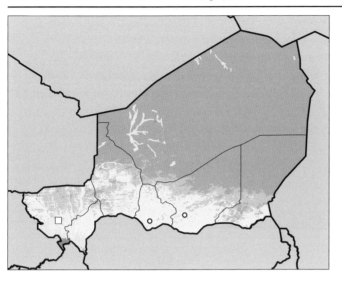

Tree cover, broadleaved, evergreen

Tree cover, broadleaved, deciduous, closed

Tree cover, broadleaved, deciduous, open

Tree cover, broadleaved, needle-leaved, evergreen

Tree cover, broadleaved, needle-leaved, deciduous

Tree cover, broadleaved, mixed leaf type

Tree cover, broadleaved, regularly flooded, fresh water

Tree cover, broadleaved, regularly flooded, saline water

Mosaic of tree cover/other natural vegetation

Tree cover, burnt

Shrub cover, closed–open, evergreen

Shrub cover, closed–open, deciduous

Herbacious cover, closed–open

Sparse herbacious or sparse shrub cover

Regularly flooded shrub or herbacious cover

Cultivated and managed areas

Mosaic of cropland/tree cover/other natural vegetation

Mosaic of cropland/shrub/grass cover

Bare areas

Water bodies

Snow and ice

Artificial surfaces and associated areas

No data

Source: GLC2000 (Global Land Cover 2000) (Bartholome and Belward 2005).

long dry period. Commonly occurring annuals include *Andropogon pseudapricus,
Hyparrhenia,* and *Loudetia* spp. A number of perennials grow vigorously:
*Andropogon gayanus, Anthrophora nigritane, Aristida stipoides, Pennisetum
setosum,* and *Hyparrhenia* spp. More to the north, trees with thorns (such as
Acacia spp.) become more common and the grasses become shorter, less tus-
socky, and more feathery. In the southern part of the country, millet, requiring a
minimum growing period of 75 days, can be grown (ILRI 1993).

Figure 9.7 shows the locations of protected areas, including parks and
reserves. These locations provide important protection for fragile environmental areas, which may also be important for the tourism industry as the country
tries to diversify its economic base.

FIGURE 9.7   Protected areas in Niger, 2009

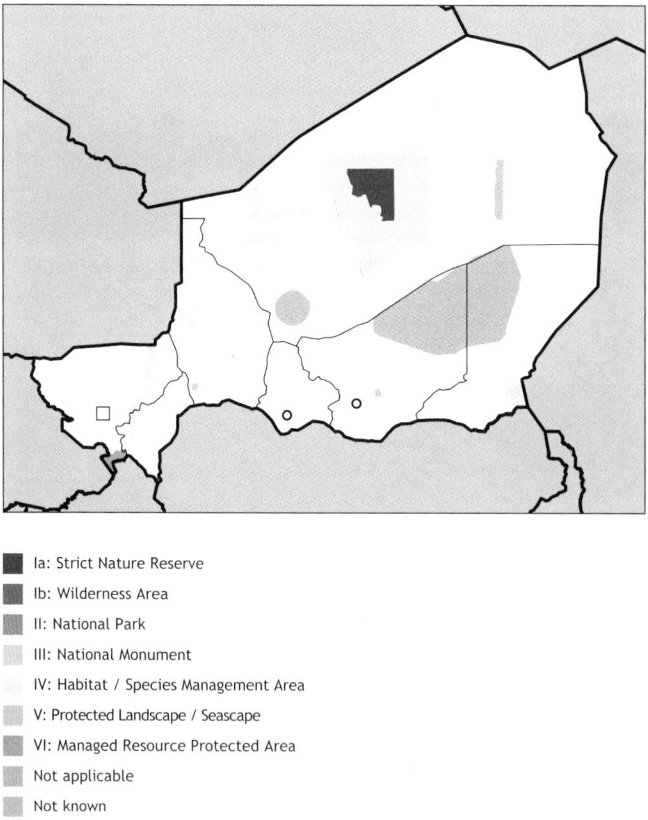

- Ia: Strict Nature Reserve
- Ib: Wilderness Area
- II: National Park
- III: National Monument
- IV: Habitat / Species Management Area
- V: Protected Landscape / Seascape
- VI: Managed Resource Protected Area
- Not applicable
- Not known

Sources: Protected areas are from the World Database on Protected Areas (UNEP and IUCN 2009). Water bodies are from the
World Wildlife Fund's Global Lakes and Wetlands Database (Lehner and Döll 2004).

Figure 9.8 shows the travel time to urban areas as potential markets for agricultural products as well as sources of agricultural inputs and consumer goods for farm households. The road network is good in the Tillabéri Region, particularly around the capital city Niamey. The southern parts of the regions bordering Nigeria have road networks, particularly around the regional

FIGURE 9.8   Travel time to urban areas of various sizes in Niger, circa 2000

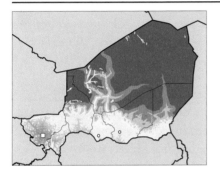

To cities of 500,000 or more people

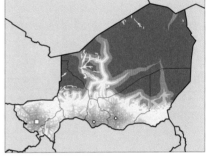

To cities of 100,000 or more people

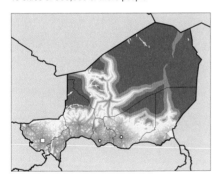

To towns and cities of 25,000 or more people

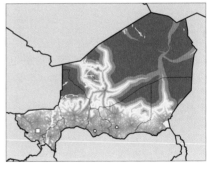

To towns and cities of 10,000 or more people

- Urban location
- < 1 hour
- 1–3 hours
- 3–5 hours
- 5–8 hours
- 8–11 hours
- 11–16 hours
- 16–26 hours
- > 26 hours

Source: Authors' calculations.

capitals. In general, the travel time to these cities ranges from one to three hours. Most of the Agadez Region—which is mainly desert—is not connected by roads. The regional capital of Agadez is connected to the regional capitals of Tillabéri, Tahoua, and Zinder; the road leading to Algeria is not paved.

Agriculture Overview

Agropastoralism is the major farming system in Niger. Livestock production is a major component, based mainly on open grazing. During the dry season, herds are moved southward across the borders to Benin, Nigeria, and Burkina Faso. The major livestock-producing regions are Agadez, Diffa, Tahoua, and Tillabéri. Recurring droughts severely affect livestock production: the drought of 1969 led to an estimated loss of 30 percent of the cattle in Agadez and at least 13 percent in the rest of the country, and the catastrophic drought of 1974 killed almost all of the livestock in the country. As recently as 2009, the livestock sector was hit by a drought leading to the loss of thousands of cattle.

Tables 9.3–9.5 show key agricultural commodities in terms of area harvested, the value of the harvest, and the provision of food for human consumption (ranked by weight). A wide range of crops is grown in the semiarid areas of Niger: finger millet, pearl millet, bulrush millet, sorghum, cowpeas, pigeon peas, groundnuts, green grams, *phaesolus* beans, and chickpeas. Millet is the

TABLE 9.3   Harvest area of leading agricultural commodities in Niger, 2006–08 (thousands of hectares)

Rank	Crop	Percent of total	Harvest area
	Total	100.0	14,761
1	Millet	43.4	6,410
2	Cowpeas	32.1	4,743
3	Sorghum	19.4	2,859
4	Groundnuts	3.1	460
5	Sesame seed	0.5	73
6	Other pulses	0.2	33
7	Mangoes, mangosteens, guavas	0.1	22
8	Rice	0.1	20
9	Beans	0.1	18
10	Cabbages and other brassicas	0.1	13

Source: FAOSTAT (FAO 2010).
Note: All values are based on the three-year average for 2006–08.

TABLE 9.4   Value of production of leading agricultural commodities in Niger, 2005–07 (millions of US$)

Rank	Crop	Percent of total	Value of production
	Total	100.0	885.1
1	Millet	44.9	397.7
2	Sorghum	13.2	117.2
3	Cowpeas	10.6	94.2
4	Onions, dry	6.6	58.2
5	Groundnuts	5.1	45.2
6	Tomatoes	3.1	27.3
7	Sugarcane	2.7	23.5
8	Cassava	1.9	17.1
9	Chilies and peppers	1.9	16.7
10	Rice	1.7	14.6

Source: FAOSTAT (FAO 2010).
Note: All values are based on the three-year average for 2005–07. US$ = US dollars.

TABLE 9.5   Consumption of leading food commodities in Niger, 2003–05 (thousands of metric tons)

Rank	Crop	Percent of total	Food consumption
	Total	100.0	4,132
1	Millet	39.8	1,646
2	Sorghum	11.9	493
3	Other vegetables	6.5	268
4	Rice	6.3	261
5	Other pulses	6.1	251
6	Onions	5.5	228
7	Cassava	3.1	127
8	Tomatoes	2.5	104
9	Sugar	2.3	94
10	Groundnuts	1.7	71

Source: FAOSTAT (FAO 2010).
Note: All values are based on the three-year average for 2003–05.

most important crop, occupying nearly half of the total cropped area of the country and being the main staple food item. The other important crops are cowpeas, sorghum, and groundnuts.

The next three figures show the estimated yields and growing areas of key crops. Millet (Figure 9.9), cowpeas (Figure 9.10), and sorghum (Figure 9.11) are grown in the southern part of the country, where it rains about three months of the year. Millet is more widely grown than the other crops. The yields of all the crops are very low, an average of 0.5 metric tons per hectare.

Economic and Demographic Scenarios

Population

Figure 9.12 shows population projections for Niger made by the United Nations (UN) population office through 2050 (UNPOP 2009). The population of Niger is projected to grow to about 24 million by 2020; after that point, estimates for the low, medium, and high variants differ. In 2050 the difference between the low and high variants is greater than 10 million people,

FIGURE 9.9   Yield (metric tons per hectare) and harvest area density (hectares) for rainfed millet in Niger, 2000

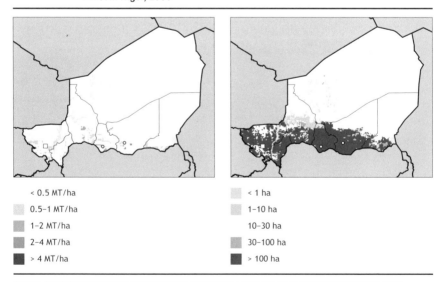

< 0.5 MT/ha	< 1 ha
0.5–1 MT/ha	1–10 ha
1–2 MT/ha	10–30 ha
2–4 MT/ha	30–100 ha
> 4 MT/ha	> 100 ha

Sources: SPAM (Spatial Production Allocation Model) (You and Wood 2006; You, Wood, and Wood-Sichra 2006, 2009).
Notes: ha = hectare; MT = metric tons.

FIGURE 9.10 Yield (metric tons per hectare) and harvest area density (hectares) for rainfed cowpeas in Niger, 2000

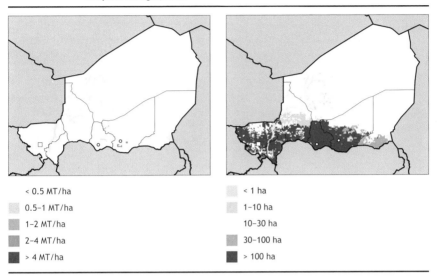

< 0.5 MT/ha

0.5–1 MT/ha

1–2 MT/ha

2–4 MT/ha

> 4 MT/ha

< 1 ha

1–10 ha

10–30 ha

30–100 ha

> 100 ha

Sources: SPAM (Spatial Production Allocation Model) (You and Wood 2006; You, Wood, and Wood-Sichra 2006, 2009).
Notes: ha = hectare; MT = metric tons.

FIGURE 9.11 Yield (metric tons per hectare) and harvest area density (hectares) for rainfed sorghum in Niger, 2000

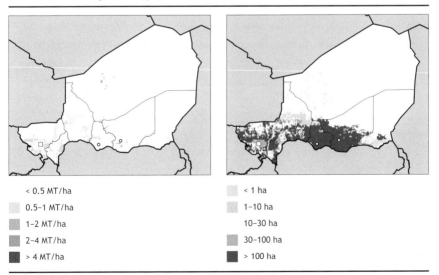

< 0.5 MT/ha

0.5–1 MT/ha

1–2 MT/ha

2–4 MT/ha

> 4 MT/ha

< 1 ha

1–10 ha

10–30 ha

30–100 ha

> 100 ha

Sources: SPAM (Spatial Production Allocation Model) (You and Wood 2006; You, Wood, and Wood-Sichra 2006, 2009).
Notes: ha = hectare; MT = metric tons.

FIGURE 9.12 Population projections for Niger, 2010–50

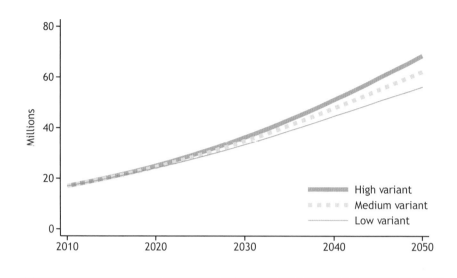

Source: UNPOP (2009).

and the high variant estimates the population at 68.5 million. That is almost triple the population of 2010. That number of people in Niger would create very high densities in the cultivable areas and put significant pressure on arable land as well as on utilities. One possible policy option is the reclamation of the desert to make it more habitable, enabling an environment for growing crops and rearing livestock. This would be an uphill task based on the limited resources of the country.

Income

Figure 9.13 presents three overall scenarios for Niger's GDP per capita derived by combining three GDP scenarios with the three population scenarios of Figure 9.12 (based on UN population data). The optimistic scenario combines high GDP with low population scenarios for all countries, the baseline scenario combines the medium GDP projection with the medium population scenario, and the pessimistic scenario combines the low GDP scenario with the high population scenario. The agricultural modeling in the next section uses these scenarios.

FIGURE 9.13   Gross domestic product (GDP) per capita in Niger, future scenarios, 2010–50

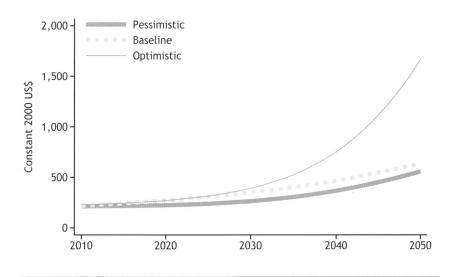

Sources: Computed from GDP data from the World Bank Economic Adaptation to Climate Change project (World Bank 2010), from the Millennium Ecosystem Assessment (2005) reports, and from population data from the United Nations (UNPOP 2009).
Note: US$ = US dollars.

The baseline and pessimistic scenarios follow a similar trend, showing only about US$600–650 per capita GDP by 2050. The optimistic scenario follows the baseline until the late 2020s. After 2030, low population and high GDP—the optimistic scenario—are predicted to result in a significant increase in per capita GDP, to US$750 in 2040 and to more than US$1,670 by 2050.

Biophysical Scenarios

Climate Scenarios

Figure 9.14 shows projected precipitation changes in Niger in the four down-scaled general circulation models (GCMs) we use in this chapter in the A1B scenario. The CSIRO Mark 3 and ECHAM 5 GCMs both show little or no change in rainfall throughout the country. The CNRM-CM3 and MIROC 3.2 medium-resolution GCMs both show an increase in rainfall

FIGURE 9.14   Changes in mean precipitation in Niger, 2000–2050, A1B scenario
(millimeters)

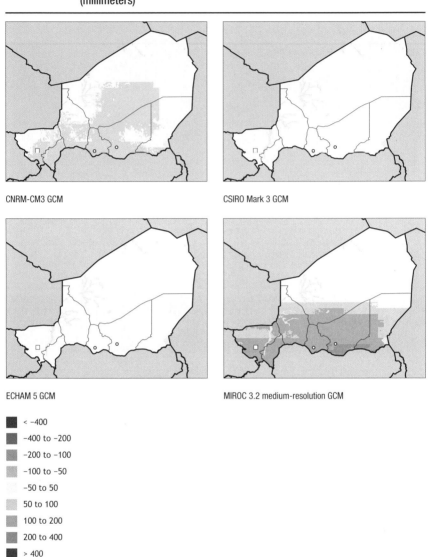

CNRM-CM3 GCM   CSIRO Mark 3 GCM

ECHAM 5 GCM   MIROC 3.2 medium-resolution GCM

- < −400
- −400 to −200
- −200 to −100
- −100 to −50
- −50 to 50
- 50 to 100
- 100 to 200
- 200 to 400
- > 400

Source: Authors' calculations based on Jones, Thornton, and Heinke (2009).

Notes: A1B = greenhouse gas emissions scenario that assumes fast economic growth, a population that peaks midcentury, and the development of new and efficient technologies, along with a balanced use of energy sources; CNRM-CM3 = National Meteorological Research Center–Climate Model 3; CSIRO = climate model developed at the Australia Commonwealth Scientific and Industrial Research Organisation; ECHAM 5 = fifth-generation climate model developed at the Max Planck Institute for Meteorology (Hamburg); GCM = general circulation model; MIROC = Model for Interdisciplinary Research on Climate, developed at the University of Tokyo Center for Climate System Research.

for the southern part of the country.[1] MIROC 3.2 predicts higher rainfall at 100–200 millimeters than does the CNRM-CM3 scenario, which shows 50–100 millimeters; however, the CNRM-CM3 GCM predicts increased rainfall in a greater part of the desert area of the country.

Figure 9.15 shows the predicted change in the average daily maximum temperature for the warmest month of the year in the A1B scenario according to various GCMs. The CNRM-CM3 and ECHAM 5 GCMs show a uniform 2.0°–2.5°C increase in temperature in the country. The CSIRO Mark 3 GCM shows the least increase in temperature, with most of the country experiencing an increase of only 1.0°–1.5°C, whereas the MIROC 3.2 medium-resolution GCM shows an increase ranging from 1.0°–1.5°C in the southernmost part of the country to 3.0°–3.5°C in the northernmost part of the country.

Crop Physiological Response to Climate Change

The effect of climate change on sorghum in Niger is mapped in Figure 9.16. Crop yields for 2050 with climate change are compared to the projected 2050 yields with an unchanged (2000) climate. All the scenarios predict a yield loss of 5–25 percent, as well as varying losses in baseline area in the southern part of the country. However, the loss in the baseline area is relatively less in CSIRO Mark 3 than in the other models.

Agricultural Vulnerability Scenarios (Crop-Specific)

The next two figures show simulation results from the International Model for Policy Analysis of Agricultural Commodities and Trade (IMPACT) associated with key agricultural crops in Niger. The figure for each featured crop has five graphs: production, yield, area, net exports, and world price.

The production and productivity of both millet (Figure 9.17) and sorghum (Figure 9.18) are seen to increase in all the scenarios. However, the area under cultivation will increase significantly only in the case of sorghum. For both crops, productivity will increase by at least 100 percent, accounting for the increase in production. The increase in productivity will be related to improvement in management rather than improved varieties; the indicated

---

1 The A1B scenario is a greenhouse gas emissions scenario that assumes fast economic growth, a population that peaks midcentury, and the development of new and efficient technologies, along with a balanced use of energy sources. CSIRO Mark 3 is a climate model developed at the Australia Commonwealth Scientific and Industrial Research Organisation. ECHAM 5 is a fifth-generation climate model developed at the Max Planck Institute for Meteorology in Hamburg. CNRM-CM3 is National Meteorological Research Center–Climate Model 3. MIROC is the Model for Interdisciplinary Research on Climate, developed at the University of Tokyo Center for Climate System Research.

FIGURE 9.15   Changes in normal daily maximum temperature in Niger for the warmest month, 2000–2050, A1B scenario (°C)

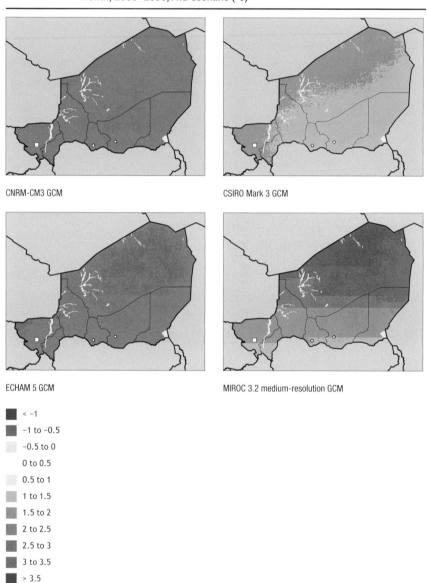

CNRM-CM3 GCM

CSIRO Mark 3 GCM

ECHAM 5 GCM

MIROC 3.2 medium-resolution GCM

■ < −1
■ −1 to −0.5
   −0.5 to 0
   0 to 0.5
   0.5 to 1
   1 to 1.5
   1.5 to 2
■ 2 to 2.5
■ 2.5 to 3
■ 3 to 3.5
■ > 3.5

Source: Authors' calculations based on Jones, Thornton, and Heinke (2009).

Notes: A1B = greenhouse gas emissions scenario that assumes fast economic growth, a population that peaks midcentury, and the development of new and efficient technologies, along with a balanced use of energy sources; CNRM-CM3 = National Meteorological Research Center–Climate Model 3; CSIRO = climate model developed at the Australia Commonwealth Scientific and Industrial Research Organisation; ECHAM 5 = fifth-generation climate model developed at the Max Planck Institute for Meteorology (Hamburg); GCM = general circulation model; MIROC = Model for Interdisciplinary Research on Climate, developed at the University of Tokyo Center for Climate System Research.

FIGURE 9.16   Yield change under climate change: Rainfed sorghum in Niger, 2000–2050, AIB scenario

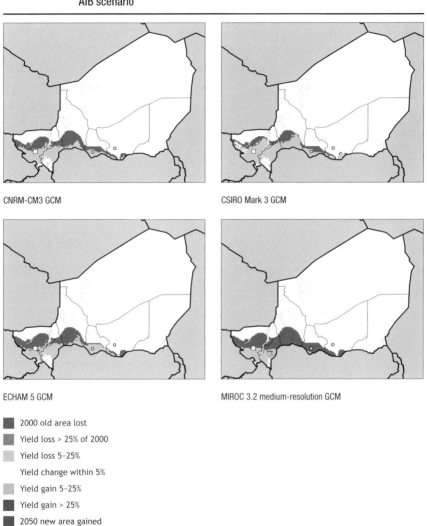

CNRM-CM3 GCM

CSIRO Mark 3 GCM

ECHAM 5 GCM

MIROC 3.2 medium-resolution GCM

- ■ 2000 old area lost
- ▨ Yield loss > 25% of 2000
- ░ Yield loss 5–25%
- Yield change within 5%
- ▓ Yield gain 5–25%
- ■ Yield gain > 25%
- ■ 2050 new area gained

Source: Authors' estimates.

Notes: A1B = greenhouse gas emissions scenario that assumes fast economic growth, a population that peaks midcentury, and the development of new and efficient technologies, along with a balanced use of energy sources; CNRM-CM3 = National Meteorological Research Center–Climate Model 3; CSIRO = climate model developed at the Australia Commonwealth Scientific and Industrial Research Organisation; ECHAM 5 = fifth-generation climate model developed at the Max Planck Institute for Meteorology (Hamburg); GCM = general circulation model; MIROC = Model for Interdisciplinary Research on Climate, developed at the University of Tokyo Center for Climate System Research.

FIGURE 9.17   Impact of changes in GDP and population on millet in Niger, 2010–50

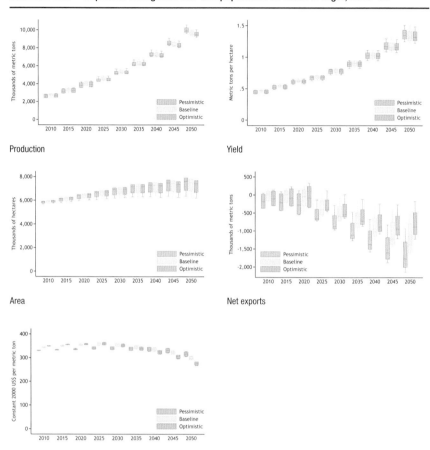

Source: Based on analysis conducted for Nelson et al. (2010).

Notes: The box and whiskers plot for each socioeconomic scenario shows the range of effects from the four future climate scenarios. GDP = gross domestic product; US$ = US dollars.

FIGURE 9.18   Impact of changes in GDP and population on sorghum in Niger, 2010–50

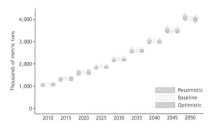

Production

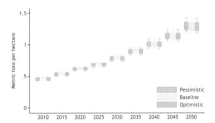

Yield

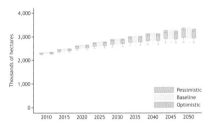

Area

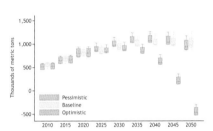

Net exports

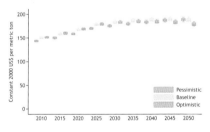

Prices

Source: Based on analysis conducted for Nelson et al. (2010).

Note: GDP = gross dom Source: Based on analysis conducted for Nelson et al. (2010).

Notes: The box and whiskers plot for each socioeconomic scenario shows the range of effects from the four future climate scenarios. GDP = gross domestic product; US$ = US dollars. estic product.

yields of both crops in 2050 will remain below the genetic potential of varieties currently available.

Millet production in Niger is still insufficient to meet demand. All scenarios project a growing deficit of millet after 2020, with the greatest deficit in the pessimistic scenario and the smallest in the optimistic scenario. The increase in imports will be driven by a decline in the world price of millet coupled with an increase in population. Sorghum exports are projected to rise in all scenarios through 2030, then level off in the pessimistic and baseline scenarios while declining in the optimistic scenario. The fall in net exports will coincide with stagnation in the world price of sorghum but also with the increased welfare of the population in the optimistic scenario, which will enable households to purchase foods.

Human Vulnerability Scenarios

In addition to agricultural scenarios, IMPACT also shows the number of malnourished children under the age of five, as well as the number of available kilocalories per capita.

Figure 9.19 shows the impact of future GDP and population scenarios on under-five malnutrition rates. The box-and-whisker plots in the figure

FIGURE 9.19   Number of malnourished children under five years of age in Niger in multiple income and climate scenarios, 2010–50

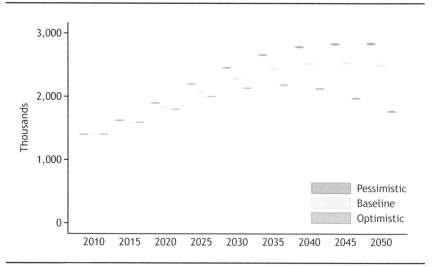

Source: Based on analysis conducted for Nelson et al. (2010).

Note: The box and whiskers plot for each socioeconomic scenario shows the range of effects from the four future climate scenarios.

indicate the range of climate scenario effects. The number of malnourished children under age five is shown to be increasing in all scenarios through 2035. After 2025 the differences between the scenarios become increasingly pronounced: the number of malnourished children under age five appears lowest in the optimistic scenario and highest in the pessimistic scenario. The optimistic scenario shows a decline after 2035, while in the baseline scenario the number will further increase, stabilizing at 2.3 million by 2040. The pessimistic scenario shows a continuing but relatively small increase after 2040. Although the absolute numbers of malnourished children are projected to rise during many of the years to come, the percentage of malnourished children is likely to decline steadily and dramatically due to the rapid population increase.

Figure 9.20 shows the available kilocalories per capita. As might be expected, there appears to be an inverse relationship between the availability of kilocalories and the number of malnourished children under age five. The increase in available kilocalories after 2025 in the optimistic scenario coincides with the decline in the number of malnourished children under age five.

FIGURE 9.20   Kilocalories per capita in Niger in multiple income and climate scenarios, 2010–50

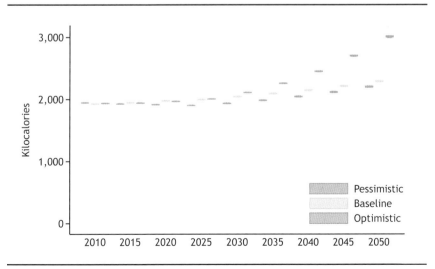

Source: Based on analysis conducted for Nelson et al. (2010).

Note: The box and whiskers plot for each socioeconomic scenario shows the range of effects from the four future climate scenarios.

Conclusions and Policy Recommendations

According to the modeled scenarios, the effects of climate change in Niger may be manifested in accelerated degradation of natural resources (farmland, pastures, rivers, and forests), militating against the country's ability to meet the food needs of its growing population. From our crop modeling analysis we found that all climate models show areas that currently grow sorghum but will be unable to do so in the future unless new heat-tolerant (and possibly drought-tolerant) varieties are developed.

IMPACT predicts increased agricultural production for the next 40 years, which it appears will be sufficient in most cases to provide many of the food needs of the nation in most scenarios.

Population growth means higher population density, which will put more pressure on the natural resource base. The models show neutral or increasing precipitation in Niger in the future. An increase in precipitation far beyond the prevailing amounts will require significant adjustments in farming as well as associated livelihoods. Decisionmakers need to design and implement policies to ensure sustainable development in the country against the background of changing climatic conditions. These policies should be designed to do the following:

- Support adequate monitoring of climate and provide information on climate change impacts.

- Provide a framework for responding to adverse climate change, for example, an increase in precipitation in a hitherto dry country. Policies for adequate housing, roads, and other infrastructure, particularly those related to agriculture, should be seriously considered.

- Provide adequate support to the agricultural research and extension system to develop appropriate crop varieties that will be adaptable to future climate conditions and to help farmers learn about them and any new agricultural techniques and technologies for cultivation and livestock husbandry.

- Support the high council for food security created in 2010 to ensure that it is effective in coordinating improved food production in the face of climate change.

- Provide adequate support for institutions responsible for managing rural areas and develop the most degraded lands.

- Promote agricultural diversification, particularly crop livestock production systems that will provide flexibility in adapting to changing climates, especially if the increased precipitation will favoring crop production more than livestock production.

- Establish water points and fodder stocks all over the country to guard against drought effects. This would require significant resources but would certainly improve livestock production.

- Develop capacity at all levels to follow up on environment management policies.

Although climate change will present some challenges to agriculture in Niger, the models used in this chapter suggest that rising temperatures will be the main challenge, because precipitation is predicted to stay the same or increase. Adopting these policy recommendations or similar ones that are designed to provide a supportive environment for farmers, including helping farmers gain access to new technologies designed for a hotter climate, will allow the positive future of some of the scenarios discussed above to be realized.

References

Bartholome, E., and A. S. Belward. 2005. "GLC2000: A New Approach to Global Land Cover Mapping from Earth Observation Data." *International Journal of Remote Sensing* 26 (9): 1959–1977.

CIESIN (Center for International Earth Science Information Network, Columbia University), Columbia University, IFPRI (International Food Policy Research Institute), World Bank, and CIAT (Centro Internacional de Agricultura Tropical). 2004. *Global Rural–Urban Mapping Project, Version 1 (GRUMPv1)*. Palisades, NY, US: Socioeconomic Data and Applications Center (SEDAC), Columbia University. http://sedac.ciesin.columbia.edu/gpw.

FAO (Food and Agriculture Organization of the United Nations). 2010. *FAOSTAT Database on Agriculture*. Rome.

ILRI (International Institute for Land Reclamation and Improvement). 1993. *Inland Valleys in West Africa: An Agro-ecological Characterization of Rice-Growing Environments,* edited by P. N. Windmeijer and W. Andriesse. Wageningen, the Netherlands.

Jones, P. G., P. K. Thornton, and J. Heinke. 2009. "Generating Characteristic Daily Weather Data Using Downscaled Climate Model Data from the IPCC's Fourth Assessment." Project report for the International Institute for Land Reclamation and Improvement, Wageningen, the Netherlands. Accessed May 7, 2010. www.ccafs-climate.org/pattern_scaling/.

Lehner, B., and P. Döll. 2004. "Development and Validation of a Global Database of Lakes, Reservoirs, and Wetlands." *Journal of Hydrology* 296 (1–4): 1–22.

Millennium Ecosystem Assessment. 2005. *Ecosystems and Human Well-being: Synthesis.* Washington, DC: Island Press. http://www.maweb.org/en/Global.aspx.

Nelson, G. C., M. W. Rosegrant, A. Palazzo, I. Gray, C. Ingersoll, R. Robertson, S. Tokgoz, et al. 2010. *Food Security, Farming, and Climate Change to 2050: Scenarios, Results, Policy Options.* Washington, DC: International Food Policy Research Institute.

UNEP and IUCN (United Nations Environment Programme and International Union for the Conservation of Nature). 2009. *World Database on Protected Areas (WDPA): Annual Release.* Accessed 2009. www.wdpa.org/protectedplanet.aspx.

UNPOP (United Nations Department of Economic and Social Affairs–Population Division). 2009. *World Population Prospects: The 2008 Revision.* New York. http://esa.un.org/unpd/wpp/.

Wood, S., G. Hyman, U. Deichmann, E. Barona, R. Tenorio, Z. Guo, et al. 2010. *Sub-national Poverty Maps for the Developing World Using International Poverty Lines: Preliminary Data Release.* Washington, DC: Harvest Choice and International Food Policy Research Institute.

World Bank. 2009. *World Development Indicators.* Accessed May 2011. http://data.worldbank.org/data-catalog/world-development-indicators.

———. 2010. *Economics of Adaptation to Climate Change: Synthesis Report.* Washington, DC. http://climatechange.worldbank.org/content/economics-adaptation-climate-change-study-homepage.

You, L., and S. Wood. 2006. "An Entropy Approach to Spatial Disaggregation of Agricultural Production." *Agricultural Systems* 90 (1–3): 329–347.

You, L., S. Wood, and U. Wood-Sichra. 2006. "Generating Global Crop Distribution Maps: From Census to Grid." Paper presented at the International Association of Agricultural Economists Conference, Brisbane, Australia, August 11–18.

———. 2009. "Generating Plausible Crop Distribution and Performance Maps for Sub-Saharan Africa Using a Spatially Disaggregated Data Fusion and Optimization Approach." *Agricultural Systems* 99 (2–3): 126–140.

Chapter 10

NIGERIA

Shuaib M. Hassan, Celestine E. Ikuenobe, Abdulai Jalloh,
Gerald C. Nelson, and Timothy S. Thomas

O ur purpose in this chapter is to help policymakers and researchers better understand and anticipate the likely impacts of climate change on
agriculture and on vulnerable households in Nigeria. We do this by
reviewing current data on agriculture and economic development, modeling
anticipated changes in climate between now and 2050, using crop models to
assess the impact of climate change on agricultural production, and globally
modeling supply and demand for food to predict food price trends.

Vulnerability to climate change is considered high in developing countries
due to social, economic, and environmental conditions that amplify suscep-
tibility to negative impacts and contribute to a low capacity to cope with and
adapt to climate hazards. Because of the high level of vulnerability in developing countries, there is an urgent need to understand the threats from climate
change that they face, formulate policies that mitigate the risks, and take necessary action. The Fourth Assessment Report of the Intergovernmental Panel
on Climate Change (Parry et al. 2007) observed that information about
the impacts of climate change on important sectors and systems in developing countries such as agriculture, forestry, fisheries, water resources, human
health, human settlements, and ecological systems is inadequate for understanding key vulnerabilities and planning appropriate adaptive strategies. It
also observed that many developing countries have an inadequate capacity
to systematically evaluate potential impacts and adaptation responses. One
of the major reasons for lack of understanding of vulnerability is the lack of
political will to prioritize the issues of climate change in policy formulation
and implementation.

The agricultural sector in Nigeria has not been sufficiently productive to
have a positive impact on the country's economy and has been associated with
environmental degradation. Consequently, the country is experiencing mount-
ing food deficits and declines in both gross domestic product (GDP) and
export earnings, while retail food prices and import bills have been increasing.
These problems could be further exacerbated by climate change if the nation's

agricultural policies do not incorporate issues aimed at understanding and mitigating the impact of climate change. There is therefore a need to establish agricultural strategies that promote political stability, self-reliance, public participation, sustained production, and environmental security.

The broad objectives of the nation's current agricultural policy enunciated in 2001 are the following:

- Achievement of self-sufficiency in basic food supply and the attainment of food security.

- Increased production of agricultural raw materials for industries.

- Increased production and processing of export crops using improved production and processing technologies.

- Generation of gainful employment.

- Rational use of agricultural resources; improved protection of agricultural land resources from drought, desert encroachment, soil erosion, and flood; and the general preservation of the environment for the sustainability of agricultural production.

- Promotion of the increased application of modern technology to agricultural production.

- Improvement in the quality of life of rural dwellers.

Resilience to climate change is crucial in attaining these objectives. Therefore, policy measures to mitigate the impact of climate change on Nigeria's agricultural sector should aim at understanding the impact of climate change on the nation's agricultural resource base.

Although the analysis in this chapter may show uncertainties about the impact of climate change, it can help those developing policies and actions to mitigate the outcomes of climate change for the livelihoods of vulnerable groups, particularly farmers. Policy measures on adaptation as suggested by NEST (2004) should aim to address the development or refinement of early warning systems to enable timely remedial measures and research into agricultural strategies.

Review of the Current Situation and Trends

Economic and Demographic Indicators

Population

Figure 10.1 shows the total and rural population counts (left axis) and the share of the urban population (right axis) in Nigeria. The rural population growth rate between 1960 and 2008 was lower than the urban population growth rate and declined to its lowest level during 2000–2008 (Table 10.1). The country has urbanized over time, as indicated by the population growth rate shown in Figure 10.1 and Table 10.1. Population growth in urban areas such as Lagos, Ibadan, Kano, and the Federal Capital Territory has been remarkable.

Figure 10.2 shows the geographic distribution of the population in Nigeria. The data are for 2000. The map shows high population densities in all of southern Nigeria, particularly Delta, Bayelsa, and parts of Edo States; the southeastern states of Anambra, Imo, Abia, Ebonyi, Rivers, and Akwa Ibom; and parts of the southwestern states of Ondo, Lagos, Ogun, Osun, and Ekiti.

FIGURE 10.1   Population trends in Nigeria: Total population, rural population, and percent urban, 1960–2008

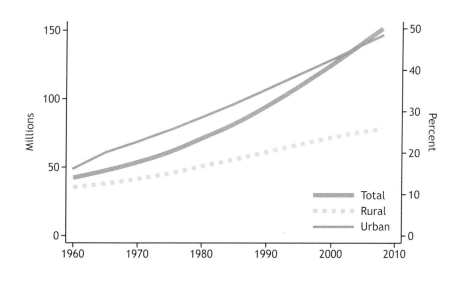

Source: World Development Indicators (World Bank 2009).

TABLE 10.1   Population growth rates in Nigeria, 1960–2008 (percent)

Decade	Total growth rate	Rural growth rate	Urban growth rate
1960–69	2.4	1.5	5.9
1970–79	2.8	2.0	5.1
1980–89	2.8	1.9	4.9
1990–99	2.8	1.6	4.7
2000–2008	2.4	1.1	4.0

Source: Authors' calculations based on World Development Indicators (World Bank 2009).

FIGURE 10.2   Population distribution in Nigeria, 2000 (persons per square kilometer)

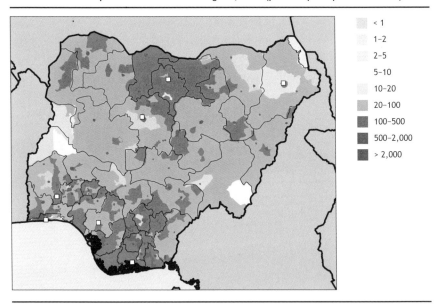

	< 1
	1–2
	2–5
	5–10
	10–20
	20–100
	100–500
	500–2,000
	> 2,000

Source: CIESIN et al. (2004).

Areas with high population densities in the central region include part of the Federal Capital Territory, Plateau, Benue, and Kogi States. The areas with high population densities in northern Nigeria are the north central states of Kaduna, Kano, Jigawa, and Katsina, as well as parts of Kebbi, Sokoto, and Gombe States.

Income

The Nigerian GDP per capita rose sharply from about US$250 (US dollars) in the late 1960s to over US$400 in the 1970s due to the oil revenue. However, the GDP per capita declined sharply with the structural adjustment programs of 1980s, recovering slightly during the 1990s and increasing again sharply since 2000. The sharp increase in GDP coincided with a rapidly declining agricultural GDP, from about 50 percent in 2000 to about 30 percent toward the end of the decade, as shown in Figure 10.3. It is worth noting that the fall in agricultural GDP in itself does not reflect declining agricultural productivity but is in fact a consequence of the increasing value of other sectors of the economy.

Vulnerability to Climate Change

Vulnerability has many dimensions. In this chapter the focus is on income, both level and sources, as we saw in the previous section and the data displayed in Figure 10.3. Table 10.2 provides some data on Nigeria's performance on additional indicators of vulnerability and resiliency to economic shocks: the level of education of the population, literacy, and the concentration of labor in the agricultural sector. The rate of enrollment in secondary school is low in Nigeria, whereas the rates of primary school enrollment and adult literacy are

FIGURE 10.3   Per capita GDP in Nigeria (constant 2000 US$) and share of GDP from agriculture (percent), 1960–2008

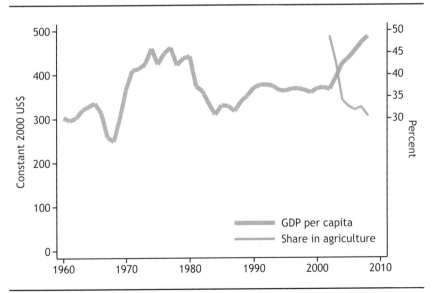

Source: World Development Indicators (World Bank 2009). Data on agricultural GDP for Nigeria were not available in the World Development Indicators prior to 2002.
Note: GDP = gross domestic product; US$ = US dollars.

TABLE 10.2 Education and labor statistics for Nigeria, 1980s and 2000s

Indicator	Year	Percent
Primary school enrollment (percent gross, three-year average)	2006	96.7
Secondary school enrollment (percent gross, three-year average)	2006	31.9
Adult literacy rate	2007	72.0
Percent employed in agriculture	1986	46.8
Under-five malnutrition (weight for age)	2003	27.2

Source: Authors' calculations based on World Development Indicators (World Bank 2009).

relatively high. The percentage of the population employed in agriculture is lower than in many West African countries, suggesting that alternative livelihoods are available. Nigeria's rate of under-five malnutrition is also relatively lower than in many neighboring countries.

Figure 10.4 shows Nigeria's performance on two noneconomic correlates of poverty, life expectancy and under-five mortality. As shown in Figure 10.4, life expectancy at birth improved from 1960 to the late 1990s, then declined

FIGURE 10.4 Well-being indicators in Nigeria, 1960–2008

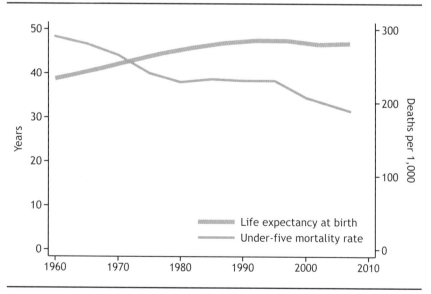

Source: World Development Indicators (World Bank 2009).

TABLE 10.3   Income distribution in Nigeria, 2004

Indicator	Measure
Gini coefficient (0 = perfect equality; 100 = perfect inequality)	42.9
Percent of total income earned by the richest 20 percent of the population	48.6
Percent of total income earned by the poorest 20 percent of the population	5.1
National poverty rate (percent)	54.7
Poverty rate, urban population (percent)	43.1
Percent of population living on less than US$1.25 a day (PPP)	63.1
Percent of population living on less than US$2.00 a day (PPP)	83.1

Source: World Bank (2012).
Notes: PPP = purchasing power parity; US$ = US dollars.

slightly. There was a solid decline in the under-five mortality rate between 1960 and 1980, a leveling off for about 15 years, and then a gradual decline. To sustain the country's drop in child mortality and improve life expectancy, policy measures should be developed that mitigate the vulnerabilities of all groups of the population to the drivers of all these indicators, including poverty and inadequate access to healthcare and food.

Table 10.3 presents some statistics related to income distribution in Nigeria. Income inequality is relatively high, as indicated by a Gini coefficient of 51, and the high level of poverty—with over 70 percent of the population living on less than US$1 a day—despite a GDP per capita of around US$500.

Given that the child malnutrition rate is also relatively high in Nigeria, special attention needs to be given to the most vulnerable in the country, particularly those who are food insecure. Circumstances that restrict the movement of food from surplus areas to deficit areas—for example, natural disasters such as flooding in Niger, Jigawa, Sokoto, and Kebbi States in 2010—could decrease food availability and affordability and increase the vulnerability of the poor to lack of access to food. Therefore, for a country with as a high population growth rate as Nigeria, policy measures should aim to provide enhanced resources that support the poorest and most vulnerable, a considerable proportion of whom are farmers. Many of them are located in the north central part of the country.

Figure 10.5 shows the geographic distribution of the population living on less than US$2 per day. Many of these individuals are located in the north central part of the country.

FIGURE 10.5   Poverty in Nigeria, circa 2005 (percentage of population living on less than US$2 per day)

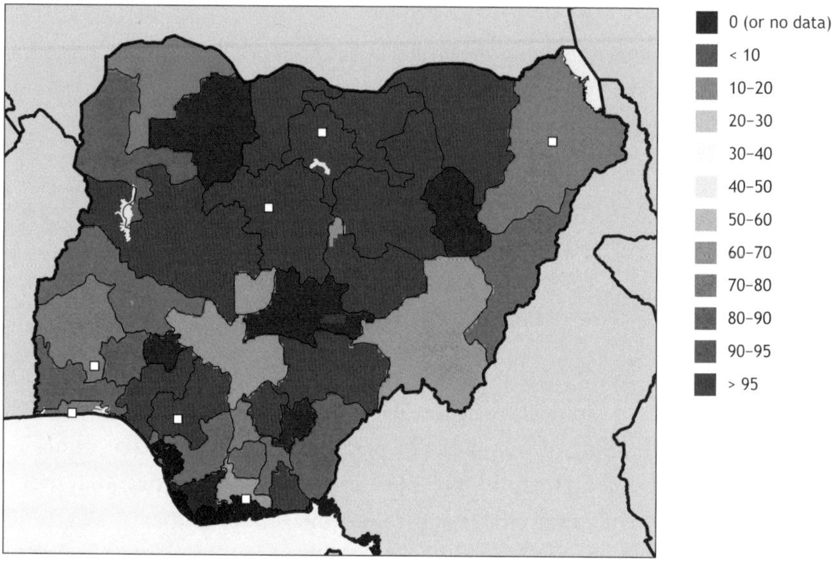

Source: Wood et al. (2010).
Note: Based on 2005 US$ (US dollars) and on purchasing power parity value.

Review of Land Use, Potential, and Limitations

Land Use Overview

Figure 10.6 shows the land cover and land use in Nigeria as of 2000. The major agricultural areas are the two regions of mosaic croplands in the north central zone and the southeast to southwestern zones in the country. The other agricultural regions are the areas of herbaceous cover in the northern part of the country, where millet and sorghum are predominantly cultivated and livestock raised. Other parts of the country also support agricultural activities in one form or another but to a lesser extent. Remnants of the country's original forest vegetation (evergreen) can be seen only in the south and the southeast, which have the relatively favorable environmental conditions that support plantation agriculture, which is itself evergreen. Open, broad-leaved deciduous forests now cover the area referred to as the middle belt in Nigeria, while mosaic tree cover or other natural vegetation is confined to the eastern margins of the Adamawa highlands. Shrub cover, closed-open, evergreen and deciduous, is scattered around the southern parts of northern Nigeria, the middle belt region, and the northern parts of southern Nigeria.

FIGURE 10.6 Land cover and land use in Nigeria, 2000

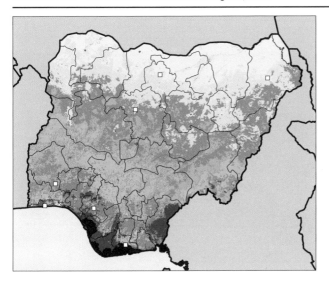

 Tree cover, broadleaved, evergreen

Tree cover, broadleaved, deciduous, closed

Tree cover, broadleaved, deciduous, open

Tree cover, broadleaved, needle-leaved, evergreen

Tree cover, broadleaved, needle-leaved, deciduous

Tree cover, broadleaved, mixed leaf type

Tree cover, broadleaved, regularly flooded, fresh water

Tree cover, broadleaved, regularly flooded, saline water

Mosaic of tree cover/other natural vegetation

Tree cover, burnt

Shrub cover, closed–open, evergreen

Shrub cover, closed–open, deciduous

Herbacious cover, closed–open

Sparse herbacious or sparse shrub cover

Regularly flooded shrub or herbacious cover

Cultivated and managed areas

Mosaic of cropland/tree cover/other natural vegetation

Mosaic of cropland/shrub/grass cover

Bare areas

Water bodies

Snow and ice

Artificial surfaces and associated areas

No data

Source: GLC2000 (Global Land Cover 2000) (Bartholome and Belward 2005).

FIGURE 10.7 Protected areas in Nigeria, 2009

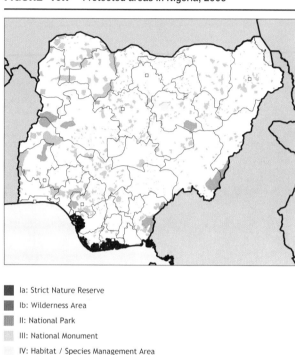

■ Ia: Strict Nature Reserve
■ Ib: Wilderness Area
▦ II: National Park
▢ III: National Monument
▢ IV: Habitat / Species Management Area
▢ V: Protected Landscape / Seascape
▢ VI: Managed Resource Protected Area
▢ Not applicable
▢ Not known

Sources: Protected areas are from the World Database on Protected Areas (UNEP and IUCN 2009). Water bodies are from the World Wildlife Fund's Global Lakes and Wetlands Database (Lehner and Döll 2004).

Major agricultural activities are also undertaken in the floodplains of the Niger and Benue Rivers and the inland valleys in the central part of the country.

Figure 10.7 shows the locations of protected areas, including parks and reserves. These locations provide important protection for fragile environmental areas, which may also be important for the tourism industry. Two categories of protected areas are shown in Figure 10.7 that are applicable to Nigeria. These are International Union for the Conservation of Nature (IUCN) category II and IUCN category not known. The IUCN category not known includes the wetlands of Yobe in the northeastern part of the country, Kainji Lake National Park, north central Nigeria, and the mosaic of forest reserves.

Figure 10.8 shows the travel time to urban areas that provide potential markets for agricultural products as well as places where agricultural inputs and

FIGURE 10.8   Travel time to urban areas of various sizes in Nigeria, circa 2000

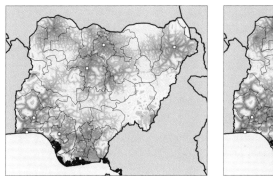

To cities of 500,000 or more people

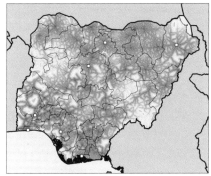

To cities of 100,000 or more people

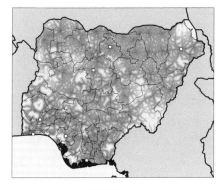

To towns and cities of 25,000 or more people

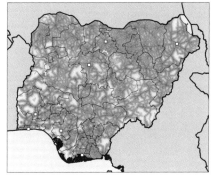

To towns and cities of 10,000 or more people

Urban location
< 1 hour
1–3 hours
3–5 hours
5–8 hours
8–11 hours
11–16 hours
16–26 hours
> 26 hours

Source: Authors' calculations.

consumer goods for farm households can be purchased. Policymakers need to keep in mind the importance of transport costs when considering areas' potential for agricultural expansion. That is, if fertile but unused land is far from markets, it represents potential land for expansion only if transportation infrastructure is put in place and if the land does not conflict with the preservation priorities seen in Figure 10.7. The maps in Figure 10.8 depict the travel times from the rural areas to towns and cities with populations of 10,000, 25,000, 100,000, and 500,000 or more people. The major population centers of Nigeria are also adequately captured. In general, most of the roads in rural areas of the country are in poor condition. In the coastal areas of Niger Delta, access to the nearest cities is made difficult by the travel times on water.

Agriculture

Table 10.4 shows key agricultural commodities in terms of area harvested. Table 10.5 reports the value of the harvest of these commodities and Table 10.6 the quantity consumed. All commodities in these tables are significant to Nigeria because they are important to the food culture of the people or are cash crops providing significant income to farm families and national foreign exchange earnings; an example is cocoa beans. Cassava and yams are the most important foodcrops in the country. Other major foodcrops include sorghum and maize.

TABLE 10.4   Harvest area of leading agricultural commodities in Nigeria, 2006–08 (thousands of hectares)

Rank	Crop	Percent of total	Harvest area
	Total	100.0	45,877
1	Sorghum	16.5	7,579
2	Millet	10.8	4,977
3	Cowpeas	9.6	4,395
4	Maize	8.5	3,898
5	Cassava	8.3	3,821
6	Oil palm fruit	6.8	3,142
7	Yams	6.7	3,068
8	Rice	5.5	2,519
9	Groundnuts	4.9	2,251
10	Cocoa beans	2.4	1,110

Source: FAOSTAT (FAO 2010).
Note: All values are based on the three-year average for 2006–08.

TABLE 10.5   Value of production of leading agricultural commodities in Nigeria, 2005–07 (millions of US$)

Rank	Crop	Percent of total	Value of production
	Total	100.0	66,008.7
1	Yams	29.4	19,380.3
2	Cassava	11.7	7,696.7
3	Sorghum	5.7	3,776.4
4	Other citrus	5.2	3,400.6
5	Millet	4.7	3,115.5
6	Maize	4.4	2,932.3
7	Other fresh vegetables	3.7	2,469.9
8	Plantains	3.1	2,075.1
9	Cowpeas	3.0	1,952.6
10	Groundnuts	2.7	1,811.3

Source: FAOSTAT (FAO 2010).
Note: All values are based on the three-year average for 2005–07. US$ = US dollars.

TABLE 10.6   Consumption of leading food commodities in Nigeria, 2003–05 (thousands of metric tons)

Rank	Crop	Percent of total	Food consumption
	Total	100.0	81,884
1	Cassava	18.5	15,139
2	Yams	12.3	10,071
3	Fermented beverages	10.1	8,291
4	Other vegetables	7.9	6,445
5	Sorghum	7.0	5,765
6	Millet	5.8	4,770
7	Rice	3.8	3,079
8	Maize	3.7	3,054
9	Other citrus	3.4	2,763
10	Other fruits	3.1	2,555

Source: FAOSTAT (FAO 2010).
Note: All values are based on the three-year average for 2003–05.

The next five figures show the estimated yield and growing areas of key crops. Both sorghum (Figure 10.9) and millet (Figure 10.10) are mainly grown in the central and northern regions of Nigeria. However, part of the northeast is not favorable to the growth of millet. As shown in Figure 10.11, cassava is now widely grown and is being introduced in the northern extremes of the country. Rainfed yams and sweet potatoes are widely grown across the country, with high concentrations in the north central and southeastern areas and on the southern flank of northeastern Nigeria (Figure 10.12). Rainfed maize is grown from the coast to the northern flank of the country (Figure 10.13). For all these crops, the yield does not vary significantly across the country.

Scenarios of the Future

Economic and Demographic Indicators

Population

Figure 10.14 shows population projections made for Nigeria by the United Nations (UN) population office through 2050. The projected population

FIGURE 10.9   Yield (metric tons per hectare) and harvest area density (hectares) for rainfed sorghum in Nigeria, 2000

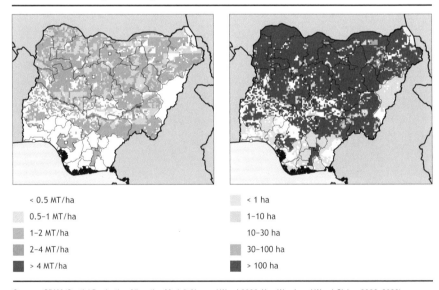

< 0.5 MT/ha	< 1 ha
0.5–1 MT/ha	1–10 ha
1–2 MT/ha	10–30 ha
2–4 MT/ha	30–100 ha
> 4 MT/ha	> 100 ha

Sources: SPAM (Spatial Production Allocation Model) (You and Wood 2006; You, Wood, and Wood-Sichra 2006, 2009).
Notes: ha = hectare; MT = metric tons.

FIGURE 10.10   Yield (metric tons per hectare) and harvest area density (hectares) for rainfed millet in Nigeria, 2000

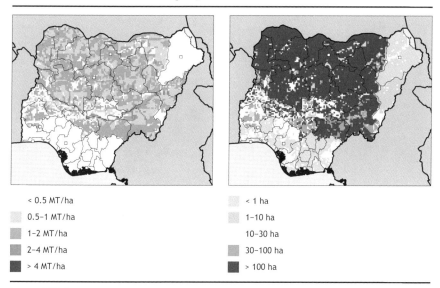

< 0.5 MT/ha
0.5–1 MT/ha
1–2 MT/ha
2–4 MT/ha
> 4 MT/ha

< 1 ha
1–10 ha
10–30 ha
30–100 ha
> 100 ha

Sources: SPAM (Spatial Production Allocation Model) (You and Wood 2006; You, Wood, and Wood-Sichra 2006, 2009).
Notes: ha = hectare; MT = metric tons.

FIGURE 10.11   Yield (metric tons per hectare) and harvest area density (hectares) for rainfed cassava in Nigeria, 2000

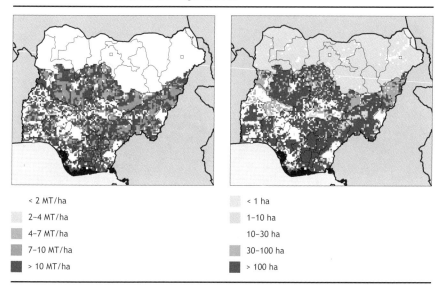

< 2 MT/ha
2–4 MT/ha
4–7 MT/ha
7–10 MT/ha
> 10 MT/ha

< 1 ha
1–10 ha
10–30 ha
30–100 ha
> 100 ha

Sources: SPAM (Spatial Production Allocation Model) (You and Wood 2006; You, Wood, and Wood-Sichra 2006, 2009).
Notes: ha = hectare; MT = metric tons.

FIGURE 10.12 Yield (metric tons per hectare) and harvest area density (hectares) for rainfed yams and sweet potatoes in Nigeria, 2000

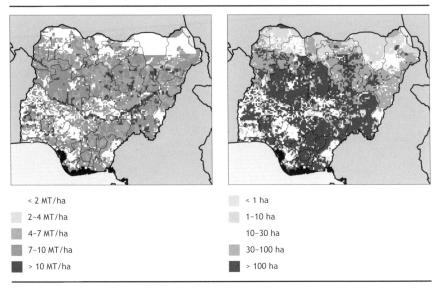

< 2 MT/ha	< 1 ha
2–4 MT/ha	1–10 ha
4–7 MT/ha	10–30 ha
7–10 MT/ha	30–100 ha
> 10 MT/ha	> 100 ha

Sources: SPAM (Spatial Production Allocation Model) (You and Wood 2006; You, Wood, and Wood-Sichra 2006, 2009).
Notes: ha = hectare; MT = metric tons.

FIGURE 10.13 Yield (metric tons per hectare) and harvest area density (hectares) for rainfed maize in Nigeria, 2000

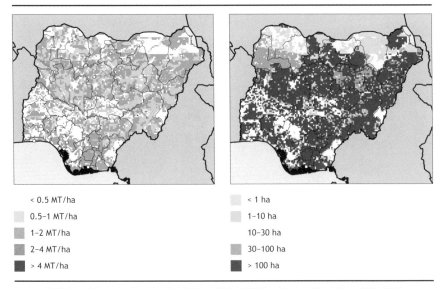

< 0.5 MT/ha	< 1 ha
0.5–1 MT/ha	1–10 ha
1–2 MT/ha	10–30 ha
2–4 MT/ha	30–100 ha
> 4 MT/ha	> 100 ha

Sources: SPAM (Spatial Production Allocation Model) (You and Wood 2006; You, Wood, and Wood-Sichra 2006, 2009).
Notes: ha = hectare; MT = metric tons.

FIGURE 10.14   Population projections for Nigeria, 2010–50

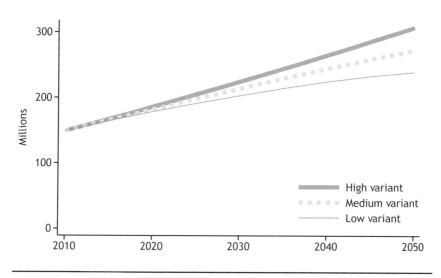

Source: UNPOP (2009).

will double in the next 40 years, from about 150 million presently to about 310 million based on the high variant projection or about 240 million, a 60 percent increase, based on the low variant projection. Challenges associated with a high rate of population growth will include providing food, shelter, and social amenities. The per capita land available for agriculture will likely be reduced (unless a substantial number of farmers give up farming to enter one of the other economic sectors), and consequently increased pressure on the land will make agricultural intensification inevitable. Farmers will therefore likely need to adjust to high-input agriculture.

Income

Figure 10.15 shows the three GDP per capita scenarios used for our study. These are the results of combining three GDP projections with the three population projections of Figure 10.14 from the UN population office. The optimistic scenario combines high GDP with low population, the baseline scenario combines the medium GDP projection with the medium population projection, and the pessimistic scenario combines the low GDP projection with the high population projection. In all of the scenarios, GDP per capita is expected to grow with time. However, the differences by 2050 are noteworthy,

FIGURE 10.15   Gross domestic product (GDP) per capita in Nigeria, future scenarios, 2010–50

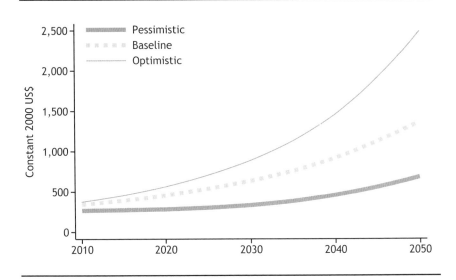

Sources: Computed from GDP data from the World Bank Economic Adaptation to Climate Change project (World Bank 2010), from the Millennium Ecosystem Assessment (2005) reports, and from population data from the United Nations (UNPOP 2009).
Note: US$ = US dollars.

with GDP in the pessimistic scenario reaching only US$684, almost exactly half that in the baseline scenario ($1,364), and much lower than that in the optimistic scenario, which is just slightly less than $2,500.

Biophysical Analysis

Climate Models

Figure 10.16 shows projected precipitation changes in Nigeria in the four downscaled general circulation models (GCMs) we use in this chapter in the A1B scenario. The CNRM-CM3 GCM predicts an increase in precipitation throughout the country except in the central portion. The ECHAM 5 GCM predicts some increase in rainfall, primarily in the coastal areas and the southeastern portion of the country along the border with Cameroon. The CSIRO Mark 3 GCM predicts less precipitation in the central and southwestern half of the country. The MIROC 3.2 medium-resolution GCM predicts a complete reversal of the climatic pattern of the

FIGURE 10.16   Changes in mean annual precipitation in Nigeria, 2000–2050, A1B scenario (millimeters)

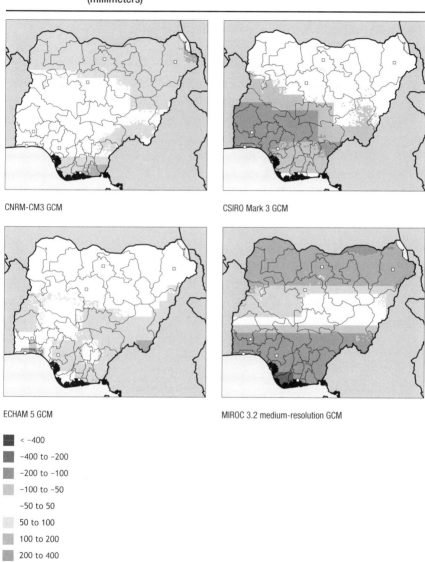

CNRM-CM3 GCM

CSIRO Mark 3 GCM

ECHAM 5 GCM

MIROC 3.2 medium-resolution GCM

- ■ < −400
- ■ −400 to −200
- ▨ −200 to −100
- ▫ −100 to −50
- −50 to 50
- 50 to 100
- 100 to 200
- 200 to 400
- ■ > 400

Source: Authors' estimates based on Jones, Thornton, and Heinke (2009).

Notes: A1B = greenhouse gas emissions scenario that assumes fast economic growth, a population that peaks midcentury, and the development of new and efficient technologies, along with a balanced use of energy sources; CNRM-CM3 = National Meteorological Research Center–Climate Model 3; CSIRO = climate model developed at the Australia Commonwealth Scientific and Industrial Research Organisation; ECHAM 5 = fifth-generation climate model developed at the Max Planck Institute for Meteorology (Hamburg); GCM = general circulation model; MIROC = Model for Interdisciplinary Research on Climate, developed at the University of Tokyo Center for Climate System Research.

geographical areas of the country.[1] Although the coastal areas of Nigeria, which currently receive more rainfall, will suffer more loss in precipitation, the northern part of the country will gain precipitation. This could create both hardship in the south and new opportunities in the north. There will be a need for change in the types of crops grown in the north and the south. Farmers may need to adjust their farming practices to accommodate the new crops they have not been used to cultivating.

Figure 10.17 shows the mean daily maximum temperature in Nigeria for the warmest month. The CNRM-CM3 GCM predicts an increase of 2.0°–2.5°C across the country. Both the CSIRO Mark 3 and the MIROC 3.2 medium-resolution GCMs predict a reasonably uniform increase of 1.0°–1.5°C, whereas the ECHAM 5 GCM predicts an increase of 2.0°–2.5°C in the northern half of the country and an increase of only 1.5°–2.0°C in the southern half.

Yield Effects from Climate Change

The effects of climate change on key crops in Nigeria are mapped in the next two figures. The comparison is between the crop yields in 2050 with climate change and the yields with a 2000 climate.

All the crop modeling results predict a loss of yield in areas planted with sorghum in the northern Sahelian zone, which is already prone to desertification (Figure 10.18). This means that the temperature increase will make it too hot for sorghum cultivation in these areas. Except in pockets of areas in Kebbi and some inland valleys, all the models predict yield loses on the order of 5–25 percent below baseline, with a few areas showing even higher losses. Maize will perform relatively better in the face of climate change, as shown in Figure 10.19, which shows a gain in yield of between 5 and 25 percent, with some areas predicted to have a yield increase greater than 25 percent. Less area is predicted to be lost to maize than to sorghum (see Figure 10.18). As in the case of sorghum, the areas predicted to be lost to maize fall within the Sahelian region of the northeastern extreme of the country (Figure 10.19).

---

1   The A1B scenario is a greenhouse gas emissions scenario that assumes fast economic growth, a population that peaks midcentury, and the development of new and efficient technologies, along with a balanced use of energy sources. CNRM-CM3 is National Meteorological Research Center–Climate Model 3. ECHAM 5 is a fifth-generation climate model developed at the Max Planck Institute for Meteorology in Hamburg. CSIRO Mark 3 is a climate model developed at the Australia Commonwealth Scientific and Industrial Research Organisation. MIROC is the Model for Interdisciplinary Research on Climate, developed at the University of Tokyo Center for Climate System Research.

FIGURE 10.17 Change in the normal daily maximum temperature in Nigeria for the warmest month, 2000–2050, A1B scenario (°C)

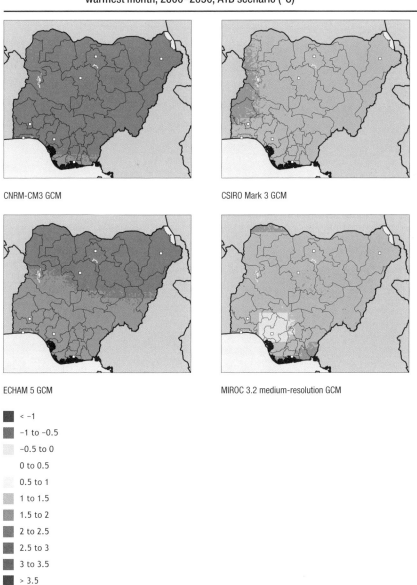

CNRM-CM3 GCM

CSIRO Mark 3 GCM

ECHAM 5 GCM

MIROC 3.2 medium-resolution GCM

- ■ < –1
- ■ –1 to –0.5
- ■ –0.5 to 0
- ■ 0 to 0.5
- ■ 0.5 to 1
- ■ 1 to 1.5
- ■ 1.5 to 2
- ■ 2 to 2.5
- ■ 2.5 to 3
- ■ 3 to 3.5
- ■ > 3.5

Source: Authors' calculations based on Jones, Thornton, and Heinke (2009).

Notes: A1B = greenhouse gas emissions scenario that assumes fast economic growth, a population that peaks midcentury, and the development of new and efficient technologies, along with a balanced use of energy sources; CNRM-CM3 = National Meteorological Research Center–Climate Model 3; CSIRO = climate model developed at the Australia Commonwealth Scientific and Industrial Research Organisation; ECHAM 5 = fifth-generation climate model developed at the Max Planck Institute for Meteorology (Hamburg); GCM = general circulation model; MIROC = Model for Interdisciplinary Research on Climate, developed at the University of Tokyo Center for Climate System Research.

FIGURE 10.18   Yield change under climate change: Rainfed sorghum in Nigeria, 2010–50, A1B scenario

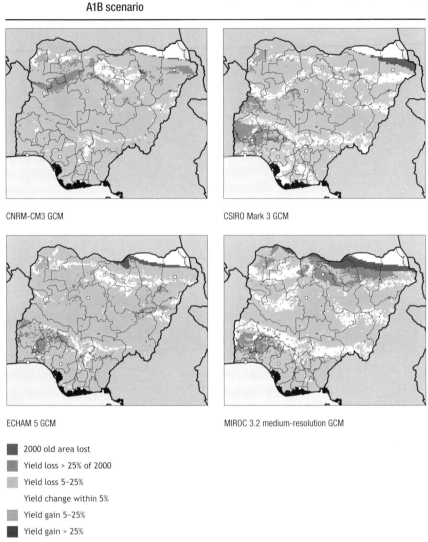

CNRM-CM3 GCM

CSIRO Mark 3 GCM

ECHAM 5 GCM

MIROC 3.2 medium-resolution GCM

■ 2000 old area lost

■ Yield loss > 25% of 2000

░ Yield loss 5–25%

   Yield change within 5%

▒ Yield gain 5–25%

■ Yield gain > 25%

■ 2050 new area gained

Source: Authors' estimates.

Notes: A1B = greenhouse gas emissions scenario that assumes fast economic growth, a population that peaks midcentury, and the development of new and efficient technologies, along with a balanced use of energy sources; CNRM-CM3 = National Meteorological Research Center–Climate Model 3; CSIRO = Australia Commonwealth Scientific and Industrial Research Organisation; ECHAM 5 = fifth-generation climate model developed at the Max Planck Institute for Meteorology (Hamburg); GCM = general circulation model; MIROC = Model for Interdisciplinary Research on Climate, developed at the University of Tokyo Center for Climate System Research.

FIGURE 10.19   Yield change under climate change: Rainfed maize in Nigeria, 2010–50, A1B
scenario

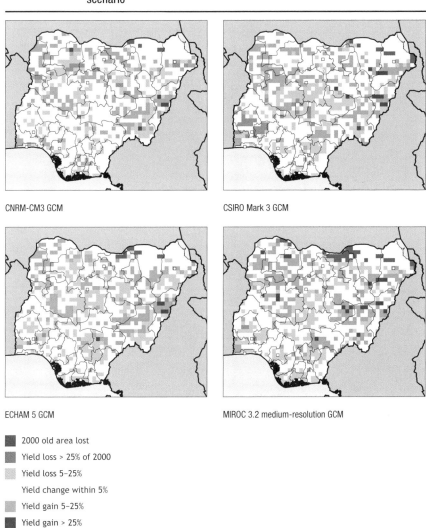

CNRM-CM3 GCM

CSIRO Mark 3 GCM

ECHAM 5 GCM

MIROC 3.2 medium-resolution GCM

- 2000 old area lost
- Yield loss > 25% of 2000
- Yield loss 5–25%
- Yield change within 5%
- Yield gain 5–25%
- Yield gain > 25%
- 2050 new area gained

Source: Authors' estimates.

Notes: A1B = greenhouse gas emissions scenario that assumes fast economic growth, a population that peaks midcentury, and the development of new and efficient technologies, along with a balanced use of energy sources; CNRM-CM3 = National Meteorological Research Center–Climate Model 3; CSIRO = climate model developed at the Australia Commonwealth Scientific and Industrial Research Organisation; ECHAM 5 = fifth-generation climate model developed at the Max Planck Institute for Meteorology (Hamburg); GCM = general circulation model; MIROC = Model for Interdisciplinary Research on Climate, developed at the University of Tokyo Center for Climate System Research.

Vulnerability

Figure 10.20 shows the impact of the future scenarios on under-five malnutrition rates. Both the optimistic and the baseline scenarios predict a decline in the number of malnourished children under the age of five in Nigeria, while the pessimistic scenario predicts an initial increase, with a slightly higher number in 2050 than at present. Although the numbers increase slightly in the pessimistic scenario, we see declines by 2020 in the optimistic scenario and by 2030 in the baseline scenario. Furthermore, with population growth we would expect that the percentage of children who are malnourished would actually be declining in all scenarios.

Figure 10.21 shows the kilocalories per capita available to each person. Given the same period shown in Figure 10.20, the scenarios in Figure 10.21 indicate that the availability of calories will not improve in the pessimistic scenario, but there will be increased availability in the optimistic scenario and in the baseline scenario after 2030.

FIGURE 10.20   Number of malnourished children under five years of age in Nigeria in multiple income and climate scenarios, 2010–50

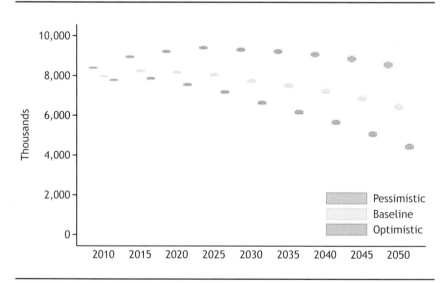

Source: Based on analysis conducted for Nelson et al. (2010).

Note: The box and whiskers plot for each socioeconomic scenario shows the range of effects from the four future climate scenarios.

FIGURE 10.21   Kilocalories per capita in Nigeria in multiple income and climate scenarios, 2010–50

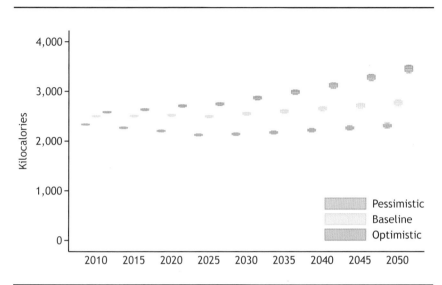

Source: Based on analysis conducted for Nelson et al. (2010).
Note: The box and whiskers plot for each socioeconomic scenario shows the range of effects from the four future climate scenarios.

Agricultural Outcomes

The next four figures show simulation results from the International Model for Policy Analysis of Agricultural Commodities and Trade associated with key agricultural crops in Nigeria. The figure for each featured crop has five graphs: one each showing production, yield, area, net exports, and world price. All scenarios predict a general increase in sorghum production, yield, area, net exports, and world price (Figure 10.22). However, area and world price will remain virtually the same after 2030. After 2040, the net exports predicted by the optimistic scenario will be greater than in the pessimistic scenario.

Millet production, yield, and net exports are predicted to increase in all the scenarios, although the area planted with the crop will remain unchanged and the world market price for millet will decline by 2050 (Figure 10.23). The net exports of millet will be virtually the same for all the scenarios in 2050 following relatively higher net exports in the pessimistic scenario until 2040.

The production of cassava and other root crops as well as sweet potatoes and yams is projected to increase in all scenarios (Figures 10.24 and 10.25).

FIGURE 10.22   Impacts of GDP, population, and climate change scenarios on sorghum area, yield, production, net exports, and prices in Nigeria, 2010–50

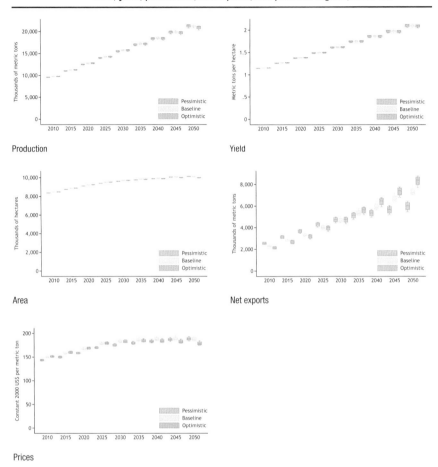

Source: Based on analysis conducted for Nelson et al. (2010).

Notes: The box and whiskers plot for each socioeconomic scenario shows the range of effects from the four future climate scenarios. GDP = gross domestic product; US$ = US dollars.

FIGURE 10.23   Impacts of GDP, population, and climate change scenarios on millet area, yield, production, net exports, and prices in Nigeria, 2010–50

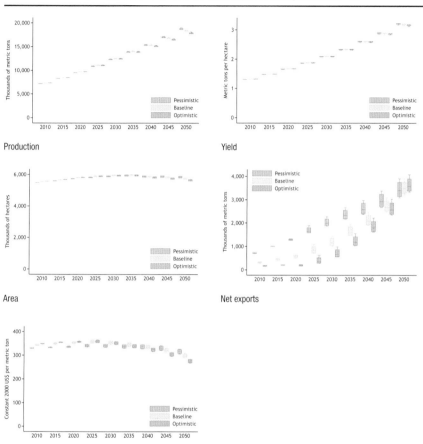

Production

Yield

Area

Net exports

Prices

Source: Based on analysis conducted for Nelson et al. (2010).

Notes: The box and whiskers plot for each socioeconomic scenario shows the range of effects from the four future climate scenarios. GDP = gross domestic product; US$ = US dollars.

FIGURE 10.24   Impacts of GDP, population, and climate change scenarios on cassava area, yield, production, net exports, and prices in Nigeria, 2010–50

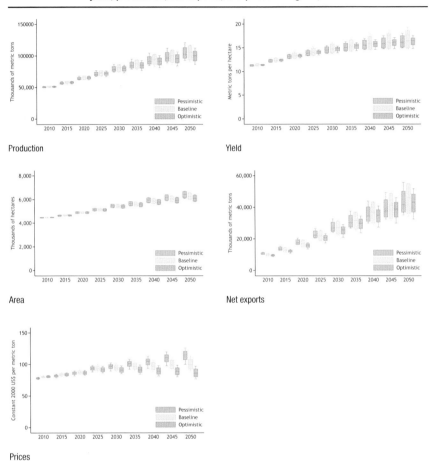

Source: Based on analysis conducted for Nelson et al. (2010).

Notes: The box and whiskers plot for each socioeconomic scenario shows the range of effects from the four future climate scenarios. GDP = gross domestic product; US$ = US dollars.

Chapter 14

SUMMARY AND CONCLUSIONS

Abdulai Jalloh, Mbène Dièye Faye, Harold Roy-Macauley, Paco Sérémé,
Robert Zougmoré, Timothy S. Thomas, and Gerald C. Nelson

Climate variability is a reality that is affecting rural livelihoods in West Africa today and presenting a growing challenge in the region, as in many other parts of the African continent and elsewhere. Climate change will have far-reaching consequences for the poor and marginalized groups among which the majority depend on agriculture for their livelihoods and have a lower capacity to adapt. Weather-related crop failures, fishery collapses, and livestock deaths in addition to losses of property are already causing economic losses and undermining food security in West Africa. This situation is likely to become more desperate and to threaten the survival of the majority of poor farmers as global warming continues. Feeding the increasing populations in a subregion with one of the highest rates of population growth in the world requires radical transformation of a largely underdeveloped agriculture over the next four decades. A major challenge is increasing agricultural production among resource-poor farmers without exacerbating environmental problems and simultaneously coping with climate change.

There is apparently a growing awareness of the potential adverse effects of climate variability and change at the levels of both national governments and regional institutions. This has resulted in various initiatives, national and regional, aimed at addressing climate change issues. Other than Côte d'Ivoire, Ghana, and Nigeria, all West African countries involved in this study have submitted National Adaptation Programmes of Action (NAPAs) to the United Nations Framework Convention on Climate Change to identify priority activities for adaptation to climate change. Though useful in providing a framework for raising awareness among policymakers and guiding resource allocation for adaptation to climate change, the NAPAs would benefit immensely from studies like the present one in providing updated information on climate change, particularly in the agricultural sector.

The results of the individual country chapters clearly underscore the general concern for climate change in West Africa. The West African economies are especially vulnerable to climate change as a result of their heavy dependence on rainfed agriculture. Despite the variation among models, there is a clear indication of changes in precipitation with either a reduction in the heavy-rainfall areas, particularly along the coast, or an increase in areas of the Sahel hitherto devoid of much rain. Côte d'Ivoire, Ghana, Guinea, Nigeria, and Togo, which are among the countries that receive the most rainfall, are shown to experience a reduction of at least 50–100 millimeters of rainfall per year, whereas Sahelian countries like Burkina Faso, Niger, and Senegal that receive little rainfall are shown to have substantial increases in rainfall (50–100 millimeters), with Niger predicted to receive as much as 200 millimeters by 2050.

Against the backdrop of the rainfall changes is an increase in temperature by an average of 2°C in all the countries, with at least one model showing a rise in temperature of up to 3.5°C in Liberia, Niger, and Sierra Leone. Certainly decreased precipitation and an increase in temperature will pose tremendous challenges to farming and related livelihoods. High temperatures above the ranges tolerated by crops will definitely affect the physiology of plants, including staple crops in the region, with consequences of decreased productivity that will affect food production. This situation could be compounded by genetic erosion due to the inability of plants to survive harsh conditions. Similarly, animal production, including livestock and fisheries, could be adversely affected. The climate projections for Africa presented in the Forth Assessment Report of the Intergovernmental Panel on Climate Change (Boko et al. 2007) include a likely average temperature increase of 1.5°–4°C in this century, which is higher than the global average (World Bank 2009). Acting now could help save the 10–15 percent of species that will otherwise likely be lost in an Africa that is 2°C warmer than in preindustrial days (Parry et al. 2007). This situation will demand actions on many fronts, including water conservation and the development of irrigation, conservation of biodiversity, and capacity building at various levels, all of which will require adequate resources and policy frameworks.

On the other hand, a drastic increase in rainfall in hitherto dry areas could pose serious challenges to adaptation and the conservation of biodiversity, at least in the short run. Increased humidity and flooding could threaten the existence of plants and animals adapted to dry conditions in the Sahel. The mosquitoes and tsetse flies that transmit the pathogens that cause malaria in human beings and sleeping sickness in cattle, respectively, abound in humid conditions. An increase in rainfall in the Sahel could pose a serious threat to the cattle industry, with a need to adjust the prevailing farming system. The growing concern for rainfall variability is clearly expressed by virtually all the authors of the country chapters and reflected in their expression of the overwhelming need to provide support to national meteorological services and other climate information and service providers to make available relevant information that will adequately inform policymaking with a view to enhancing adaptation to climate change. This situation could open up opportunities for the private sector to play key roles in adaptation to climate change in the region, particularly in providing reliable climate information and disseminating such information as well as insurance for crops and animals.

In the meantime it is worthy to note the important role being played by key continental and regional institutions with regard to climate change information. These include the Regional Centre for Agriculture, Hydrology, and Meteorology (AGRHYMET), a specialized institute of the Permanent Interstate Committee for Drought Control in the Sahel, composed of nine member states (Burkina Faso, Cape Verde, Chad, Gambia, Guinea-Bissau, Mali, Mauritania, Niger, and Senegal) and with headquarters in Niamey, Niger. AGRHYMET provides training and information in the areas of agroclimatology, hydrology, and crop protection. The African Centre of Meteorological Applications for Development, also based in Niger, contributes to strengthening the capacities of national meteorological services in climate monitoring and making predictions for short-range (daily or weekly), medium-range (10-day), long-range (monthly), and seasonal timescales. The African Monsoon Multidisciplinary Analysis Network brings together more than 200 scientists who are stakeholders in African monsoon multidisciplinary analysis, which is aimed at improving understanding of the African monsoon and its influence on the physical, chemical, and biological environment regionally and globally. Strengthening the capacities of national meteorological services is imperative if reliable climate information is to be available to inform decisionmaking in the region.

The results of the study presented in this monograph clearly show that climate change will adversely affect the productivity of the major staples in the region, with relatively greater effects on sorghum and groundnuts, which are key crops in the Sahelian countries. Sorghum is the leading cereal crop in Burkina Faso and Nigeria and the second most important crop in Niger. These three countries cultivate more than 50 percent of the sorghum area in the region. It is interesting to note, however, that despite the adverse effects of climate change on the productivity of crops in the region, the production of all the crops is shown to increase in all countries, due mainly to improved productivity rather than to an increase in the area under cultivation. It is worrying to note that the yields achieved by 2050 are still predicted to be far less than the current genetic potential of the respective crops, including landraces of such crops. A possible scenario is that the harsh climatic conditions will pose serious challenges to the attainment of the genetic potential of the crops. The importance of ensuring improved productivity under adverse climatic conditions is highlighted by all the country authors and reflected in the recommendations for increased support to research for the development of improved crop varieties that are resilient to the adverse effects of the weather in addition to appropriate management practices.

The challenges of climate change are also opening the avenue for serious consideration of the farming systems in the area with regard to crop diversification as well as crop–livestock integration to minimize the risk of crop failure or livestock deaths. This was specifically identified for Burkina Faso and Niger in the Sahel as well as for Togo, which stretches from the coast into the Sahel. Interestingly, the three countries share borders. The Niger chapter reports that the drought in 1969 led to an estimated loss of 30 percent of the cattle in Agadez and at least 13 percent in the rest of the country and that the catastrophic drought of 1974 killed almost all the livestock in the country. As recently as 2009, the Niger livestock sector was hit by a drought leading to the loss of thousands of cattle. Livestock production is also a key economic activity in both Burkina Faso and northern Togo. It is against this background that agricultural diversification is being promoted in these countries. Most of the country chapter authors advocate for crop diversification to reduce the risk of crop failure. In Nigeria cassava, which is relatively drought tolerant compared to a crop like rice or maize, is increasingly being grown in the hitherto cereal-dominated northern part of the country. On the other hand, the drastic reduction in precipitation predicted for some parts of the coastal countries like Nigeria, Benin, Togo, and Ghana could erode the advantage of growing tree crops like cocoa and coffee that require a longer rainy season and convince farmers of the need to grow drought-tolerant crops like sorghum and millet based on the reduced precipitation predicted for parts of this region by 2050.

Even though the scenarios show crop production increasing in all the countries, net exports generally decrease except in Nigeria, where net exports increase for all the crops considered in our study, including the two major staple foodcrops, sorghum and cassava. The decline in exports is related to both population and income growth. All countries have recorded improvements in under-five mortality and life expectancy due to increased vaccinations against key diseases as well as improvements in per capita income. Unfortunately, the dismal level of family planning among the vast majority of the population in West Africa, particularly in rural areas, has resulted in a rapidly growing population that is not matched by the stagnant or slow increase in food production, which largely remains in the hands of smallholders who lack the vital inputs to deal with the growing challenges of the climate. Only in Nigeria and Burkina Faso does the total population based on the median variant not double by 2050. It is therefore very clear from the results of our study that population growth against the background of slow growth in crop productivity is a driver of negative net exports. The chapters on Benin, Côte d'Ivoire, Liberia, and Sierra Leone put specific emphasis on the need for appropriate action to slow population growth.

Beyond population growth, net rural–urban migration, particularly by youth, is identified by most of the country authors as a challenge in meeting the consequences of climate change, such as high unemployment rates, overcrowding, and inadequate social services, which are also leading to armed robberies and increased strikes, all of which are part of a recipe for civil unrest that can undermine political stability. This trend has been driven by low agricultural productivity coupled with the lack of improved socioeconomic conditions in the rural areas. Climate change is bound to worsen this situation, especially the adverse effects on agricultural productivity. As reported in the Senegal chapter, the severe drought in the late 1960s and early 1970s contributed significantly to the migration of the rural population to urban areas, particularly youth in search of jobs. The majority of the country authors specifically recommend actions related to rural development, including the construction of roads and market infrastructure as well as the provision of inputs for farmers, as indicated in the case of Burkina Faso.

It should also be noted that in addition to the direct effects of climate on crop productivity, heavy rains could pose a serious challenge to the condition of roads, particularly the unpaved feeder roads vital for the transport of inputs to farming areas and produce to market. This is likely to be a problem especially in the humid forest regions of countries along the coast. Several of the country authors, particularly in the cases of Liberia and Sierra Leone, indicated that some of the roads are impassable during the peak of the rainy season. The increasing rainfall for some of the Sahelian countries (Burkina Faso, Niger, and Senegal) shown by the results of our study could pose similar problems for these countries, particularly in view of the fact that roads and other structures in this region have not been built to withstand rainfall conditions.

A growing phenomenon in all the countries covered by our study is the decreasing proportion of the agricultural sector in total gross domestic product. Invariably this has mainly been due to the diversification of the economies of these countries. Nevertheless, this situation reveals the inefficiency of the agricultural sector, because the sector still employs the majority of the workforce in each of these countries. There is therefore a need to make the necessary changes to improve agricultural productivity with special attention given to climate change, which has been clearly identified as a critical force driving low agricultural productivity in the region.

In view of the foregoing, we make the following suggestions for consideration by the regional economic body the Economic Community of West African States (ECOWAS) as well as relevant regional organizations that have a stake in the development of the region, particularly with regard to agricultural development related to climate change adaptation in the region.

- AGRHYMET, which is responsible for weather monitoring in the Sahelian countries, should be supported in extending its activities to the remaining countries in the West African region to ensure reliable weather data collection for the region.

- There is a need for targeted research on climate change related to agriculture. The strategic framework of CORAF/WECARD (Conseil Ouest et Centre Africain pour la Recherche et le Developpement Agricoles / Western and Central African Council for Agricultural Research and Development) for climate change research needs support for both promotion and implementation.

- The many rivers in the region (such as the Niger, Senegal, and Volta Rivers) have a tremendous potential for irrigation. Most of the major rivers run through several countries that have an increasing need to develop dams for electricity and irrigation. There is definitely a need for the effective coordination of such dams along the rivers to ensure maximum benefit and avoid conflict in their exploitation.

- There is a growing awareness of the need for conservation of natural resources, particularly forests, and the development of parks. Many such designated areas are adjacent to neighboring countries, which necessitates collaboration between or among countries sharing such common borders and goals. An example is the Gola Peace Park between Sierra Leone and Liberia.

- ECOWAS should pursue efforts in economic integration, particularly the adoption of a common currency and harmonization of the multiple trade policies of member states to encourage trade within the region. Effective implementation of the ECOWAS Agricultural Policy will be a step in the right direction.

- The international road network in the region should be improved to facilitate the movement of goods and people throughout the region.

In the wake of the growing awareness of climate change, it is imperative that there be developments in climate science as well as the biophysical sciences related to agriculture, particularly innovations that will contribute to realistic adaptation to climate change. It is a reality that basic science is not a prerogative of countries in the West African region. However, there is room for collaboration between research institutions in the national agricultural research systems and advanced institutions in the north. Certainly such collaboration can be fostered bilaterally, but an effort should be made to advance regional initiatives. This calls for proactive strides by ECOWAS and synergy between the CGIAR centers in the region, particularly the Climate Change, Agriculture, and Food Security Research Program of the CGIAR and the International Food Policy Research Institute, to collaborate with CORAF/ WECARD, which has been designated by ECOWAS and the Forum for Agricultural Research in Africa to coordinate agricultural research in the region with a view to promoting the effective implementation of innovative food and agricultural research programs, satisfying the requirements of the citizens of member countries, promoting economic development, and reducing poverty.

The German government is supporting the West African scientific community that deals with the impact of climate change by establishing a Science Service Center on Climate and Adapted Land Use (WASCAL) linked with the scientific community in Germany. Its initial geographic target area is the Guinea Savanna agroecological zone in the riparian countries of the Volta River Basin (Benin, Burkina Faso, Côte d'Ivoire, Ghana, Mali, and Togo). The initiative involves the construction of a Competence Center in Ouagadougou to be shared with the Volta Basin Authority. This Competence Center will assist partner countries to collect panel data on climate, hydrology, land use, biodiversity, demography, and economic development. In addition, WASCAL will formulate a research program to be jointly implemented by a German and regional research consortium. The Core Research Program will target the advancement of knowledge on the impact of climate change on West African land resources through the promotion of resilience through adapted land use to ensure sustainable development.

Also, as part of WASCAL a series of graduate schools are being sponsored in the participating countries to address the deficit in human resources in the region in areas dealing with the impact of climate change in West Africa. In this regard, a Masters Research Program in Climate Change and Adapted Land Use is being hosted by the Federal University of Technology, Minna (FUT Minna), Niger State, Nigeria, while the Kwame Nkrumah University of Science and Technology, Kumasi Ghana, is focusing on capacity building at the PhD level. The postgraduate program ultimately aims at strengthening the research, educational, and policy capacity and competency of West African countries to deal with issues of climate change through adapted land use on a scientific basis in partnership with German institutions. It is expected that upon graduation these postgraduate fellows will be competent for engagement by universities, research institutes, and public services.

The resilience of resource-poor farmers to the effects of climate change in West Africa will be supported by the availability of reliable climate information that will guide farmers' management of scarce resources. Improved modeling could guide farmers' decisionmaking as well as policy formulation. Developing and making available crop varieties with a wide range of adaptations to moisture and temperature could ensure the preservation of a valuable gene pool in a changing climate situation. Every effort should be made to capitalize on indigenous knowledge across the region to provide adequate information on relevant entry points for research and development. There will be a need for the harmonization of efforts and procedures to reflect the regional perspective.

The actions to be taken over the next 10 years and beyond will be especially critical. New initiatives are needed—ones that integrate and apply the best and most promising approaches, tools, and technologies. The involvement of farmers, policymakers, researchers, the private sector, and civil society in the research process is vital. Successful mitigation of climate change and adaptation to it will entail changes in individual behavior, technology, institutions, agricultural systems, and socioeconomic systems. These changes cannot be achieved without improving interactions among scientists and decisionmakers at all levels of society.

It is critical that the all-inclusive IAR4D (Integrated Agricultural Research for Development), a multistakeholder and multiinstitutional participatory process that puts the farmer or entrepreneur at the center of the process, be adopted to achieve the common goals of adaptation to climate change and sustainable food production. In this novel approach, which is characterized by systemic facilitation and mutual learning among all actors, value-chain and innovation approaches are employed. In it the development of innovation platforms where mutual learning occurs among all stakeholders (including producers, processors, researchers, policymakers, and others) is essential. In the meantime it is absolutely critical that an appropriate forum that facilitates interactions among key stakeholders be established to adequately and appropriately inform policymakers in developing policies aimed at enhancing adaptation to climate change in Africa. To fill this gap, CORAF/WECARD, through AfricaInteract, a project funded by the International Development Research Centre, aims to establish an effective platform that will provide the much-needed forum for dialogue among key stakeholders in research and development, among them policymakers. This initiative is expected to stimulate the formation and development of meaningful partnerships in the quest to improve livelihoods in the face of the growing climate change challenges on the continent.

Finally, it is worth noting that the actions of individual countries will have consequences for neighboring countries with regard to climate. It is therefore in the interest of all countries to collaborate as much as possible in meeting the challenges of climate change, improving livelihoods in a way that will ensure the realization of economic development and improved welfare goals, and attaining the Millennium Development Goals.

References

Boko, M., I. Niang, A. Nyong, C. Vogel, A. Githeko, M. Medany, B. Osman-Elasha, R. Tabo, and P. Yanda. 2007. Africa. "Climate Change 2007: Impacts, Adaptation and Vulnerability." Contribution of Working Group II to the *Fourth Assessment Report of the Intergovernmental Panel on Climate Change,* edited by M. L. Parry, O. F. Canziani, J. P. Palutikof, P. J. van der Linden, and C. E. Hanson. Cambridge, UK: Cambridge University Press.

Parry, M., O. F. Canaziani, J. P. Palutikof, P. J. van der Linden, and C. E. Hanson. 2007. "Technical Summary." In *Climate Change 2007: Impacts, Adaptation and Vulnerability.* Contribution of Working Group II to the Fourth Assessment Report of the Intergovernmental Panel on Climate Change, edited by M. Parry, O. F. Canziani, J. P. Palutikof, P. J. Van der Linden, and C. E. Hanson. Cambridge, UK: Cambridge University Press.

World Bank. 2009. *Africa's Development in a Changing Climate.* Washington, DC: International Bank for Reconstruction and Development/World Bank.

Contributors

Kadio Ahossane (kahossane@gmail.com or kahossane@yahoo.com), Head, Climate Change Unit, National Polytechnic Institutes, Côte d'Ivoire

P. B. Irénikatché Akponikpè (akponikpe@yahoo.com), Faculty Member, Environmental Soil Physics and Hydraulics Unit (PSHE), Université de Parakou (UP), Benin

Sidafa Condé (sidafac2000@yahoo.fr), Head, Research and Development Division of the Extension Service (RD/ANPROCA), Ministry of Agriculture, Republic of Guinea, Conakry, Guinea

Adamou Danguioua (adamoudanguioua@yahoo.fr), Economist, Bureau d'Études, de Formation, et d'Appui-conseil à la Réduction de la Pauvreté (BEFACREP), Niger

Mbène Dièye Faye (mbene.faye@coraf.org), Programme Manager, Policy, Markets, and Trade Programme, West and Central African Council for Agricultural Research and Development (WECARD)

Shuaib M. Hassan (hassanalabo@yahoo.com), Lecturer, Department of Geography and Environmental Management, University of Abuja, Nigeria

Celestine E. Ikuenobe (ceeikuenobe@yahoo.com), Agronomist and Director of Research, Nigerian Institute for Oil Palm Research, Benin City, Nigeria

Abdulai Jalloh (Abdulai.jalloh@coraf.org), Programme Manager, Natural Resources Management, West and Central African Council for Agricultural Research and Development (WECARD)

Raymond G. Johnson (traymond12001@yahoo.com), Senior Lecturer, Institute of Marine Biology and Oceanography, University of Sierra Leone

Mohamed Kandeh, Officer-in-Charge, Magbosi Land and Water Research Centre, Sierra Leone Agricultural Research Institute (SLARI), Sierra Leone

Benjamin S. Karmorh, Jr. (benkarmorh@yahoo.com or benkamorh@yahoo .com), National Focal Point, Climate Change, Environmental Protection Agency of Liberia (EPA), Liberia

Mamadou Khouma (khoumamamadu@yahoo.fr), Ingénieur Agronome, Senegal

Agnidé Emmanuel Lawin (ewaari@yahoo.fr), Instructor, Faculté des Sciences et Techniques (FAST), Université d'Abomey–Calavi (UAC), Benin

Daniel Mason-d'Croz (D.MASON-DCROZ@cgiar.org), Research Analyst, International Food Policy Research Institute (IFPRI)

Gerald C. Nelson (g.nelson@cgiar.org), Senior Research Fellow, International Food Policy Research Institute (IFPRI)

Delali Kofi Nutsukpo (kofi_nutsukpo@live.com), Deputy Director, Environment and Land Management Division, Ministry of Food and Agriculture, Ghana

Amanda Palazzo (palazzo@iiasa.ac.at), Research Scholar, International Institute for Applied Systems Analysis. While working on this monograph, she was a Research Analyst at International Food Policy Research Institute (IFPRI).

Richard Robertson (R.Robertson@cgiar.org), Research Fellow, International Food Policy Research Institute (IFPRI)

Harold Roy-Macauley (h.roy-macauley@coraf.org), Director of Programmes, Natural Resources Management, West and Central African Council for Agricultural Research and Development (WECARD)

Paco Sérémé (paco.sereme@coraf.org), Executive Director, West and Central African Council for Agricultural Research and Development (WECARD)

Léopold Somé (bsomel@yahoo.fr; someleopold@fasonat.bf), Senior Researcher, Institut de l'Environnement et de Recherches Agricoles (INERA), Burkina Faso

Abiziou Tchinguilou (ptching17@yahoo.fr; abiziou.tchinguilou@hotmail.com), Ingénieur Agronome, Ministère de l'Environnement et des Ressources Forestières, Direction de l'Environnement, Togo

Timothy S. Thomas (T.S.Thomas@cgiar.org), Research Fellow, International Food Policy Research Institute (IFPRI)

Hassane Yayé (befacrep@yahoo.fr), Independent Agroeconomist, Siege Social; Immeuble UNC, Niger

Robert Zougmoré (r.zougmore@cgiar.org), Regional Program Leader, West Africa, Research Program on Climate Change, Agriculture, and Food Security (CCAFS), Consultative Group on International Agricultural Research (CGIAR)

Index

Page numbers for entries occurring in figures are followed by an *f;* those for entries in notes, by an *n;* and those for entries in tables, by a *t.*

FAO (Food and Agriculture Organization of the United Nations). 2010. *FAOSTAT Database on Agriculture.* Rome.

Jones, P. G., P. K. Thornton, and J. Heinke. 2009. "Generating Characteristic Daily Weather Data Using Downscaled Climate Model Data from the IPCC's Fourth Assessment." Project report for the International Institute for Land Reclamation and Improvement, Wageningen, the Netherlands. Accessed May 7, 2010. www.ccafs-climate.org/pattern_scaling/.

Lehner, B., and P. Döll. 2004. "Development and Validation of a Global Database of Lakes, Reservoirs, and Wetlands." *Journal of Hydrology* 296 (1–4): 1–22.

Millennium Ecosystem Assessment. 2005. *Ecosystems and Human Well-being: Synthesis.* Washington, DC: Island Press. http://www.maweb.org/en/Global.aspx.

Nelson, G. C., M. W. Rosegrant, A. Palazzo, I. Gray, C. Ingersoll, R. Robertson, S. Tokgoz, et al. 2010. *Food Security, Farming, and Climate Change to 2050: Scenarios, Results, Policy Options.* Washington, DC: International Food Policy Research Institute.

Sierra Leone, MOAFFS and MOF (Ministry of Agriculture, Forestry, and Food Security and Ministry of Fisheries). 2004. *Agricultural Sector Review.* Freetown.

Sierra Leone, MOFED (Ministry of Finance and Economic Development). 2009. *Development Assistance Data.* Freetown.

———. 2010. *Millennium Development Goals Progress Report, 2010.* Freetown.

———. 2011. *Agricultural Tracking Survey, 2011.* Freetown.

Spencer, D.S.C., S. Deen, and C. Williams. 2009. *Economics of Rice Production in Sierra Leone: Report of a Survey in Three Northern Districts.* Funded by the Soros Economic Development Fund, New York. Freetown, Sierra Leone: Enterprise Development Services.

SSL and MI (Statistics Sierra Leone and Macro International Inc.). 2008. *Sierra Leone Demographic and Health Survey (DHS) 2008, Preliminary Report.* Freetown.

Statistics Sierra Leone. 2005. *Multiple Indicator Cluster Survey 2005, Final Report.* Freetown.

———. 2006. *2004 Population and Housing Census.* Freetown.

UNEP and IUCN (United Nations Environment Programme and International Union for the Conservation of Nature). 2009. *World Database on Protected Areas* (*WDPA*): *Annual Release.* Accessed 2009.

UNPOP (United Nations Department of Economic and Social Affairs–Population Division). 2009. *World Population Prospects: The 2008 Revision.* New York. http://esa.un.org/unpd/wpp/.

USAID (U.S. Agency for International Development) Sierra Leone. 2007. *118/119 Biodiversity and Tropical Forest Assessment for Sierra Leone.* Freetown.

Wood, S., G. Hyman, U. Deichmann, E. Barona, R. Tenorio, Z. Guo, et al. 2010. *Sub-national Poverty Maps for the Developing World Using International Poverty Lines: Preliminary Data Release.* Washington, DC: Harvest Choice and International Food Policy Research Institute. http://labs.harvestchoice.org/2010/08/poverty-maps/.

World Bank. 2009. *World Development Indicators.* Accessed May 2011. http://data.worldbank.org/data-catalog/world-development-indicators.

You, L., and S. Wood. 2006. "An Entropy Approach to Spatial Disaggregation of Agricultural Production." *Agricultural Systems* 90 (1–3): 329–347.

You, L., S. Wood, and U. Wood-Sichra. 2006. "Generating Global Crop Distribution Maps: From Census to Grid." Paper presented at the International Association of Agricultural Economists Conference, Brisbane, Australia, August 11–18.

———. 2009. "Generating Plausible Crop Distribution and Performance Maps for Sub-Saharan Africa Using a Spatially Disaggregated Data Fusion and Optimization Approach." *Agricultural Systems* 99 (2–3): 126–140.

Chapter 13

TOGO

Abiziou Tchinguilou, Abdulai Jalloh, Timothy S. Thomas, and
Gerald C. Nelson

L ocated on the coast of the Gulf of Guinea in West Africa, Togo has a surface area of 56,600 square kilometers, bordering the Atlantic Ocean in the south, Burkina Faso in the north, Benin in the east, and Ghana in the west. The Togolese population was estimated at 6.3 million inhabitants in 2007. The Human Development Index ranked Togo 152nd out of 177 countries across the world, with an index of 0.512 (UNDP 2007).

The agricultural sector employs approximately 70 percent of the country's workforce and plays a crucial economic and social role in Togo, contributing to food security, creating jobs, and generating income as well as providing goods and services. Agriculture accounts for 38 percent of Togo's gross domestic product (GDP): 26.0 percent from foodcrops, 3.4 percent from cash crops, 5.1 percent from livestock products, 1.4 percent from fishery products and aquaculture, and 2.1 percent from forestry production. It produces 20 percent of the country's export earnings (Togo 2009). The Togolese agricultural sector is dominated by the small-scale rainfed farming of millet, sorghum, maize, and rice.

Productivity is generally low in Togolese agriculture for several reasons, including limited banking facilities, minimal training, and such natural factors as variable climate and poor soils. Togo's agricultural sector and the country's economic development are thus particularly susceptible to the effects of climate change. According to some climate scenarios, Togo is located in the area that will experience a decrease in rainfall and a rise in temperature, with an adverse impact on agricultural productivity and thus on the well-being of the population, particularly in rural areas.

Some national policy strategies have been adopted by the government to improve agricultural production and the well-being of rural dwellers, as summarized in the conclusions to this chapter. These strategies need to be revisited to mainstream adaptation to climate change and thus ensure that the expected results will be achieved.

Review of the Current Situation

Population

Figure 13.1 shows total and rural population trends in Togo (left axis) and the share of the urban population (right axis). The population of Togo approximately doubled between 1985 and 2010, with increasing urbanization (currently over 40 percent of the population lives in urban areas). The overall population growth rate has been declining slightly since 1980 (Table 13.1).

FIGURE 13.1   Population trends in Togo: Total population, rural population, and percent urban, 1960–2008

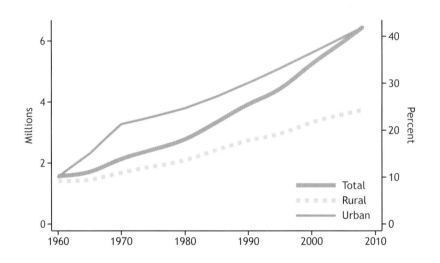

Source: World Development Indicators (World Bank 2009).

TABLE 13.1   Population growth rates in Togo, 1960–2008 (percent)

Decade	Total growth rate	Rural growth rate	Urban growth rate
1960–69	3.0	1.7	10.5
1970–79	2.6	2.1	4.0
1980–89	3.6	2.8	5.5
1990–99	2.8	1.9	4.8
2000–2008	2.6	1.4	4.3

Source: Authors' calculations based on World Development Indicators (World Bank 2009).

FIGURE 13.2   Population distribution in Togo, 2000 (persons per square kilometer)

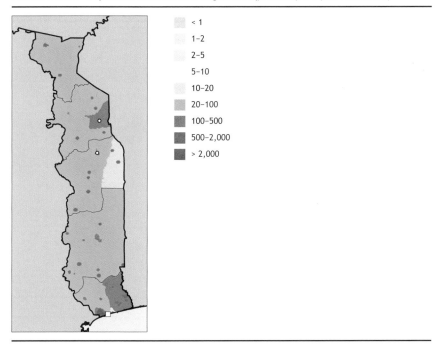

Source: CIESIN et al. (2004).

Figure 13.2 shows the geographic distribution of the population in Togo in 2000. The population is very unevenly distributed; arable areas (mostly in the south) as well as the areas around the capital city host more than 66 percent of the total population. All the major urban areas have population densities of 100–500 people per square kilometer, while the rural areas have a density of 20–100 people per square kilometer. Higher population densities continue to present serious challenges to governments including the Togolese government, particularly with regard to providing essential infrastructure and social services for the people. On the other hand, the largely human labor–intensive agriculture in rural areas has an increasingly dwindling labor force.

Income

Figure 13.3 shows trends in GDP per capita in Togo as well as the proportion of GDP from agriculture. GDP per capita, estimated at about US$180 (US dollars) in 1960, had almost doubled by 1980, reflecting the increased production of cash crops (coffee, cocoa, and cotton) and the mining sector (mainly phosphate). GDP per capita decreased sharply thereafter until 1994, to a low

FIGURE 13.3   Per capita GDP in Togo, 1960–2008 (constant 2000 US$) and share of GDP
from agriculture (percent)

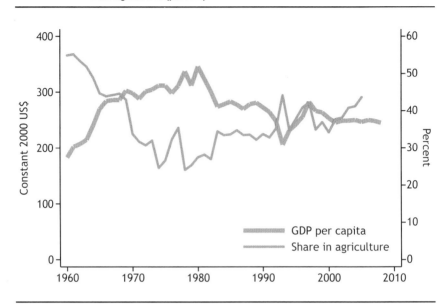

Source: World Development Indicators (World Bank 2009).
Notes: GDP = gross domestic product; US$ = US dollars.

of around US$200, due to structural adjustments imposed by the World Bank.
GDP per capita then increased sharply and peaked at the level of the 1980s,
followed by a more moderate decline and stabilizing at just below US$250 in
the mid-2000s. The reduction in donor funding as a consequence of bad governance largely accounted for the stagnation of the economy after 2000.

The agricultural sector occupies a prominent place in Togo's economy,
accounting for 38 percent or more of GDP in recent years and providing over
20 percent of export earnings. During the past 10 years, while GDP per capita
has been stagnant, the contribution of agricultural gross domestic product has
been increasing.

Vulnerability to Climate Change

Table 13.2 provides some data on Togo's performance on several indicators of a
population's vulnerability and resiliency to economic shocks: level of education,
literacy, and concentration of labor in poorer or less dynamic sectors. School
enrollment is 97.1 percent in primary school but only 39.3 percent in secondary

TABLE 13.2   Education and labor statistics for Togo, 1990s and 2000s

Indicator	Year	Percent
Primary school enrollment (percent gross, three-year average)	2007	97.1
Secondary school enrollment (percent gross, three-year average)	2007	39.3
Adult literacy rate	2000	53.2
Percent employed in agriculture	2010	66.0
Under-five malnutrition (weight for age)	1998	23.2

Source: Authors' calculations based on World Development Indicators (World Bank 2009).

school. The high dropout rate between primary and secondary levels is driven by such factors as the need for farm labor, an inability to pay school fees, and early marriage for girls. Only about half of the population is literate.

Figure 13.4 shows Togo's performance on two noneconomic correlates of poverty: life expectancy and under-five mortality. Life expectancy increased from 45 years in 1960 to 57 years in 1990 and then continued to increase slightly to around 63 years in 2008; infant mortality has been reduced by more than half, from more than 260 deaths per 1,000 in 1960 to about 100 per 1,000 in 2008.

FIGURE 13.4   Well-being indicators in Togo, 1960–2008

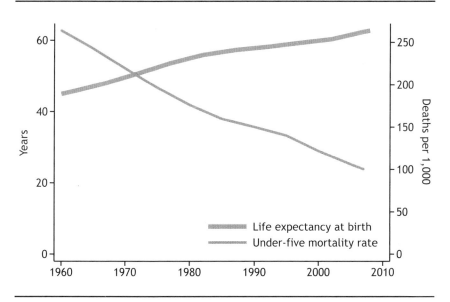

Source: World Development Indicators (World Bank 2009).

The vaccination of children as well as urbanization—which gives people better access to medical and social services—may partly account for these improvements.

Wood et al. (2010) report that 69 percent of the country is living on less than US$2 per person per day based on the 2005 US dollar and the purchasing power parity measure. Poverty is overwhelmingly rural: the rural incidence is 74.3 percent, representing 79.9 percent of the poor (Togo, MEF 2008). In urban areas the incidence of poverty is 36.7 percent. In general, the Savanna Region is the poorest (90.5 percent incidence), followed by the Central Region (77.7 percent), Kara (75.0 percent), Maritime (69.4 percent), Plateaux (56.2 percent), and Lomé, the least poor region (24.5 percent). Except for the city of Lomé and the Plateaux Region, all the regions have urban poverty rates of at least 50 percent; in the Savannah Region, 76.8 percent of the urban population is poor (Togo, MEF 2008).

Review of Land Use and Agriculture

Land Use Overview

Figure 13.5 shows the land cover and land use in Togo. Approximately 17 percent of Togo is forested, of which about 90 percent (3,480 square kilometers) is natural forest and 10 percent (380 square kilometers) is plantation (USAID Togo 2008). The Guinean savanna, an area of dry forests in the middle of the country, is the single most extensive vegetation cover; the major crops grown there are maize, sorghum, and cassava. The second-largest area of land cover is the Sudanian savanna in the far north of the country, with some parts in dry forests; there the major crops are cereals (maize, sorghum, millet, and rice) and legumes (peanuts, beans, and soy). In part of the Guinean savannah there is a zone of semideciduous forests where the major crops are maize, coffee, cocoa, and cassava.

Figure 13.6 shows the locations of protected areas, including parks and reserves. Togo has 83 protected areas covering 14 percent of the land, but most of these areas have been invaded by settlements, and at best about 10 percent of Togo has protected status (Amegadje 2007). This encroachment began occurring following the political turmoil that started in the 1990s. The government's rehabilitation program of protected areas (1999–2002) has set a goal of restoring and securing 578,246 hectares of 10 of the 83 priority protected areas, representing 10.2 percent of the national territory (Togo, MERF 2009). These areas are designed to conserve biodiversity and to improve the environments and living conditions of the people. The following existing protected areas are considered priorities: Malfakassa, Anié,

FIGURE 13.5   Land cover and land use in Togo, 2000

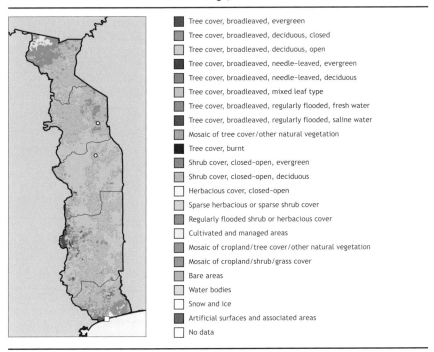

Tree cover, broadleaved, evergreen
Tree cover, broadleaved, deciduous, closed
Tree cover, broadleaved, deciduous, open
Tree cover, broadleaved, needle-leaved, evergreen
Tree cover, broadleaved, needle-leaved, deciduous
Tree cover, broadleaved, mixed leaf type
Tree cover, broadleaved, regularly flooded, fresh water
Tree cover, broadleaved, regularly flooded, saline water
Mosaic of tree cover/other natural vegetation
Tree cover, burnt
Shrub cover, closed-open, evergreen
Shrub cover, closed-open, deciduous
Herbacious cover, closed-open
Sparse herbacious or sparse shrub cover
Regularly flooded shrub or herbacious cover
Cultivated and managed areas
Mosaic of cropland/tree cover/other natural vegetation
Mosaic of cropland/shrub/grass cover
Bare areas
Water bodies
Snow and ice
Artificial surfaces and associated areas
No data

Source: GLC2000 (Bartholome and Belward 2005).

FIGURE 13.6   Protected areas in Togo, 2009

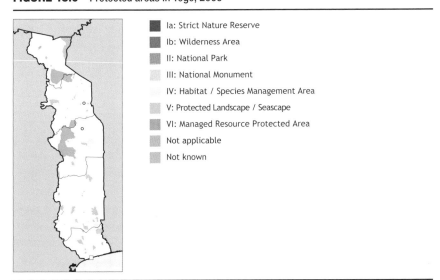

Ia: Strict Nature Reserve
Ib: Wilderness Area
II: National Park
III: National Monument
IV: Habitat / Species Management Area
V: Protected Landscape / Seascape
VI: Managed Resource Protected Area
Not applicable
Not known

Sources: Protected areas are from the World Database on Protected Areas (UNEP and IUCN 2009). Water bodies are from the World Wildlife Fund's Global Lakes and Wetlands Database (Lehner and Döll 2004).

Abdoulaye, Oti-Keran, Oti-Mandouri Aledjo, Togodo–South, North Togodo, Bayeme, Amu Mono, Galangashi, Tchilla-Monot, Fosse aux Lions, and Asséué Godjinmé. These protected areas cover nearly 595,848 hectares. By 2009 an estimated 7.22 percent of the protected areas had been reclassified and their boundaries delineated with the participation of local populations. Only the following protected areas can be classified according to the International Union for the Conservation of Nature categories: Aledjo, Togodo–South, North Togodo, Bayeme, Galangashi, and Fosse aux Lions. Several of the protected areas in northern Togo are part of a transboundary conservation corridor providing a large area for the migration of large game animals like elephants. Flora and fauna are threatened by anthropogenic activities, such as hunting pressure, overharvesting, and converting land to agriculture (USAID Togo 2008).

Figure 13.7 shows travel times to urban areas of various sizes in Togo as potential markets for agricultural products and as sources of agricultural inputs and consumer goods for rural households. The underdeveloped road transport infrastructure remains a problem for the growth of the Togolese economy, especially agricultural activities. Only 21 percent of the national road network is paved, and paved roads and engineering structures (bridges) are largely in disrepair due to a lack of maintenance and monitoring in recent years. The feeder roads linking major agricultural production areas with potential markets are often not passable, particularly during the rainy season, and some areas remain isolated.

It is difficult for farmers in remote areas to sell their agricultural produce in an urban center with more than 100,000 inhabitants (such as Lomé or Kara) with larger markets and better prices. Generally farmers must sell their products in smaller urban centers of fewer than 10,000 inhabitants, particularly in periodic markets.

Agriculture

Togo has two principal climate zones, north and south. In the north the rainy season extends from May to October, and the dry season lasts from November to April. Rainfall varies from 900 to 1,100 millimeters per year in this region, with an average temperature of 28°C. The southern region has two wet seasons of unequal duration, with annual rainfall between 1,000 and 1,600 millimeters and an average temperature of 27°C.

Tables 13.3–13.5 show key agricultural commodities in terms of area harvested, the value of the harvest, and the provision of food for human

FIGURE 13.7   Travel time to urban areas of various sizes in Togo, circa 2000

To cities of 500,000 or more
people

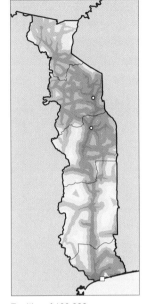

To cities of 100,000 or more
people

To cities of 25,000 or more
people

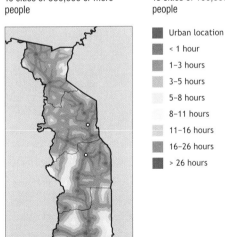

Urban location

< 1 hour

1–3 hours

3–5 hours

5–8 hours

8–11 hours

11–16 hours

16–26 hours

> 26 hours

To cities of 5,000 or more people

Source: Authors' calculations.

TABLE 13.3   Harvest area of leading agricultural commodities in Togo, 2006–08 (thousands of hectares)

Rank	Crop	Percent of total	Harvest area
	Total	100.0	1,532
1	Maize	31.0	475
2	Sorghum	14.4	221
3	Beans	12.3	188
4	Cassava	8.5	130
5	Cocoa beans	6.8	104
6	Millet	4.5	69
7	Seed cotton	4.4	67
8	Yams	3.9	60
9	Groundnuts	3.7	57
10	Coffee	2.2	34

Source: FAOSTAT (FAO 2010).
Note: All values are based on the three-year average for 2006–08.

consumption (ranked by weight). Maize has the largest area under cultivation. Cassava has the largest area for roots and tubers, and cocoa has the largest area for a cash crop (see Table 13.3). The greatest potential value is derived from cocoa beans followed by maize (see Table 13.4); cassava and yams are the first and second major foodcrops consumed in the country in terms of weight consumed (see Table 13.5).

The next five figures show the estimated yield and growing areas of key crops. Maize is the most widely cultivated crop in Togo (Figure 13.8). It is grown in all parts of the country, with yields ranging from 1 to 2 metric tons per hectare, though in some areas the yields are lower.[1] Sorghum, also widely grown, is concentrated mostly in the central and extreme southern parts of the country (Figure 13.9). In many areas the sorghum yields are also in the range of 1–2 tons per hectare. Beans are grown mainly in the middle belt, with a yield of less than 0.5 tons per hectare (Figure 13.10). Both cassava (Figure 13.11) and sweet potatoes and yams (Figure 13.12) are grown in the south and middle parts of Togo, though cassava is grown far more in the middle part of the country and cassava is grown in the far north as well. Cassava yields are mostly in the range of 4–7 tons per hectare, whereas yam and sweet potato yields are mostly in the category of yields greater than 10 tons per hectare.

---

1 All tons are metric tons.

TABLE 13.4   Value of production of leading agricultural commodities in Togo, 2005–07 (millions of US$)

Rank	Crop	Percent of total	Value of production
	Total	100.0	783.4
1	Cocoa beans	20.3	159.3
2	Maize	16.7	130.9
3	Yams	16.0	125.0
4	Other fresh vegetables	12.9	100.9
5	Cassava	10.4	81.5
6	Sorghum	7.6	59.8
7	Beans	3.5	27.5
8	Rice	2.5	19.4
9	Groundnuts	2.0	15.5
10	Seed cotton	1.9	15.1

Source: FAOSTAT (FAO 2010).
Note: All values are based on the three-year average for 2005–07. US$ = US dollars.

TABLE 13.5   Consumption of leading food commodities in Togo, 2003–05 (thousands of metric tons)

Rank	Crop	Percent of total	Food consumption
	Total	100.0	2,314
1	Cassava	26.5	614
2	Yams	19.7	456
3	Maize	15.7	363
4	Rice	5.7	132
5	Other vegetables	5.2	119
6	Sorghum	4.9	113
7	Wheat	3.1	73
8	Beans	2.0	46
9	Beer	1.5	34
10	Sugar	1.4	32

Source: FAOSTAT (FAO 2010).
Note: All values are based on the three-year average for 2003–05.

FIGURE 13.8   Yield (metric tons per hectare) and harvest area density (hectares) for rainfed maize in Togo, 2000

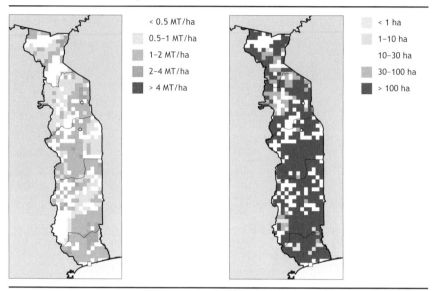

Sources: SPAM (Spatial Production Allocation Model) (You and Wood 2006; You, Wood, and Wood-Sichra 2006, 2009).

FIGURE 13.9   Yield (metric tons per hectare) and harvest area density (hectares) for rainfed sorghum in Togo, 2000

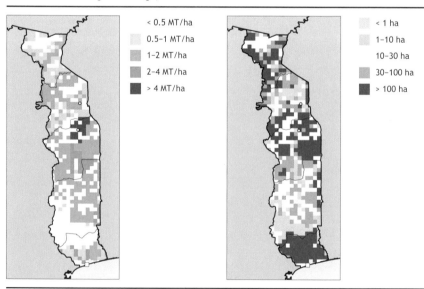

Sources: SPAM (Spatial Production Allocation Model) (You and Wood 2006; You, Wood, and Wood-Sichra 2006, 2009).

FIGURE 13.10   Yield (metric tons per hectare) and harvest area density (hectares) for rainfed beans in Togo, 2000

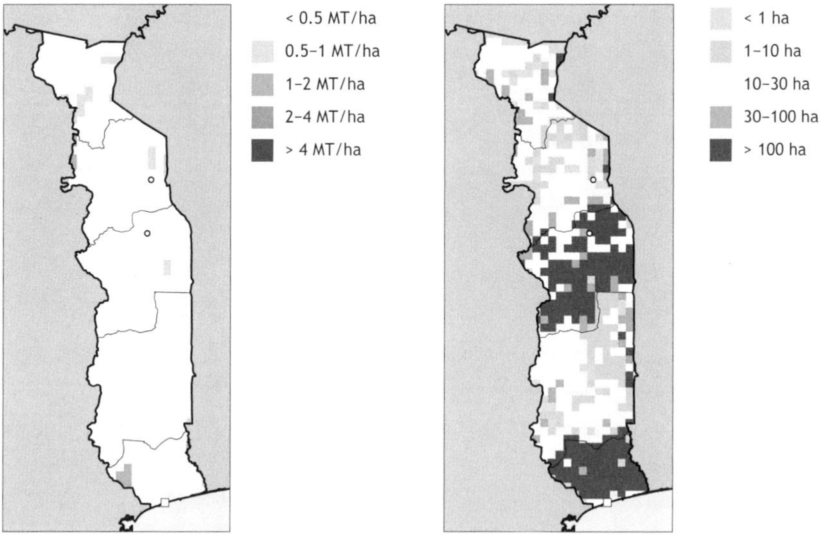

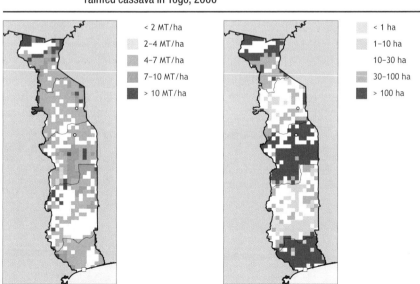

< 0.5 MT/ha
0.5–1 MT/ha
1–2 MT/ha
2–4 MT/ha
> 4 MT/ha

< 1 ha
1–10 ha
10–30 ha
30–100 ha
> 100 ha

Sources: SPAM (Spatial Production Allocation Model) (You and Wood 2006; You, Wood, and Wood-Sichra 2006, 2009).

FIGURE 13.11   Yield (metric tons per hectare) and harvest area density (hectares) for rainfed cassava in Togo, 2000

< 2 MT/ha
2–4 MT/ha
4–7 MT/ha
7–10 MT/ha
> 10 MT/ha

< 1 ha
1–10 ha
10–30 ha
30–100 ha
> 100 ha

Sources: SPAM (Spatial Production Allocation Model) (You and Wood 2006; You, Wood, and Wood-Sichra 2006, 2009).

FIGURE 13.12   Yield (metric tons per hectare) and harvest area density (hectares) for rainfed yams and sweet potatoes in Togo, 2000

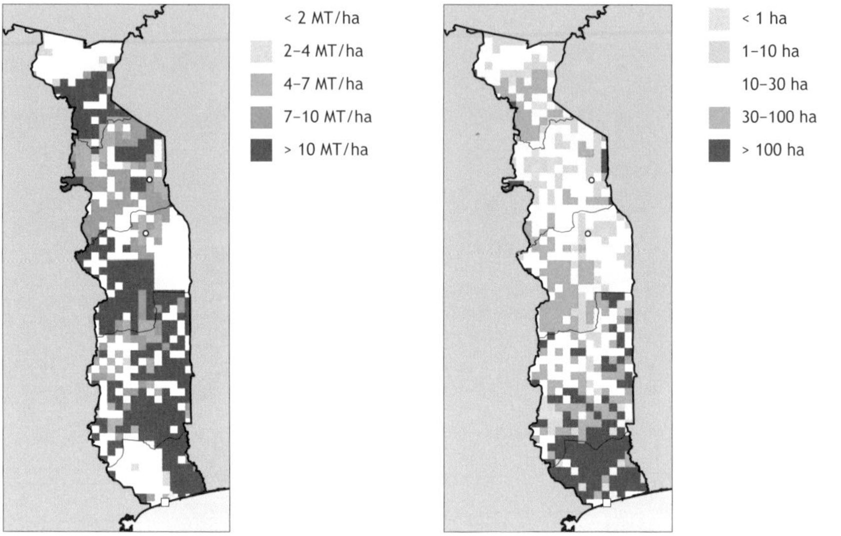

< 2 MT/ha	< 1 ha
2–4 MT/ha	1–10 ha
4–7 MT/ha	10–30 ha
7–10 MT/ha	30–100 ha
> 10 MT/ha	> 100 ha

Sources: SPAM (Spatial Production Allocation Model) (You and Wood 2006; You, Wood, and Wood-Sichra 2006, 2009).

Economic and Demographic Scenarios

Population

Figure 13.13 shows population projections for Togo by the United Nations (UN) population office through 2050 (UNPOP 2009). The population in 2050 is projected to be 15 million people (high variant scenario), 13 million (medium variant scenario), or almost 12 million (low variant scenario). These projected population levels will pose serious challenges to feed the increasing number of people. Population growth also poses serious environmental problems, including deforestation, bush fires, reduction of the length of the fallow period, inadequate farming techniques (leading to soil loss due to erosion), and overgrazing. Other challenges related to overcrowding include those related to the management of solid waste and industrial and commercial waste, pollution of the air and water, the emergence of toxic waste, and emissions of greenhouse gases.

Income

Figure 13.14 presents three overall scenarios for Togo's GDP per capita derived by combining three GDP scenarios with the three population scenarios of

FIGURE 13.13 Population projections for Togo, 2010–50

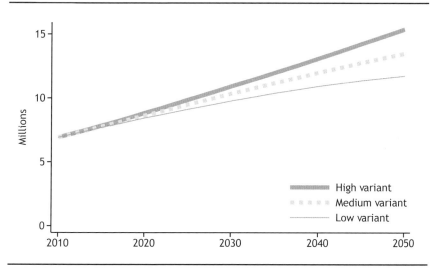

Source: UNPOP (2009).

FIGURE 13.14 Gross domestic product (GDP) per capita in Togo, future scenarios, 2010–50

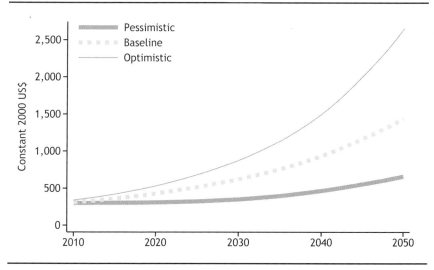

Sources: Computed from GDP data from the World Bank Economic Adaptation to Climate Change project (World Bank 2010), from the Millennium Ecosystem Assessment (2005) reports, and from population data from the United Nations (UNPOP 2009).
Note: US$ = US dollars.

Figure 13.13 (based on UN population projections). The optimistic scenario combines high GDP with low population scenarios for all countries, the baseline scenario combines the medium GDP projection with the medium population scenario, and the pessimistic scenario combines the low GDP scenario with the high population scenario. The agricultural modeling in the next section uses these scenarios.

The pessimistic scenario shows GDP per capita increasing only very slightly between 2030 and 2040, with a high of just US$700 in 2050. In the optimistic scenario GDP per capita is shown to double by 2025, reaching more than US$2,600 in 2050; the baseline scenario shows GDP per capita reaching about US$1,400 in 2050.

Biophysical Scenarios

Climate Scenarios

Figure 13.15 shows precipitation changes in the four downscaled general circulation models (GCMs) we use in this chapter in the A1B scenario.[2] The models show varying scenarios: the CNRM-CM3 GCM shows the average rainfall for 2000–2050 changing very little (between –50 and 50 millimeters) across the entire country; the CSIRO Mark 3 GCM, the most pessimistic model, shows for the same period a reduction of –100 to –50 millimeters for the far north (the Maritime Region and much of the Kara Region) and –200 to –100 millimeters for the rest of the country; the ECHAM 5 GCM shows little change (between –50 and 50 millimeters) in the extreme north (the Savanna Region and much of the Kara Region) and a moderate increase (between 50 and 100 millimeters) in the south; and the MIROC 3.2 medium-resolution GCM shows rainfall increasing in the north (100 to 200 millimeters) and diminishing southward, with substantial rainfall decreases in the southern third of the country (–200 to –100 millimeters).[3]

---

2 The A1B scenario is a greenhouse gas emissions scenario that assumes fast economic growth, a population that peaks midcentury, and the development of new and efficient technologies, along with a balanced use of energy sources.

3 CNRM-CM3 is the National Meteorological Research Center–Climate Model 3. CSIRO is a climate model developed at the Australia Commonwealth Scientific and Industrial Research Organisation. ECHAM 5 is a fifth-generation climate model developed at the Max Planck Institute for Meteorology in Hamburg. MIROC is the Model for Interdisciplinary Research on Climate, developed at the University of Tokyo Center for Climate System Research.

FIGURE 13.15   Changes in mean annual precipitation in Togo, 2000–2050, A1B scenario (millimeters)

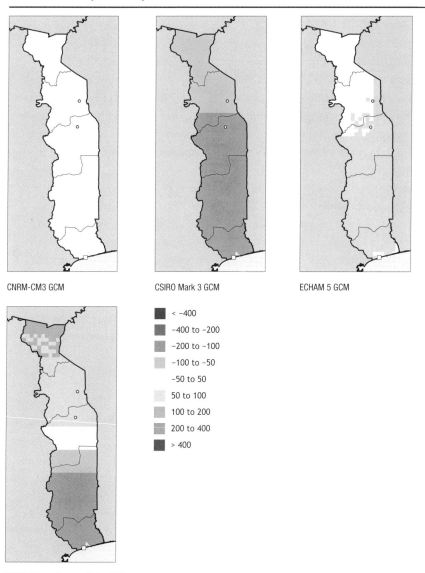

CNRM-CM3 GCM

CSIRO Mark 3 GCM

ECHAM 5 GCM

■ < –400
■ –400 to –200
■ –200 to –100
  –100 to –50
  –50 to 50
  50 to 100
  100 to 200
■ 200 to 400
■ > 400

MIROC 3.2 medium-resolution GCM

Source: Authors' calculations based on Jones, Thornton, and Heinke (2009).

Notes: A1B = greenhouse gas emissions scenario that assumes fast economic growth, a population that peaks midcentury, and the development of new and efficient technologies, along with a balanced use of energy sources; CNRM-CM3 = National Meteorological Research Center–Climate Model 3; CSIRO = climate model developed at the Australia Commonwealth Scientific and Industrial Research Organisation; ECHAM 5 = fifth-generation climate model developed at the Max Planck Institute for Meteorology (Hamburg); GCM = general circulation model; MIROC = Model for Interdisciplinary Research on Climate, developed at the University of Tokyo Center for Climate System Research.

Figure 13.16 shows the change in average daily maximum temperature for the warmest month in Togo in the A1B scenario according to various GCMs. CNRM-CM3 and MIROC 3.2 each show a uniform increase in temperature across the country of differing amounts. CNRM-CM3 is the most pessimistic of the four, with an increase of 2.0°–2.5°C; MIROC 3.2 shows the least increase, 1°–1.5 °C. CSIRO Mark 3 and ECHAM 5 show increases in most parts of the country in the range of 1.5°–2.0°C. Overall, the models show a minimum temperature increase of 1°C and a maximum of 2.5°C. Any sustained increase in temperature, especially with declining rains, could pose a serious challenge to the resource-poor farmers in the country.

Crop Scenarios

The effect of climate change on maize is mapped in Figure 13.17 as a comparison of 2050 crop yields under climate change with yields assuming an unchanged (2000) climate. All the models show a widespread reduction in the maize yield of varying degrees, ranging from 5 to 25 percent of baseline for CNRM-CM3 and ECHAM 5 to a loss of more than 25 percent for parts of the country in CSIRO Mark 3 and MIROC 3.2. However, all models show an increase of 5–25 percent of baseline in some grids in the northern part of the country.

Agricultural Vulnerability Scenarios (Crop-Specific)

The next three figures show simulation results from the International Model for Policy Analysis of Agricultural Commodities and Trade (IMPACT) associated with key agricultural crops in Togo. The figure for each featured crop has five graphs: production, yield, area, net exports, and world price. The box-and-whisker graphs in the figure indicate the range of possible climate change effects for each of the overall scenarios.

Maize production increases through 2030 and stabilizes thereafter, while the area under cultivation decreases from 2015 onward (Figure 13.18). The increase in production will thus be driven by productivity increases, reflecting the increased use of inputs and improved management practices as well as improved varieties. All scenarios suggest that there will be declining net exports after 2025, even though the world market price for maize is projected to continue to rise. The decline might be due to the increased domestic demand for maize as a result of population growth, as well as increased demand from the feed industry.

FIGURE 13.16 Change in the daily maximum temperature in Togo for the warmest month, 2010–50, A1B scenario (°C)

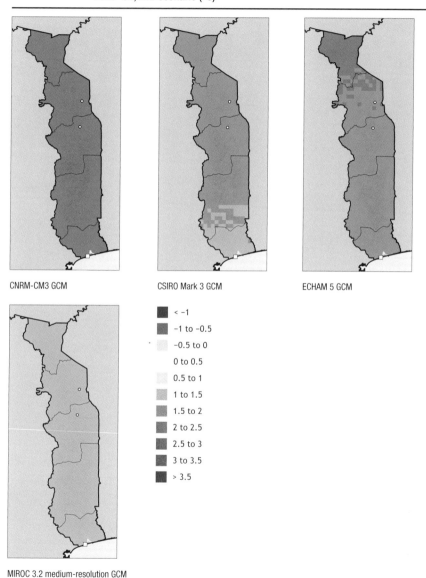

CNRM-CM3 GCM   CSIRO Mark 3 GCM   ECHAM 5 GCM

■ < −1
■ −1 to −0.5
−0.5 to 0
0 to 0.5
0.5 to 1
1 to 1.5
1.5 to 2
2 to 2.5
2.5 to 3
3 to 3.5
> 3.5

MIROC 3.2 medium-resolution GCM

Source: Authors' calculations based on Jones, Thornton, and Heinke (2009).

Notes: A1B = greenhouse gas emissions scenario that assumes fast economic growth, a population that peaks midcentury, and the development of new and efficient technologies, along with a balanced use of energy sources; CNRM-CM3 = National Meteorological Research Center–Climate Model 3; CSIRO = climate model developed at the Australia Commonwealth Scientific and Industrial Research Organisation; ECHAM 5 = fifth-generation climate model developed at the Max Planck Institute for Meteorology (Hamburg); GCM = general circulation model; MIROC = Model for Interdisciplinary Research on Climate, developed at the University of Tokyo Center for Climate System Research.

FIGURE 13.17   Yield change under climate change: Rainfed maize in Togo, 2000–2050, A1B scenario

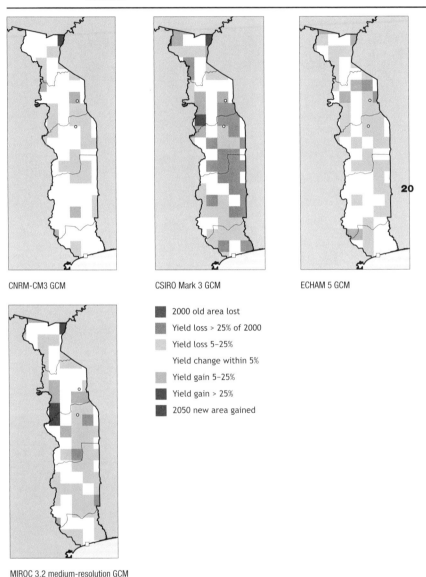

CNRM-CM3 GCM   CSIRO Mark 3 GCM   ECHAM 5 GCM

■ 2000 old area lost
■ Yield loss > 25% of 2000
  Yield loss 5–25%
  Yield change within 5%
  Yield gain 5–25%
■ Yield gain > 25%
■ 2050 new area gained

MIROC 3.2 medium-resolution GCM

Source: Authors' calculations based on Jones, Thornton, and Heinke (2009).
Notes: A1B = greenhouse gas emissions scenario that assumes fast economic growth, a population that peaks midcentury, and the development of new and efficient technologies, along with a balanced use of energy sources; CNRM-CM3 = National Meteorological Research Center–Climate Model 3; CSIRO = climate model developed at the Australia Commonwealth Scientific and Industrial Research Organisation; ECHAM 5 = fifth-generation climate model developed at the Max Planck Institute for Meteorology (Hamburg); GCM = general circulation model; MIROC = Model for Interdisciplinary Research on Climate, developed at the University of Tokyo Center for Climate System Research.

FIGURE 13.18 Impact of changes in GDP and population on maize in Togo, 2010–50

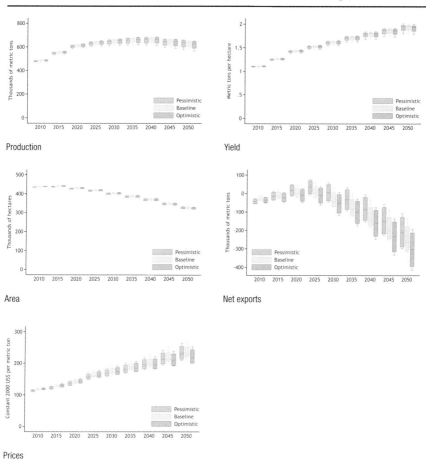

Production

Yield

Area

Net exports

Prices

Source: Based on analysis conducted for Nelson et al. (2010).

Notes: The box and whiskers plot for each socioeconomic scenario shows the range of effects from the four future climate scenarios. GDP = gross domestic product; US$ = US dollars.

Sorghum production, productivity, and area increase until 2050 (Figure 13.19). The world market price increases until 2030 and then stabilizes through 2050. In the optimistic scenario net exports decline as the world market price stabilizes in 2030; in the pessimistic scenario net exports will continue to increase. The trend in the baseline scenario is similar to that in the optimistic scenario.

Cassava production and productivity in Togo increase even while the area planted with the crop decreases (Figure 13.20). Increased productivity will be driven by technological improvements. The world price for cassava increases, and net exports are shown to decline after around 2030.

Human Vulnerability Scenarios

In addition to agricultural scenarios, IMPACT also estimates the number of malnourished children under the age of five, as well as the available kilocalories per capita. Figure 13.21 shows the impact of future GDP and population scenarios on under-five malnutrition rates in Togo. The box-and-whisker plots in the figure indicate the range of climate scenario effects. Based on the pessimistic scenario, the number of malnourished children under age five will be somewhat higher in 2050 (about 300,000) than at present (260,000); the optimistic scenario shows a reduction of more than 50 percent (from 260,000 to 100,000) by 2050. Although the pessimistic scenario shows an increase in the absolute number of malnourished children, with the population rising this probably represents a decline in the percentage of malnourished children under age five.

Figure 13.22 shows the average kilocalories per capita available. The pessimistic scenario shows fewer kilocalories available in 2050 than today; the optimistic scenario shows an increase, from about 2,000 kilocalories per person now to about 3,000 in 2050.

Conclusions and Policy Recommendations

Like other countries of the region, Togo is currently experiencing climate disruption characterized by irregularity in onset as well as overall shortening of the rainy season. There is also poor distribution of rainfall over the year. These changes are adversely affecting agricultural production. In the future (specifically by 2050), precipitation may rise or fall on average, depending on which model we look to. The temperature is expected to increase between 1°C and 2.5°C.

FIGURE 13.19   Impact of changes in GDP and population on sorghum in Togo, 2010–50

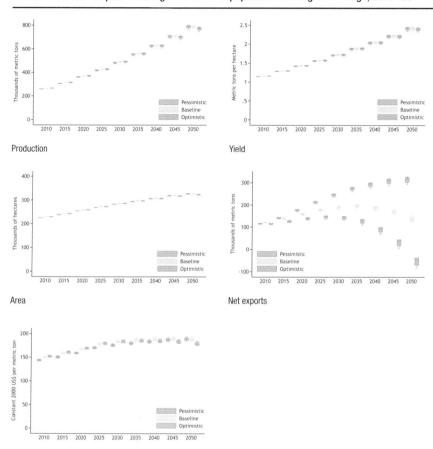

Production

Yield

Area

Net exports

Prices

Source: Based on analysis conducted for Nelson et al. (2010).

Notes: The box and whiskers plot for each socioeconomic scenario shows the range of effects from the four future climate scenarios. GDP = gross domestic product; US$ = US dollars.

FIGURE 13.20   Impact of changes in GDP and population on cassava in Togo, 2010–50

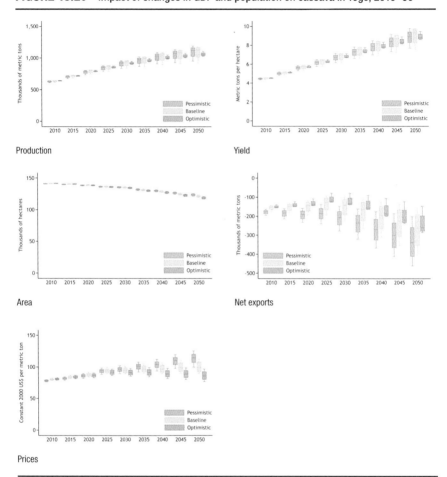

Production

Yield

Area

Net exports

Prices

Source: Based on analysis conducted for Nelson et al. (2010).

Notes: The box and whiskers plot for each socioeconomic scenario shows the range of effects from the four future climate scenarios. GDP = gross domestic product; US$ = US dollars.

FIGURE 13.21   Number of malnourished children under five years of age in Togo in multiple income and climate scenarios, 2010–50

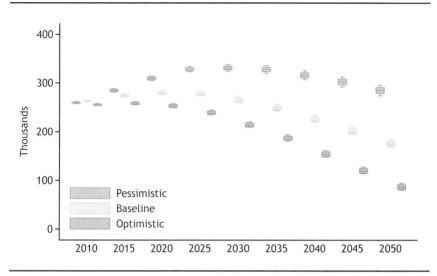

Source: Based on analysis conducted for Nelson et al. (2010).
Note: The box and whiskers plot for each socioeconomic scenario shows the range of effects from the four future climate scenarios.

FIGURE 13.22   Kilocalories per capita in Togo in multiple income and climate scenarios, 2010–50

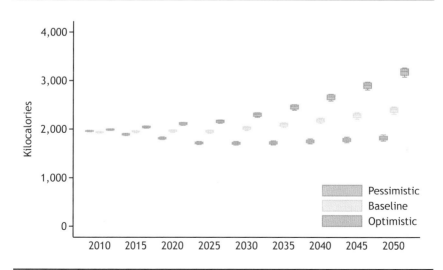

Source: Based on analysis conducted for Nelson et al. (2010).
Note: The box and whiskers plot for each socioeconomic scenario shows the range of effects from the four future climate scenarios.

In general, Togolese agriculture, which depends almost entirely on rainfall, will be strongly influenced by climate change. All models show declines in the yield of maize of between 5 and 25 percent due to adverse climate conditions, taking into consideration only climate impacts. However, the total production of maize, sorghum, and roots and tubers is shown to increase when anticipated technological improvement is factored in. The increase in productivity could be due to the development of adaptive varieties and improved management. It is therefore imperative that the required policies be developed and implemented to ensure that improved productivity is realized and sustained. The following are therefore suggested policy priorities to respond to the urgent threat to food production posed by climate change and to mitigate potential future harm.

- Support meteorological services to effectively monitor the weather and make relevant information available that will guide farmers in timing their operations and taking other important measures.

- Support the development of small-scale irrigation in lowland areas.

- Promote and encourage the diversification of crops so that the risk of failure of one crop is minimized.

- Provide adequate support for the National Agricultural Research System to develop appropriate crop varieties as well as improved management systems that will ensure improved productivity even under adverse weather conditions.

- Ensure the ability of the agricultural extension services to present their research to farmers in such a way that the farmers will be able to put the findings into practice.

- Create income-generating activities as alternative livelihoods to climate-sensitive activities.

- Strengthen prevention efforts related to flood-related disasters and other risks to the agricultural sector.

- Build technical capacity to manage climate change risks and impacts.

Some national policy strategies have been adopted by the government to improve agricultural production and the well-being of rural populations. The following strategies need to be revisited to mainstream climate change in all relevant programs and policies:

- The Agricultural Policy Note providing a strategic framework for interventions in the agricultural sector over the period 2007–11, adopted in December 2006

- The growth strategy of the agricultural and rural sectors, adopted in June 2004

- The strategy and action plan to boost agricultural production in 2008–11, adopted in July 2008

- The poverty reduction strategy, adopted in May 2009

- The long-term national strategy based on the UN Millennium Development Goals, ratified in May 2007

- The national food security program, adopted in December 2008

- The national agricultural investment program, discussed with development partners in July 2009

Although the structural transition may reduce the importance of agriculture in the overall economy, agriculture is likely to remain an important sector in Togo for both income and employment in the foreseeable future. Climate change may act to slow agricultural growth, but continued investment in agriculture can counteract the slowing and enable rural people to share in the overall economic growth that Togo is expected to enjoy in the decades to come.

References

Amegadje, M. K. 2007. "Profil Environnemental du Togo." Final report prepared for the European Commission and the Ordonnateur National du Fonds Européen de Développement. Ministère de la Cooperation et du Nouveau Partenariat pour le Développement en Afrique, Republic of Togo, Lomé.

Bartholome, E., and A. S. Belward. 2005. "GLC2000: A New Approach to Global Land Cover Mapping from Earth Observation Data." *International Journal of Remote Sensing* 26 (9): 1959–1977.

CIESIN (Center for International Earth Science Information Network, Columbia University), Columbia University, IFPRI (International Food Policy Research Institute), World Bank, and CIAT (Centro Internacional de Agricultura Tropical). 2004. *Global Rural–Urban Mapping Project, Version 1 (GRUMPv1)*. Palisades, NY, US: Socioeconomic Data and Applications Center (SEDAC), Columbia University. http://sedac.ciesin.columbia.edu/gpw.

FAO (Food and Agriculture Organization of the United Nations). 2010. *FAOSTAT Database on Agriculture*. Rome.

Jones, P. G., P. K. Thornton, and J. Heinke. 2009. "Generating Characteristic Daily Weather Data Using Downscaled Climate Model Data from the IPCC's Fourth Assessment." Project report for the International Institute for Land Reclamation and Improvement, Wageningen, the Netherlands. Accessed May 7, 2010. www.ccafs-climate.org/pattern_scaling/.

Lehner, B., and P. Döll. 2004. "Development and Validation of a Global Database of Lakes, Reservoirs, and Wetlands." *Journal of Hydrology* 296 (1–4): 1–22.

Nelson, G. C., M. W. Rosegrant, A. Palazzo, I. Gray, C. Ingersoll, R. Robertson, S. Tokgoz, et al. 2010. *Food Security, Farming, and Climate Change to 2050: Scenarios, Results, Policy Options*. Washington, DC: International Food Policy Research Institute.

Togo. 2009. *Poverty Reduction Strategy Paper* (*PRSP*). Lomé.

Togo, MEF (Ministère de l'Economie et des Finances). 2008. *Document complet de stratégie de réduction de la pauvreté* (*DSRP–C*). Cellule DSRP. Lomé.

Togo, MERF (Ministère de l'Environnement et des Ressources Forestières). 2009. *Plan d'action national d'adaptation aux changements climatiques* (*PANA*). Lomé.

UNDP (United Nations Development Programme). 2007. *Human Development Report 2007/2008*. New York.

UNEP and IUCN (United Nations Environment Programme and International Union for the Conservation of Nature). 2009. *World Database on Protected Areas* (*WDPA*): *Annual Release*. Accessed 2009. www.wdpa.org/protectedplanet.aspx.

UNPOP (United Nations Department of Economic and Social Affairs–Population Division). 2009. *World Population Prospects: The 2008 Revision*. New York. http://esa.un.org/unpd/wpp/.

USAID (U.S. Agency for International Development) Togo. 2008. *Togo: 118/119 Biodiversity and Tropical Forest Assessment*. Lomé.

Wood, S., G. Hyman, U. Deichmann, E. Barona, R. Tenorio, Z. Guo, et al. 2010. *Sub-national Poverty Maps for the Developing World Using International Poverty Lines: Preliminary Data Release*. Washington, DC: Harvest Choice and International Food Policy Research Institute. http://labs.harvestchoice.org/2010/08/poverty-maps/.

World Bank. 2009. *World Development Indicators*. Accessed May 2011. http://data.worldbank.org/data-catalog/world-development-indicators.

———. 2010. *Economics of Adaptation to Climate Change: Synthesis Report*. Washington, DC. http://climatechange.worldbank.org/content/economics-adaptation-climate-change-study-homepage.

You, L., and S. Wood. 2006. "An Entropy Approach to Spatial Disaggregation of Agricultural Production." *Agricultural Systems* 90 (1–3): 329–347.

You, L., S. Wood, and U. Wood-Sichra. 2006. "Generating Global Crop Distribution Maps: From Census to Grid." Paper presented at the International Association of Agricultural Economists Conference, Brisbane, Australia, August 11–18.

———. 2009. "Generating Plausible Crop Distribution and Performance Maps for Sub-Saharan Africa Using a Spatially Disaggregated Data Fusion and Optimization Approach." *Agricultural Systems* 99 (2–3): 126–140.

FIGURE 11.26 Kilocalories per capita in Senegal in multiple income and climate scenarios, 2010–50

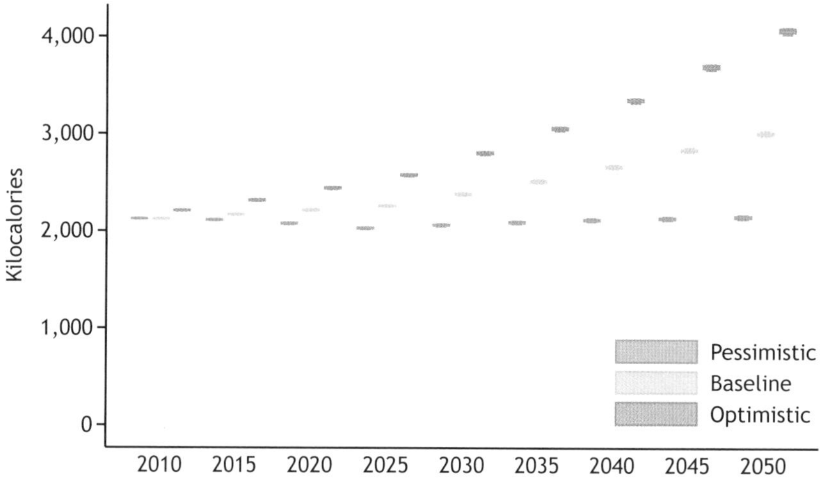

Source: Based on analysis conducted for Nelson et al. (2010).
Note: The box and whiskers plot for each socioeconomic scenario shows the range of effects from the four future climate scenarios.

Conclusions and Policy Recommendations

Senegalese agriculture is highly vulnerable to the effects of climate change, with its reliance on rainfed agriculture (representing 97 percent of the total cropped area). Currently agriculture's share of GDP is still declining despite noticeable improvement during the past decade, in part driven by the emergence and growing dominance of a service sector. Low agricultural productivity is linked to the low level of fertilizer use, poor seeds, and old agricultural equipment, as well as the poor performance of the livestock sector.

Water supply for an increasing population is a permanent challenge for Senegal. With most industrial and horticultural activities concentrated in the Dakar Region, current indications point to an increasing competition for water among domestic, industrial, and agricultural uses. Water is therefore central to any adaptation strategy in Senegal. Higher temperatures and unpredictable rainfall would put Senegalese agriculture at risk. All climatic models show negative anomalies in mean annual rainfall. The cereals maize and rice are shown to be less negatively affected by changing climate conditions than are legumes such as groundnuts.

Appropriate policies are required for a sound adaptation strategy that will minimize the potential negative effects of climate change and to build ecosystem resilience. These policies should aim at the following:

- Strengthening and modernizing the meteorological division to effectively collect weather data and make relevant information available in a timely and appropriate manner.

- Establishing early warning systems to allow farmers to plan cropping systems before the onset of the rainy season.

- Increasing investments in research and extension so that appropriate technologies can be developed, tested under local conditions, and presented as options to farmers.

The research presented in this chapter has shown that although Senegal faces a number of challenges from climate change in the agricultural sector, continued broad-based economic growth coupled with good policies and appropriate technologies will help the country succeed in facing these.

References

Bartholome, E., and A. S. Belward. 2005. "GLC2000: A New Approach to Global Land Cover Mapping from Earth Observation Data." *International Journal of Remote Sensing* 26 (9): 1959–1977.

CIESIN (Center for International Earth Science Information Network, Columbia University), Columbia University, IFPRI (International Food Policy Research Institute), World Bank, and CIAT (Centro Internacional de Agricultura Tropical). 2004. *Global Rural–Urban Mapping Project, Version 1 (GRUMPv1)*. Palisades, NY, US: Socioeconomic Data and Applications Center (SEDAC), Columbia University. http://sedac.ciesin.columbia.edu/gpw.

FAO (Food and Agriculture Organization of the United Nations). 2010. *FAOSTAT Database on Agriculture*. Rome.

Gaye, A. T., and M. B. Sylla. 2008. "Scenarios climatiques au Sénégal." Laboratoire de Physique de l'Atmosphère et de l'Océan S.F. (LPAO–SF), Ecole Supérieure Polytechnique Université Cheikh Anta Diop, Dakar, Sénégal.

Jones, P. G., P. K. Thornton, and J. Heinke. 2009. "Generating Characteristic Daily Weather Data Using Downscaled Climate Model Data from the IPCC's Fourth Assessment." Project report for the International Institute for Land Reclamation and Improvement, Wageningen, the Netherlands. Accessed May 7, 2010. www.ccafs-climate.org/pattern_scaling/.

Lehner, B., and P. Döll. 2004. "Development and Validation of a Global Database of Lakes, Reservoirs, and Wetlands." *Journal of Hydrology* 296 (1–4): 1–22.

Millennium Ecosystem Assessment. 2005. *Ecosystems and Human Well-being: Synthesis.* Washington, DC: Island Press. http://www.maweb.org/en/Global.aspx.

Nelson, G. C., M. W. Rosegrant, A. Palazzo, I. Gray, C. Ingersoll, R. Robertson, S. Tokgoz, et al. 2010. *Food Security, Farming, and Climate Change to 2050: Scenarios, Results, Policy Options.* Washington, DC: International Food Policy Research Institute.

PNUD (Programme des Nations Unies pour le Développement)–Senegal. 2009. *Rapport national sur le développement humain 2009.* Dakar.

Senegal, ANSD (Agence Nationale de la Statistique et de la Demographie). 2010. "Situation economique et Sociale du Senegal en 2009." Dakar. Accessed November 17, 2011. www.ansd.sn/publications/annuelles/SES_2009.pdf.

Senegal, MEPN (Ministère de l'Environnement et de la Protection de la Nature). 2005. *Politique forestière du Sénégal 2005–2025.* Dakar. 144 pp.

UNEP and IUCN (United Nations Environment Programme and International Union for the Conservation of Nature). 2009. *World Database on Protected Areas (WDPA): Annual Release.* Accessed 2009. www.wdpa.org/protectedplanet.aspx.

UNPOP (United Nations Department of Economic and Social Affairs–Population Division). 2009. *World Population Prospects: The 2008 Revision.* New York. http://esa.un.org/unpd/wpp/.

USAID (US Agency for International Development) Senegal. 2008. *Senegal Biodiversity and Tropical Forests Assessment: Prosperity, Livelihoods and Conserving Ecosystems (PLACE) IQC Task Order #1.* Prepared by the Senegal 118/119 Assessment Team of ECODIT. Dakar.

WHO (World Health Organization). 2010. *Roll Back Malaria.* Progress and Impact Series 4 (November). Focus on Senegal. Geneva. www.rbm.who.int/ProgressImpactSeries/docs/report4-en.pdf.

Wood, S., G. Hyman, U. Deichmann, E. Barona, R. Tenorio, Z. Guo, et al. 2010. *Sub-national Poverty Maps for the Developing World Using International Poverty Lines: Preliminary Data Release.* Washington, DC: Harvest Choice and International Food Policy Research Institute. http://labs.harvestchoice.org/2010/08/poverty-maps/.

World Bank. 2009. *World Development Indicators.* Accessed May 2011. http://data.worldbank.org/data-catalog/world-development-indicators.

——— . 2010. *Economics of Adaptation to Climate Change: Synthesis Report.* Washington, DC. http://climatechange.worldbank.org/content/economics-adaptation-climate-change-study-homepage.

You, L., and S. Wood. 2006. "An Entropy Approach to Spatial Disaggregation of Agricultural Production." *Agricultural Systems* 90 (1–3): 329–347.

You, L., S. Wood, and U. Wood-Sichra. 2006. "Generating Global Crop Distribution Maps: From Census to Grid." Paper presented at the International Association of Agricultural Economists Conference, Brisbane, Australia, August 11–18.

———. 2009. "Generating Plausible Crop Distribution and Performance Maps for Sub-Saharan Africa Using a Spatially Disaggregated Data Fusion and Optimization Approach." *Agricultural Systems* 99 (2–3): 126–140.

Chapter 12

SIERRA LEONE

Raymond G. Johnson, Mohamed Kandeh, Abdulai Jalloh,
Gerald C. Nelson, and Timothy S. Thomas

Sierra Leone has an area of 72,325 square kilometers and is bordered in the northeast by the Republic of Guinea, in the south and southeast by the Republic of Liberia, and in the west by the North Atlantic Ocean. The country is divided into five main geographical regions: coastline, interior lowland plains, interior plateau, mountains, and Freetown Peninsula. The coastline is part of the general coastline of the West and Central Africa region, a low plain, sandy and surf beaten. The general coastline orientation, northwest–southeast, is strongly influenced by the local structural and lithological framework.

Agriculture is the largest sector in the economy of Sierra Leone, providing employment for over 65 percent of the labor force and contributing about 35–47 percent of the gross domestic product (GDP) (Sierra Leone, MOAFFS and MOF 2004). Rice is the staple foodcrop in Sierra Leone, grown mainly by small-scale farmers. The impact of climate change is already felt in the country in seasonal droughts, strong winds, thunderstorms, landslides, heat waves, floods, and changed rainfall patterns. As reported in Sierra Leone's National Adaptation Programme of Action, poor communities suffer the most from climate change impacts as floods destroy their crops and increased droughts cause water shortages in some areas of the country (Sierra Leone, MOFED 2009).

Deforestation, a major environmental problem for Sierra Leone, has many adverse effects on crop production. Conversely, continued reliance on subsistence farming through shifting cultivation will accelerate the process of deforestation and the associated land degradation. The potential impacts could be more serious for Sierra Leone than for countries that have resources to cope with these effects.

Crop production is highly vulnerable to climatic change and has been affected by prolonged periods of dry days—even during the rainy season (July–September). In recent years, unprecedented heavy rains of greater than the usual frequency in March have disrupted the burning and planting of farmland, with serious consequences including weed infestation. A recent report by the government noted that erratic rainfall caused acute water shortages in Freetown and its environs in 2006 and floods in Port Loko and Kambia Districts in 2004 (Sierra Leone, MOFED 2009). The report also noted that a rise in sea level could damage infrastructure and cause increased erosion in coastal areas, as well as increase the risk of land- and mudslides. Considering that food production depends entirely on subsistence farming, a decline in agricultural productivity—coupled with the increasing trend of food prices—is expected to ultimately worsen food insecurity problems in Sierra Leone. The Government of Sierra Leone notes that the effect of climate change on water availability, agricultural productivity, and population distribution could have an impact on the accomplishment of every one of the United Nations' Millennium Development Goals (Sierra Leone, MOFED 2010). The purpose of this chapter is to help policymakers and researchers better understand and anticipate the likely impacts of climate change on agriculture, as well as on vulnerable households in Sierra Leone.

Review of the Current Situation and Trends

Population

According to the 2004 national census, Sierra Leone had a population of 5 million that year (Statistics Sierra Leone 2006). Figure 12.1 shows trends in the total and rural populations (left axis) as well as the share of the urban population (right axis). The population grew from 2.2 million in 1963 to a projected 5.6 million in 2008 (World Bank 2009). The percentage change in the population of Sierra Leone over the two decades between 1985 and 2004 was 41.6 percent, representing an annual rate of growth of 1.85 percent. The annual growth rate was even higher between 1974 and 1985, at 2.3 percent. Figure 12.1 shows the steady growth of both the urban and the rural populations from 1960 to 1990—when the civil war started—and an increase again after 2000.

Table 12.1 shows that the highest urban population growth rate (4.7 percent) occurred between 1960 and 1969; the lowest (0.7 percent) occurred between 1990 and 1999, coinciding with the decade of civil war. The sharp 4.3 percent urban growth rate after the war—from 2000 to 2008—can be attributed to the return of refugees to the main urban towns.

Figure 12.2 shows the geographic distribution of the population for the year 2000 in Sierra Leone based on census data and other sources. The population is concentrated in the district headquarters towns as well as in the Western Area, including the capital city, Freetown. The northernmost part of

FIGURE 12.1   Population trends in Sierra Leone: Total population, rural population, and percent urban, 1960–2008

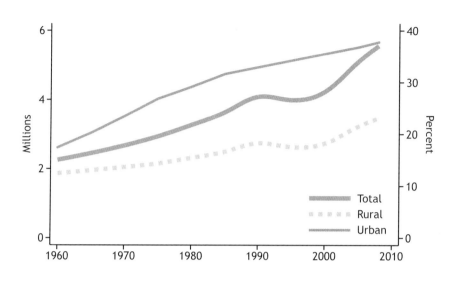

Source: World Development Indicators (World Bank 2009).

TABLE 12.1   Population growth rates in Sierra Leone, 1960–2008 (percent)

Decade	Total growth rate	Rural growth rate	Urban growth rate
1960–69	1.7	0.9	4.7
1970–79	2.0	1.2	4.2
1980–89	2.4	1.8	3.7
1990–99	−0.1	−0.5	0.7
2000–2008	3.5	3.1	4.3

Source: Authors' calculations based on World Development Indicators (World Bank 2009).

Sierra Leone is less densely populated, with large tracts of grasslands neighboring the Republic of Guinea.

Income

The share of Sierra Leone's GDP earned in agriculture shows the importance of agriculture as a sector of the economy. Figure 12.3 shows trends in GDP per capita and the proportion of GDP from agriculture.

FIGURE 12.2   Population distribution in Sierra Leone, 2000 (persons per square kilometer)

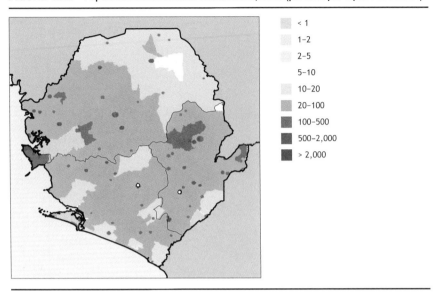

Source: CIESIN et al. (2004).

FIGURE 12.3   Per capita GDP in Sierra Leone (constant 2000 US$) and share of GDP from agriculture (percent), 1960–2008

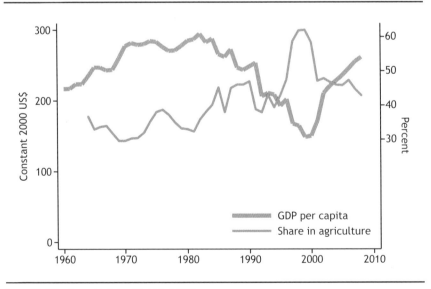

Source: World Development Indicators (World Bank 2009).
Note: GDP = gross domestic product; US$ = US dollars.

Despite its significant resource endowments, the country has suffered prolonged deterioration and an accompanying low standard of living for the vast majority of the population. The policies of successive governments since the 1970s failed to address the long-term challenges of the country's economy. Consequently, the standard of living of the majority of Sierra Leoneans has been generally marginal. GDP per capita rose only moderately between 1960 and 1982, from US$220 (US dollars) in 1960 to US$280 in 1982. Its lowest level was in 1998–99 following a decline that began in 1989–90 with the start of the decade-long civil war. GDP began to rise again after 2000, reaching US$260 by 2008. Agriculture and associated activities make up the dominant sector of the economy, accounting for approximately 40 percent of GDP and sustaining two-thirds of the population, mostly at a subsistence level. The share of GDP from agriculture ranged from 30 to 40 percent throughout the 1960s and 1970s, rising to between 40 and 60 percent in the 1980s and 1990s. The sudden rise in the share of agriculture in GDP in the late 1990s was driven by the crippling of other economic activities at the peak of the war. The decline in the share of GDP in 2000 coincided with the severe disruption of economic activities in other sectors when the war was raging in Freetown. The manufacturing sector is small, composed mostly of import-substituting industries and employing 2 percent of the labor force. The service sector—consisting mainly of transport, communications, insurance, finance, and government service—accounts for about 15 percent of GDP.

The two-decades-long decline in the economy from 1980 to 2000 can be attributed to a combination of factors, including weak internal management policies, the poor performance of the economic recovery programs, and weak export prices combined with rising import prices. The Structural Adjustment Program mandated by the World Bank and the International Monetary Fund—incorporating trade liberalization, stabilization of the exchange rate, and the removal of subsidies on petroleum products and staple foods—has had mixed results for the overall economy, and escalating prices for staple foods in fact reversed whatever gains these policies may have achieved. Strategies such as the privatization of public enterprises and restructuring of the civil service are in the planning and implementation stages, but signs of any positive impact are yet to be identified.

Vulnerability to Climate Change

Table 12.2 provides some data on Sierra Leone's performance on indicators of a population's vulnerability or resiliency to economic shocks: level of education, literacy, and concentration of labor in poorer or less dynamic sectors.

TABLE 12.2   Education and labor statistics for Sierra Leone, 2000s

Indicator	Year	Percent
Primary school enrollment (percent gross, three-year average)	2007	47.1
Secondary school enrollment (percent gross, three-year average)	2007	31.6
Adult literacy rate	2007	38.1
Percent employed in agriculture	2004	68.5
Under-five malnutrition (weight for age)	2005	28.3

Source: Authors' calculations based on World Development Indicators (World Bank 2009).

The majority of the population—68.5 percent—is engaged in the agricultural sector, which is largely underdeveloped. The adult literacy rate is extremely low, and both primary and secondary school enrollment are below 50 percent. The primary school enrollment rate is lower than in most countries in the subregion, but the secondary school enrollment rate is about normal for the region. The decade-long war and the preceding era of economic mismanagement contributed to this situation.

Figure 12.4 shows Sierra Leone's performance on two noneconomic correlates of poverty: life expectancy and under-five mortality. The current estimate of the crude birth rate is 42 births per 1,000 people. The current total fertility rate is 6.1 children per woman based on the 2004 census (Statistics Sierra Leone 2006)—a slight decrease from 6.5 in 1974 (SSL and MI 2008). The government has viewed the country's fertility levels as unacceptably high since the 1980s.

With a crude death rate of 20 per 1000, Sierra Leone remains one of the African countries south of the Sahara with the highest death rates. Until recently, Sierra Leone had the world's highest child mortality rate, 262 deaths per 1,000 live births; in 2000 its under-five and infant mortality rates were 286 and 170 per 1,000 live births, respectively. In 2005 there was a slight improvement in both indicators, with a decrease in the under-five mortality rate to 267 per 1,000 and in the infant mortality rate to 158 (Statistics Sierra Leone 2005). Life expectancy is still low, at 48.4 years according to the 2004 census. This, however, reflects an increase over time.

Overall, 70–80 percent of the population of Sierra Leone lives on less than US$2 a day based on the 2005 US dollar and the purchasing power parity measure, which turns out to reflect only a moderate amount of poverty compared to the country's immediate neighbors (Wood et al. 2010).

FIGURE 12.4   Well-being indicators in Sierra Leone, 1960–2008

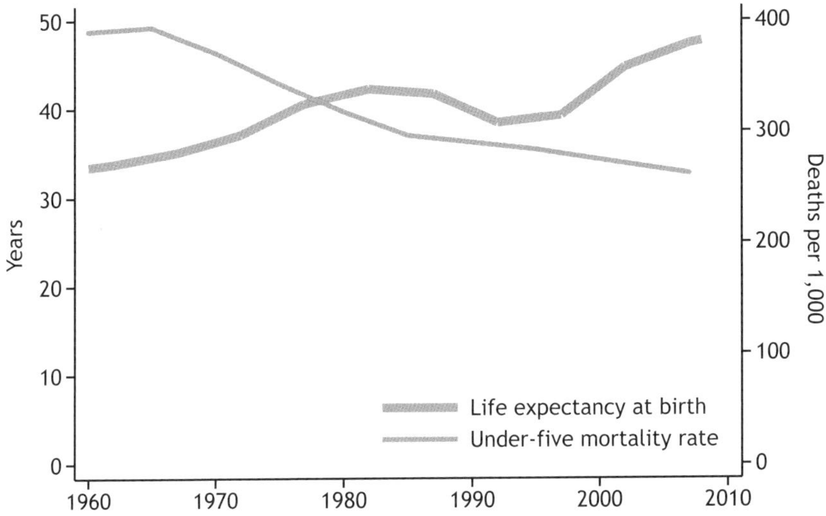

Source: World Development Indicators (World Bank 2009).

Review of Land Use and Agriculture

Land Use Overview

Figure 12.5 shows the land cover and land use in Sierra Leone as of 2000. The actual forest cover is not known. However, information from various sources indicates that deforestation in Sierra Leone has led to a decrease in the forest cover from an estimated 70 percent decades ago to less than 5 percent in recent years (USAID Sierra Leone 2007). Logging, slash-and-burn agriculture, and the cutting of trees for use as fuelwood are the primary causes of deforestation in the country. The savannah is limited to the northern parts of the country and is increasingly being subjected to frequent uncontrolled fires. The combined effects of poor farming practices such as shifting cultivation, recurrent bushfires, and overgrazing, along with the increasing population and the resulting shortening of the fallow periods for the land, have all been identified as factors contributing to land degradation. In addition to the increasing demand for agricultural land, urban development has increased the requirements for timber and fuelwood, which has led to additional deforestation (Sierra Leone, MOFED 2010). The mangrove forests along the coasts are also

FIGURE 12.5   Land cover and land use in Sierra Leone, 2000

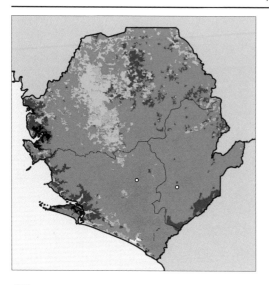

■	Tree cover, broadleaved, evergreen
▨	Tree cover, broadleaved, deciduous, closed
▢	Tree cover, broadleaved, deciduous, open
■	Tree cover, broadleaved, needle-leaved, evergreen
▢	Tree cover, broadleaved, needle-leaved, deciduous
▢	Tree cover, broadleaved, mixed leaf type
▨	Tree cover, broadleaved, regularly flooded, fresh water
■	Tree cover, broadleaved, regularly flooded, saline water
▨	Mosaic of tree cover/other natural vegetation
■	Tree cover, burnt
▨	Shrub cover, closed–open, evergreen
▨	Shrub cover, closed–open, deciduous
▢	Herbacious cover, closed–open
▨	Sparse herbacious or sparse shrub cover
▨	Regularly flooded shrub or herbacious cover
▢	Cultivated and managed areas
■	Mosaic of cropland/tree cover/other natural vegetation
▨	Mosaic of cropland/shrub/grass cover
▨	Bare areas
▢	Water bodies
▢	Snow and ice
■	Artificial surfaces and associated areas
▢	No data

Source: GLC2000 (Global Land Cover 2000) (Bartholome and Belward 2005).

being increasingly exploited for fuelwood and converted to rice cultivation. This has led to increased exposure to storms, as well as the destruction of natural breeding grounds for marine and estuarine fish.

Both artisanal and industrial mining have also affected the country's land resources in mineral-rich areas. With population pressure and commercial logging, the rate of exploitation has far outstripped the rate of regeneration by natural means. The results are deforestation and an acute threat to biodiversity (Sierra Leone, MOFED 2010). Inadequate mitigating policies and conservation programs over the years, along with weak enforcement of the existing ones, have worsened the situation.

Figure 12.6 shows the locations of protected areas, including parks and reserves. There are several forest reserves in various parts of Sierra Leone, including nonhunting forest reserves. The Gola Forest Reserve is the most notable, consisting of Gola East (22,800 hectares), Gola North (45,000 hectares), and Gola West (6,200 hectares), all in eastern Sierra Leone bordering Liberia. Other forest reserves include the Loma Mountains in northern Sierra Leone (33,201 hectares) and Kambui North (20,348 hectares). Outamba-Kilimi National Park (80,813 hectares) in northern Sierra Leone is the only national park.

Figure 12.7 shows travel times to urban areas of various sizes. Travel time is important because it can serve as a proxy for the cost of transporting

FIGURE 12.6   Protected areas in Sierra Leone, 2009

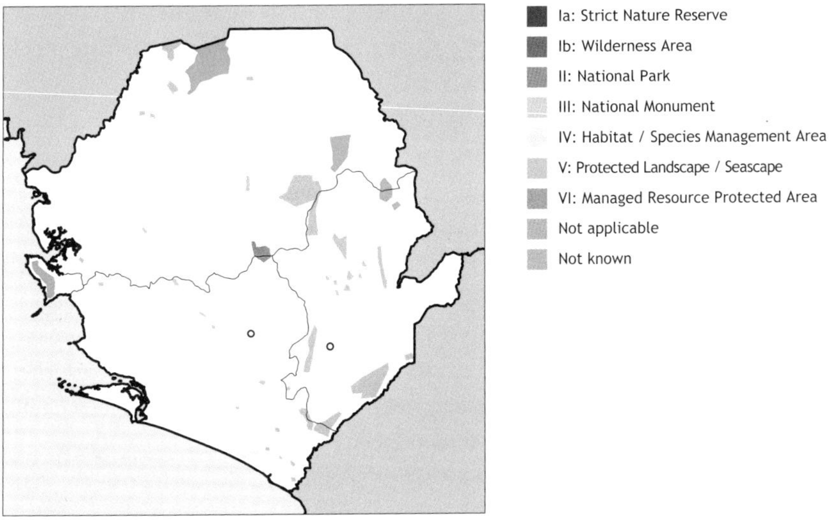

Ia: Strict Nature Reserve
Ib: Wilderness Area
II: National Park
III: National Monument
IV: Habitat / Species Management Area
V: Protected Landscape / Seascape
VI: Managed Resource Protected Area
Not applicable
Not known

Sources: Protected areas are from the World Database on Protected Areas (UNEP and IUCN 2009). Water bodies are from the World Wildlife Fund's Global Lakes and Wetlands Database (Lehner and Döll 2004).

agricultural goods to potential markets and can also indicate how costly
it might be to transport agricultural inputs and consumer goods to farms.
Sierra Leone has less than 1,000 kilometers of paved roads and more than
10,000 kilometers of unpaved roads. The upper northern and eastern regions
of the country are not well connected with road networks. Most of the roads
in remote areas are impassable during the rainy season. The main road leading
to the far eastern region—with the largest cocoa and coffee plantations—is
unpaved. Transporting agricultural produce from and inputs to various farming communities is thus a huge challenge in the country.

Agriculture Overview

Agriculture is the largest sector in the economy of Sierra Leone, providing employment for over 65 percent of the labor force and contributing
35–47 percent of the GDP (Sierra Leone, MOAFFS and MOF 2004). Crop
production is mostly carried out on the uplands, where slash-and-burn is the
main method for clearing land, invariably with traditional implements. The
majority of households (85 percent is the national average) are livestock or
poultry owners. Some 81 percent of farming households nationwide own at
least one chicken. At a national level, other commonly owned animals are
goats (owned by 25 percent of households), sheep (17 percent), and ducks
(9 percent). Other livestock and poultry are not owned by a high percentage
of farming households nationally. For example, bulls and cows are owned by
only about 1 percent of households nationally, and the same applies to pigs.
The rates of ownership of calves, work oxen, rabbits, and guinea fowl are much
less than 1 percent (Sierra Leone, MOFED 2011).

Tables 12.3 and 12.4 show key agricultural commodities of Sierra Leone in
terms of area harvested and food for human consumption (ranked by weight).
Rice, the staple food, is grown by more than 80 percent of the farmers, particularly in the southern and northern regions. The annual per capita consumption of rice (104 kilograms) is among the highest in Africa south of the
Sahara. Sierra Leone has not been able to produce enough rice to meet local
consumption demand since the late 1970s. From 1960 to 1975 the production of rice increased through the expansion of the land area planted with the
crop and to some extent an increase in yield. In the late 1980s, production fell
to an average of just above 500,000 metric tons, further declining to about
460,000 tons in the mid-1990s when civil war engulfed the entire nation.[1] The
lowest level of production (198,000 tons of paddy) was recorded at the peak of

---

1 All tons are metric tons.

FIGURE 12.7   Travel time to urban areas of various sizes in Sierra Leone, circa 2000

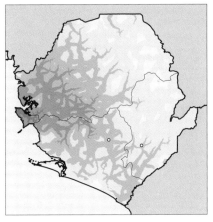

To cities of 500,000 or more people

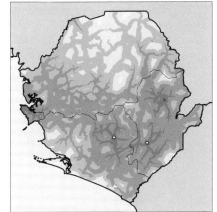

To cities of 100,000 or more people

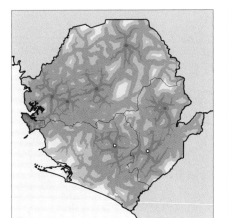

To towns and cities of 25,000 or more people

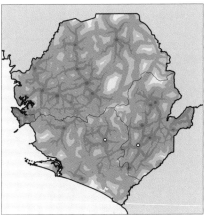

To towns and cities of 10,000 or more people

Urban location
< 1 hour
1–3 hours
3–5 hours
5–8 hours
8–11 hours
11–16 hours
16–26 hours
> 26 hours

Source: Authors' calculations.

TABLE 12.3   Harvest area of leading agricultural commodities in Sierra Leone, 2006–08 (thousands of hectares)

Rank	Crop	Percent of total	Harvest area
	Total	100.0	1,619
1	Rice	61.8	1,000
2	Groundnuts	9.3	150
3	Other pulses	5.4	88
4	Cassava	4.5	73
5	Maize	3.7	60
6	Other fresh vegetables	2.4	40
7	Cocoa beans	2.3	38
8	Millet	1.5	25
9	Oil palm fruit	1.5	24
10	Sorghum	1.4	22

Source: FAOSTAT (FAO 2010).
Note: All values are based on the three-year average for 2006–08.

TABLE 12.4   Consumption of leading food commodities in Sierra Leone, 2003–05 (thousands of metric tons)

Rank	Crop	Percent of total	Food consumption
	Total	100.0	1,893
1	Rice	22.3	422
2	Cassava	16.4	311
3	Fermented beverages	11.3	213
4	Other vegetables	11.2	212
5	Other citrus	4.1	78
6	Wheat	4.1	78
7	Pelagic fish	3.6	68
8	Other fruits	3.4	65
9	Other pulses	3.2	60
10	Palm oil	1.8	34

Source: FAOSTAT (FAO 2010).
Note: All values are based on the three-year average for 2003–05.

the civil war in 1999. Since then, rice production is estimated to have increased from 310,000 tons of paddy in 2000 to 637,983 tons in 2007 produced on 659,487 hectares (Spencer, Deen, and Williams 2009). Groundnuts are second to rice in the area under cultivation; cassava is the most important root crop and the second staple crop after rice.

The next three figures show the estimated yields and growing areas of key crops. Rice is grown in all districts of Sierra Leone; the districts with the largest rice fields are Pujehun, Bo, Koinadugu, Tonkolili, and Kambia (Figure 12.8). Rice yields are very low, averaging about 1 metric ton per hectare on the uplands and 2 metric tons per hectare in the lowlands. Cassava is also grown throughout the country, with greater production in the northern regions and yields ranging from 4 to 7 metric tons per hectare (Figure 12.9). Like rice and cassava, groundnuts are grown in all parts of the country—most extensively in the northern regions; yields are slightly more than 1 metric ton per hectare (Figure 12.10).

FIGURE 12.8   Yield (metric tons per hectare) and harvest area density (hectares) for rainfed rice in Sierra Leone, 2000

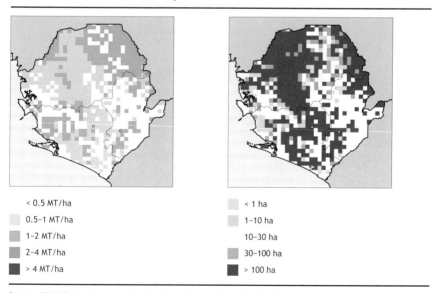

< 0.5 MT/ha
0.5–1 MT/ha
1–2 MT/ha
2–4 MT/ha
> 4 MT/ha

< 1 ha
1–10 ha
10–30 ha
30–100 ha
> 100 ha

Sources: SPAM (Spatial Production Allocation Model) (You and Wood 2006; You, Wood, and Wood-Sichra 2006, 2009).
Notes: ha = hectare; MT = metric tons.

FIGURE 12.9 Yield (metric tons per hectare) and harvest area density (hectares) for rainfed cassava in Sierra Leone, 2000

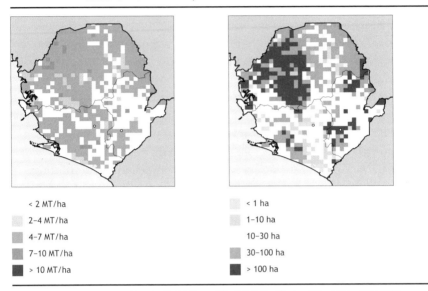

< 2 MT/ha	< 1 ha
2–4 MT/ha	1–10 ha
4–7 MT/ha	10–30 ha
7–10 MT/ha	30–100 ha
> 10 MT/ha	> 100 ha

Sources: SPAM (Spatial Production Allocation Model) (You and Wood 2006; You, Wood, and Wood-Sichra 2006, 2009).
Notes: ha = hectare; MT = metric tons.

FIGURE 12.10 Yield (metric tons per hectare) and harvest area density (hectares) for rainfed groundnuts in Sierra Leone, 2000

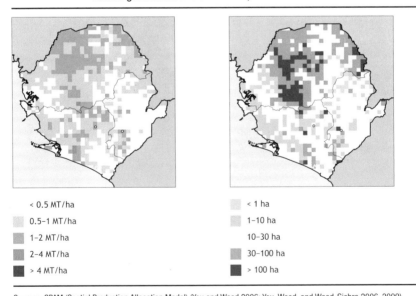

< 0.5 MT/ha	< 1 ha
0.5–1 MT/ha	1–10 ha
1–2 MT/ha	10–30 ha
2–4 MT/ha	30–100 ha
> 4 MT/ha	> 100 ha

Sources: SPAM (Spatial Production Allocation Model) (You and Wood 2006; You, Wood, and Wood-Sichra 2006, 2009).
Notes: ha = hectare; MT = metric tons.

Economic and Demographic Scenarios

Population

Figure 12.11 shows population projections for Sierra Leone for 2010–50. In the high variant the 2010 population will double soon after 2040. In the medium variant the population will double just before 2050, whereas in the low variant the population will be only 77 percent greater in 2050 than it was in 2010. Higher population growth can adversely affect resources.

Income

Figure 12.12 presents three overall scenarios for Sierra Leone's GDP per capita derived by combining three GDP scenarios with the three population scenarios of Figure 12.11 (based on United Nations population data). The optimistic scenario combines high GDP with low population scenarios for all countries, the baseline scenario combines the medium GDP projection with the medium population scenario, and the pessimistic scenario combines the low GDP scenario with the high population scenario. The agricultural modeling in the next section uses these scenarios as well.

FIGURE 12.11   Population projections for Sierra Leone, 2010–50

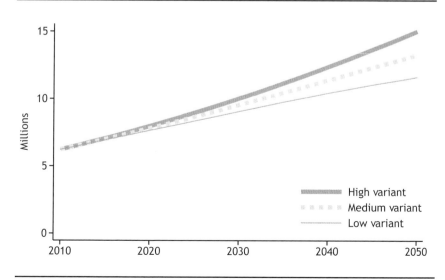

Source: UNPOP (2009).

FIGURE 12.12   Gross domestic product (GDP) per capita in Sierra Leone, future scenarios, 2010–50

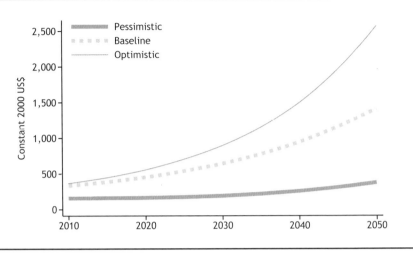

Sources: Computed from GDP data from the World Bank Economic Adaptation to Climate Change project (World Bank 2010), from the Millennium Ecosystem Assessment (2005) reports, and from population data from the United Nations (UNPOP 2009).
Note: US$ = US dollars.

The pessimistic scenario shows GDP per capita barely approaching US$400 by 2050 (see Figure 12.12). GDP per capita increases to US$1,400 in the baseline scenario and rises above $2,500 in the optimistic scenario over the same period—a rapid growth rate that is driven by substantial hypothetical gains in productivity.

Biophysical Scenarios

Climate Scenarios

Figure 12.13 shows precipitation changes in the four downscaled general circulation models (GCMs) we use in this chapter in the A1B scenario. The CNRM-CM3, CSIRO Mark 3, and ECHAM 5 GCMs show rainfall varying by −50 to 50 millimeters in most areas, with an increase of 50 to 100 millimeters in one-fifth of the country.[2] Interestingly, the three models differ regarding the specific

---

2   The A1B scenario is a greenhouse gas emissions scenario that assumes fast economic growth, a population that peaks midcentury, and the development of new and efficient technologies, along with a balanced use of energy sources. CNRM-CM3 is the National Meteorological Research Center–Climate Model 3. CSIRO Mark 3 is a climate model developed at the Australia Commonwealth Scientific and Industrial Research Organisation. ECHAM 5 is a fifth-generation climate model developed at the Max Planck Institute for Meteorology in Hamburg.

FIGURE 12.13   Changes in mean annual precipitation in Sierra Leone, 2000–2050, A1B
scenario (millimeters)

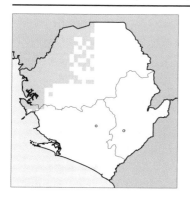

CNRM-CM3 GCM

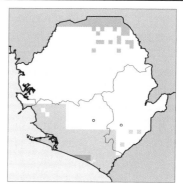

CSIRO Mark 3 GCM

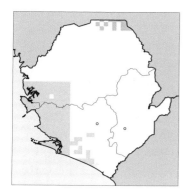

ECHAM 5 GCM

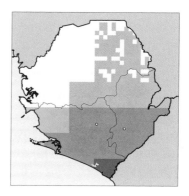

MIROC 3.2 medium-resolution GCM

- < −400
- −400 to −200
- −200 to −100
- −100 to −50
- −50 to 50
- 50 to 100
- 100 to 200
- 200 to 400
- > 400

Source: Authors' estimates based on Jones, Thornton, and Heinke (2009).

Notes: A1B = greenhouse gas emissions scenario that assumes fast economic growth, a population that peaks midcentury, and the development of new and efficient technologies, along with a balanced use of energy sources; CNRM-CM3 = National Meteorological Research Center–Climate Model 3; CSIRO = climate model developed at the Australia Commonwealth Scientific and Industrial Research Organisation; GCM = general circulation model; ECHAM 5 = fifth-generation climate model developed at the Max Planck Institute for Meteorology (Hamburg); MIROC = Model for Interdisciplinary Research on Climate, developed at the University of Tokyo Center for Climate System Research.

region that will experience this increase: CNRM-CM3 shows the 50–100 millimeter increase in the northwestern region, CSIRO Mark 3 in the southern region and part of the western region, and ECHAM 5 in parts of the northwestern and southwestern regions. The MIROC 3.2 medium-resolution GCM shows a severe reduction in rainfall in all parts of the country except the northwestern region.[3] Moving from north to south, the map shows increasing reductions, from −50 to −100 in the northern regions to −200 to −400 in the southern regions.

Figure 12.14 shows the change in the average daily maximum temperature in Sierra Leone for the warmest month of the year in the A1B scenario according to various GCMs from 2000 to 2050. CNRM-CM3 shows an increase of 2.0°–2.5°C throughout the country except for a small portion, mainly in the coastal area. CSIRO Mark 3 and MIROC 3.2 show increases of 1°–1.5°C. ECHAM 5 shows the northern and northeastern regions experiencing greater temperature changes than the rest of the country, with the highest increases ranging from 2.0° to 2.5°C. The extreme heat might adversely affect all forms of agricultural activity (crops, livestock, and fisheries).

Crop Physiological Response to Climate Change

The effect of climate change on key crops in Sierra Leone is mapped in the next two figures. Crop yields for 2050 with climate change are compared to the yields with unchanged (2000) climate. Both CNRM-CM3 and CSIRO Mark 3 show rainfed rice doing well under climate change, particularly in the northern regions of the country (Figure 12.15). These scenarios show yield gains of between 5 and 25 percent of baseline in areas throughout the country. ECHAM5 shows the greatest losses of the four models, though there is also a lot of area with no significant change, and some with yield increases of 5–25 percent.

In the climate change scenarios, rainfed groundnuts show a yield loss of 5–25 percent of baseline in many areas of the country (Figure 12.16). The CSIRO Mark 3 GCM shows relatively less area being affected, as well as a yield increase of 5–25 percent along the coast. ECHAM 5 shows that most of the country will be adversely affected, with yields decreasing by 5 to 25 percent.

---

3   The MIROC is the Model for Interdisciplinary Research on Climate, developed at the University of Tokyo Center for Climate System Research.

FIGURE 12.14   Change in the daily maximum temperature in Sierra Leone for the warmest month, 2010–50, A1B scenario (°C)

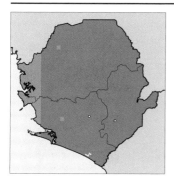

CNRM-CM3 GCM

CSIRO Mark 3 GCM

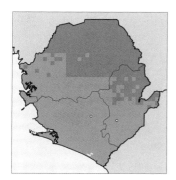

ECHAM 5 GCM

MIROC 3.2 medium-resolution GCM

- ■ < −1
- ■ −1 to −0.5
- −0.5 to 0
- 0 to 0.5
- 0.5 to 1
- 1 to 1.5
- 1.5 to 2
- 2 to 2.5
- 2.5 to 3
- 3 to 3.5
- ■ > 3.5

Source: Authors' calculations based on Jones, Thornton, and Heinke (2009).

Notes: A1B = greenhouse gas emissions scenario that assumes fast economic growth, a population that peaks midcentury, and the development of new and efficient technologies, along with a balanced use of energy sources; CNRM-CM3 = National Meteorological Research Center–Climate Model 3; CSIRO = climate model developed at the Australia Commonwealth Scientific and Industrial Research Organisation; GCM = general circulation model; ECHAM 5 = fifth-generation climate model developed at the Max Planck Institute for Meteorology (Hamburg); MIROC = Model for Interdisciplinary Research on Climate, developed at the University of Tokyo Center for Climate System Research.

FIGURE 12.15   Yield change under climate change: Rainfed rice in Sierra Leone, 2000–2050, A1B scenario

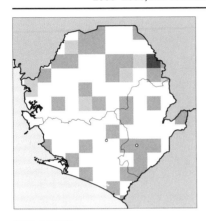

CNRM-CM3 GCM

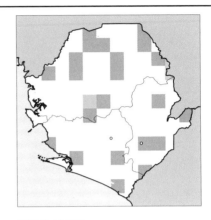

CSIRO Mark 3 GCM

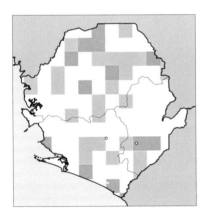

ECHAM 5 GCM

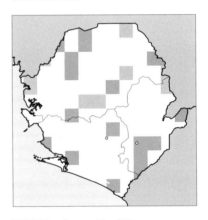

MIROC 3.2 medium-resolution GCM

■ 2000 old area lost
  Yield loss > 25% of 2000
  Yield loss 5–25%
  Yield change within 5%
  Yield gain 5–25%
■ Yield gain > 25%
■ 2050 new area gained

Source: Authors' estimates.

Notes: A1B = greenhouse gas emissions scenario that assumes fast economic growth, a population that peaks midcentury, and the development of new and efficient technologies, along with a balanced use of energy sources; CNRM-CM3 = National Meteorological Research Center–Climate Model 3; CSIRO = climate model developed at the Australia Commonwealth Scientific and Industrial Research Organisation; GCM = general circulation model; ECHAM 5 = fifth-generation climate model developed at the Max Planck Institute for Meteorology (Hamburg); MIROC = Model for Interdisciplinary Research on Climate, developed at the University of Tokyo Center for Climate System Research.

FIGURE 12.16   Yield change under climate change: Rainfed groundnuts in Sierra Leone, 2000–2050, A1B scenario

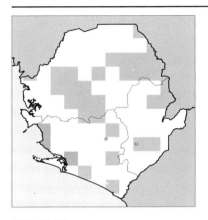

CNRM-CM3 GCM

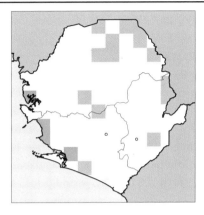

CSIRO Mark 3 GCM

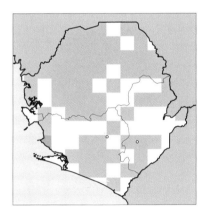

ECHAM 5 GCM

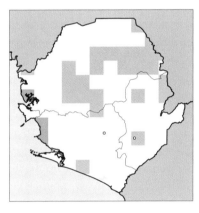

MIROC 3.2 medium-resolution GCM

- ■ 2000 old area lost
- ■ Yield loss > 25% of 2000
- ▢ Yield loss 5–25%
- Yield change within 5%
- ▨ Yield gain 5–25%
- ■ Yield gain > 25%
- ■ 2050 new area gained

Source: Authors' estimates.

Notes: A1B = greenhouse gas emissions scenario that assumes fast economic growth, a population that peaks midcentury, and the development of new and efficient technologies, along with a balanced use of energy sources; CNRM-CM3 = National Meteorological Research Center–Climate Model 3; CSIRO = climate model developed at the Australia Commonwealth Scientific and Industrial Research Organisation; GCM = general circulation model; ECHAM 5 = fifth-generation climate model developed at the Max Planck Institute for Meteorology (Hamburg); MIROC = Model for Interdisciplinary Research on Climate, developed at the University of Tokyo Center for Climate System Research.

Agricultural Vulnerability Scenarios (Crop-Specific)

The next three figures show simulation results from the International Model for Policy Analysis of Agricultural Commodities and Trade associated with key agricultural crops in Sierra Leone. The figure for each crop has five graphs: production, yield, area, net exports, and world price.

Rice production and productivity are shown to increase; the area of production increases relatively less (Figure 12.17). All of the scenarios show increasingly negative trends for net rice exports—though much less so in the case of the pessimistic scenario. All three scenarios also show a general increasing trend in the world price for rice. Rice productivity needs to improve to meet domestic consumption demand; increasing production will also benefit farmers through higher world prices.

The scenarios for the production and yield of cassava show an increase toward 2050, with only a slight increase in the area under cultivation (Figure 12.18). Net exports of cassava are shown increasing up to 2030, followed by a decline up to 2050, in all the scenarios. Net exports are higher in the pessimistic scenario than in either the baseline or the optimistic scenario. Between 2035 and 2050, all three scenarios give very broad ranges for net exports that overlap.

Groundnut production is shown to increase as a result of expansion of the area under production; productivity is shown to remain essentially constant, though there is a slight increase observed out to around 2030, followed by a slight decrease, reflecting the negative impact of climate change, which outweighs the positive impact of technological change (Figure 12.19). Depending on the scenario, net exports are shown to increase through 2020 and to decline thereafter. The world price for groundnuts is shown to increase until 2050 only in the pessimistic scenario. With decreasing productivity, more area will have to be brought under cultivation to meet the demand for groundnuts as the population increases, while increased land degradation will likely force farmers to use expensive inputs to maintain yields.

Human Vulnerability Scenarios

Figure 12.20 shows the impact of future GDP and population scenarios on under-five malnutrition rates in Sierra Leone. The box-and-whisker plots in the figure indicate the range of climate scenario effects. The optimistic scenario shows the number of malnourished children under age five decreasing by 50 percent in 2050; the baseline scenario shows a minimal decline by 2050 after rising slightly through 2025. The pessimistic scenario shows an increase in the number of malnourished children under age five up to 2040,

FIGURE 12.17   Impact of changes in GDP and population on rice in Sierra Leone, 2010–50

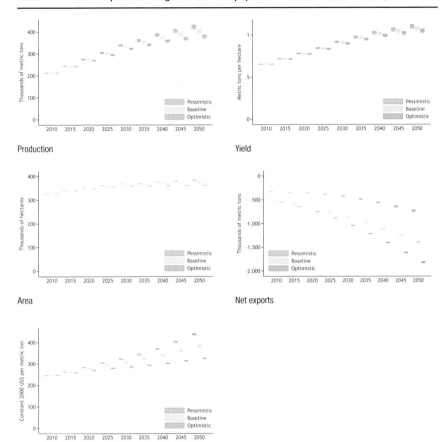

Production

Yield

Area

Net exports

Prices

Source: Based on analysis conducted for Nelson et al. (2010).

Notes: The box and whiskers plot for each socioeconomic scenario shows the range of effects from the four future climate scenarios. GDP = gross domestic product; US$ = US dollars.

FIGURE 12.18 Impact of changes in GDP and population on cassava in Sierra Leone,
2010–50

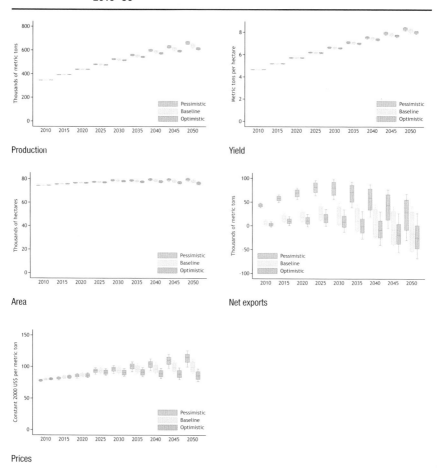

Source: Based on analysis conducted for Nelson et al. (2010).

Notes: The box and whiskers plot for each socioeconomic scenario shows the range of effects from the four future climate
scenarios. GDP = gross domestic product; US$ = US dollars.

FIGURE 12.19   Impact of changes in GDP and population on groundnuts in Sierra Leone, 2010–50

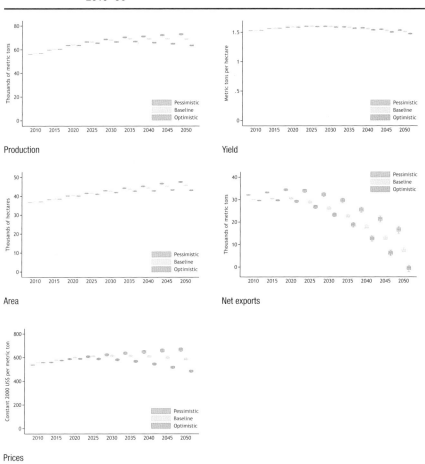

Production

Yield

Area

Net exports

Prices

Source: Based on analysis conducted for Nelson et al. (2010).

Notes: The box and whiskers plot for each socioeconomic scenario shows the range of effects from the four future climate scenarios. GDP = gross domestic product; US$ = US dollars.

FIGURE 12.20   Number of malnourished children under five years of age in Sierra Leone in multiple income and climate scenarios, 2010–50

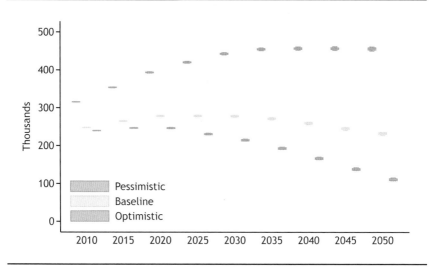

Source: Based on analysis conducted for Nelson et al. (2010).
Note: The box and whiskers plot for each socioeconomic scenario shows the range of effects from the four future climate scenarios.

but the rate then holds steady. Although some increases in the numbers of malnourished children are noted in all scenarios for at least some of the years projected in the graph, we also recognize that the population will be growing and that the number of children under five will grow along with the rest of the population, implying that the percentage of children who are malnourished will likely decline in all scenarios and possibly for all years.

Figure 12.21 shows the available kilocalories per capita. The optimistic scenario shows a greater increase in kilocalories per capita than does the baseline scenario. The pessimistic scenario shows a decrease in kilocalories per capita through 2030 and an increasing pattern afterward, though by 2050 the kilocalories per capita will still be fewer than we saw in 2010. Comparison with Figure 12.20 suggests that the increased availability of kilocalories is correlated with a reduction in the number of malnourished children under five years of age.

Conclusions and Policy Recommendations

Crop production in Sierra Leone is very sensitive to climate and climate variation, as seen in recent experience as well as in the modeled outcomes. Rainfall is becoming increasingly sporadic. For example, in 2010 and 2011 more rain

FIGURE 12.21   Kilocalories per capita in Sierra Leone in multiple income and climate scenarios, 2010–50

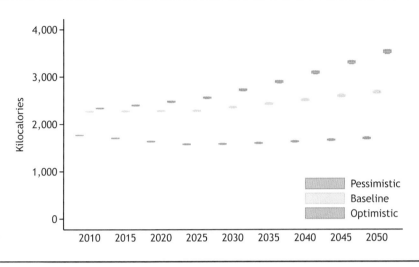

Source: Based on analysis conducted for Nelson et al. (2010).
Note: The box and whiskers plot for each socioeconomic scenario shows the range of effects from the four future climate scenarios.

fell in March (the driest month of the year) than in any March in the past three decades. The model outputs, based on climate scenarios, show specific climate change impacts: for temperatures above 25°C, for example, rice production is expected to show decreasing yields. Other crops such as maize, millet, and cocoa are also shown to be negatively affected by climate change.

The various models show different results while differing significantly from the baseline scenarios. The most significant results are those relating to possible declines in the production of basic foodcrops: the vulnerability of crops to climate change also poses a direct threat to farmers' livelihoods and to overall food security. These disturbing scenarios would undermine the government's plans to expand agricultural production, alleviate poverty, and secure affordable food for all.

The following specific agricultural policy measures are strongly urged to mitigate the impact of current and future climate challenges:

• Support the establishment of adequate weather stations around the country to provide reliable and adequate weather data that will be useful to properly inform farmers.

- Provide adequate support to the Sierra Leone Agricultural Research Institute as well as Njala University to develop appropriate crop varieties and production practices that will enhance crops' resilience to adverse weather conditions

- Develop and maintain seed banks (or become part of international efforts to do so) to provide a variety of seed types that preserve biological diversity and enable farmers to make informed choices.

- Promote innovative and adaptive approaches such as irrigation and water harvesting to protect farmers from variability in rainfall.

- Provide for the construction of appropriate roads, particularly feeder roads, in the rural areas that will be able to withstand increasing rainfall.

- Take appropriate measures to control the rapid increase in population as well as to provide appropriate infrastructure, social services, and mechanization of agriculture in the rural areas to slow massive movements of youth into urban areas.

- Support and promote awareness of climate change, specifically water storage and management methods. This effort should be backed by the development of efficient irrigation schemes.

- Provide adequate support to the agricultural research system to develop short-duration crop varieties, particularly groundnuts, that will be adaptable to drying as well as wetter conditions as indicated by the results of our study.

With a supportive policy environment, farmers will find it much easier to adapt to the challenges presented by climate change, and that, in turn, will help provide stability for Sierra Leone in terms of lower rates of poverty and unemployment and greater food security and GDP per capita.

References

Bartholome, E., and A. S. Belward. 2005. "GLC2000: A New Approach to Global Land Cover Mapping from Earth Observation Data." *International Journal of Remote Sensing* 26 (9): 1959–1977.

CIESIN (Center for International Earth Science Information Network, Columbia University), Columbia University, IFPRI (International Food Policy Research Institute), World Bank, and CIAT (Centro Internacional de Agricultura Tropical). 2004. *Global Rural–Urban Mapping Project, Version 1 (GRUMPv1)*. Palisades, NY, US: Socioeconomic Data and Applications Center (SEDAC), Columbia University. http://sedac.ciesin.columbia.edu/gpw.

FIGURE 10.25 Impacts of GDP, population, and climate change scenarios on sweet potatoes and yams area, yield, production, net exports, and prices in Nigeria, 2010–50

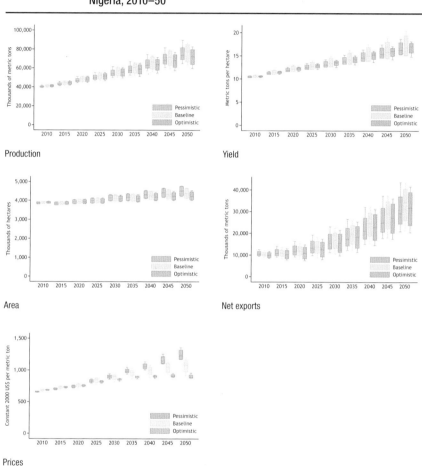

Production

Yield

Area

Net exports

Prices

Source: Based on analysis conducted for Nelson et al. (2010).

Notes: The box and whiskers plot for each socioeconomic scenario shows the range of effects from the four future climate scenarios. GDP = gross domestic product; US$ = US dollars.

The yield, area under production, world price, and net exports are all projected to generally increase. Toward 2050 the world price for roots and tubers will be higher in the pessimistic scenario than in the optimistic scenario.

For all crops presented here, exports are projected to grow, indicating a projected food surplus for the country.

Conclusions and Policy Recommendations

In this chapter we have attempted to assess the vulnerability of agriculture in Nigeria to climate change using different GCMs. The GCMs are not in agreement with each other regarding the degree of temperature change or the direction of precipitation change and therefore indicate a need to develop some flexibility in policies, research, and extension to optimize adaptation strategies. It seems that temperature changes will cause the most difficulties in terms of projecting the loss of crop areas in the northern part of the country. It also seems that sorghum may be most adversely affected by climate change. Maize may actually experience some increase in yields, most likely due to increases in rainfall.

If the situation projected by the MIROC 3.2 medium-resolution GCM comes to pass, the reduction of rainfall in the southern parts of the country could adversely affect the rainforests and the yields of tree crops such as palm oil, cocoa, and rubber.

This chapter does not analyze the likely impact of climate change on livestock production. However, given the likely shift in vegetation patterns, the areas of concentration of the production of livestock, especially cattle, sheep, and goats, may be particularly affected by the increase in rainfall shown by the CNRM-CM3 and the MIROC 3.2 medium-resolution GCMs. Increasing rainfall could support the production of fodder crops but could also create favorable conditions for the proliferation of animal diseases and pests.

Following from these likely scenarios, the following policy measures are recommended to help farmers adapt to climate change:

- Institute early warning systems through the strengthening and coordination of the nation's meteorological services and the integration of indigenous knowledge of climate and early warning signals.

- Strengthen the nation's agricultural database.

- Improve agricultural productivity through the promotion and strengthening of the national agricultural research and extension institutions.

- Formalize and promote environmental standards to mitigate environmental degradation.

- Promote and strengthen the nation's food reserve and storage programs.

- Promote rural development strategies that can reduce rural–urban migration and depletion of the rural population and enhance rural infrastructure and road linkages with the urban areas.

These measures not only make sense in the face of climate change but also will be good for overall economic development in the agricultural sector even without climate change, as farmers strive to improve the yields and profitability of their farm operations.

References

Bartholome, E., and A. S. Belward. 2005. "GLC2000: A New Approach to Global Land Cover Mapping from Earth Observation Data." *International Journal of Remote Sensing* 26 (9): 1959–1977.

CIESIN (Center for International Earth Science Information Network, Columbia University), Columbia University, IFPRI (International Food Policy Research Institute), World Bank, and CIAT (Centro Internacional de Agricultura Tropical). 2004. *Global Rural–Urban Mapping Project, Version 1 (GRUMPv1).* Palisades, NY, US: Socioeconomic Data and Applications Center (SEDAC), Columbia University. http://sedac.ciesin.columbia.edu/gpw.

FAO (Food and Agriculture Organization of the United Nations). 2010. *FAOSTAT Database on Agriculture.* Rome.

Jones, P. G., P. K. Thornton, and J. Heinke. 2009. "Generating Characteristic Daily Weather Data Using Downscaled Climate Model Data from the IPCC's Fourth Assessment." Project report for the International Institute for Land Reclamation and Improvement, Wageningen, the Netherlands. Accessed May 7, 2010. www.ccafs-climate.org/pattern_scaling/.

Lehner, B., and P. Döll. 2004. "Development and Validation of a Global Database of Lakes, Reservoirs, and Wetlands." *Journal of Hydrology* 296 (1–4): 1–22.

Millennium Ecosystem Assessment. 2005. *Ecosystems and Human Well-being: Synthesis.* Washington, DC: Island Press. http://www.maweb.org/en/Global.aspx.

Nelson, G. C., M. W. Rosegrant, A. Palazzo, I. Gray, C. Ingersoll, R. Robertson, S. Tokgoz, et al. 2010. *Food Security, Farming, and Climate Change to 2050: Scenarios, Results, Policy Options.* Washington, DC: International Food Policy Research Institute.

NEST (Nigerian Environmental Study / Action Team). 2004. *Regional Climate Modelling and Climate Scenarios Development in Support of Vulnerability and Adaptation*. Canada–Nigeria Climate Change Capacity Development Project. Ibadan.

Parry, M., O. F. Canaziani, J. P. Palutikof, P. J. van der Linden, and C. E. Hanson. 2007. "Technical Summary." In *Climate Change 2007: Impacts, Adaptation and Vulnerability*. Contribution of Working Group II to the Fourth Assessment Report of the Intergovernmental Panel on Climate Change, edited by M. Parry, O. F. Canaziani, J. P. Palutikof, P. J. Van der Linden, and C. E. Hanson. Cambridge, UK: Cambridge University Press.

UNEP and IUCN (United Nations Environment Programme and International Union for the Conservation of Nature). 2009. *World Database on Protected Areas (WDPA): Annual Release*. Accessed 2009.

UNPOP (United Nations Department of Economic and Social Affairs–Population Division). 2009. *World Population Prospects: The 2008 Revision*. New York. http://esa.un.org/unpd/wpp/.

Wood, S., G. Hyman, U. Deichmann, E. Barona, R. Tenorio, Z. Guo, et al. 2010. *Sub-national Poverty Maps for the Developing World Using International Poverty Lines: Preliminary Data Release*. Washington, DC: Harvest Choice and International Food Policy Research Institute. http://labs.harvestchoice.org/2010/08/poverty-maps/.

World Bank. 2009. *World Development Indicators*. Accessed May 2011. http://data.worldbank.org/data-catalog/world-development-indicators.

———. 2010. *Economics of Adaptation to Climate Change: Synthesis Report*. Washington, DC. http://climatechange.worldbank.org/content/economics-adaptation-climate-change-study-homepage.

———. 2012. *World Development Indicators*. Accessed September 2012. http://data.worldbank.org/data-catalog/world-development-indicators..

You, L., and S. Wood. 2006. "An Entropy Approach to Spatial Disaggregation of Agricultural Production." *Agricultural Systems* 90 (1–3): 329–347.

You, L., S. Wood, and U. Wood-Sichra. 2006. "Generating Global Crop Distribution Maps: From Census to Grid." Paper presented at the International Association of Agricultural Economists Conference, Brisbane, Australia, August 11–18.

———. 2009. "Generating Plausible Crop Distribution and Performance Maps for Sub-Saharan Africa Using a Spatially Disaggregated Data Fusion and Optimization Approach." *Agricultural Systems* 99 (2–3): 126–140.

Chapter 11

SENEGAL

Mamadou Khouma, Abdulai Jalloh, Timothy S. Thomas, and
Gerald C. Nelson

S enegal is the most westerly state of West Africa. The country is relatively flat, with low relief. Its total land area is 196,192 square kilometers. Its northern border, which is shared with Mauritania, is defined
by the Senegal River. The Falémé River delineates part of the eastern border
with Mali; Guinea and Guinea-Bissau are Senegal's southern neighbors, and
Gambia forms an enclave along the Gambia River in the southern part of the
country. The population of Senegal is estimated at more than 12 million. The
severe drought at the end of the 1960s and in the early 1970s exacerbated the
already substantial rural–urban migration that was taking place. The rural
population still represents 58 percent of the total population (World Bank
2009) and will continue to be the most important sector; most job seekers are
in rural areas. The country's gross domestic product (GDP) in agriculture continues to fall as a percentage of its total GDP, despite the noticeable improvement during the past decade. This poor performance is mainly due to low
productivity linked to the low level of fertilizer use, poor seeds, and old agricultural equipment, along with the poor performance of the livestock sector.

Like all areas near the northern limits of the southwesterlies, Senegal suf-
fers from extremely variable rainfall. Its average rainfall varies from over
1,500 millimeters in the southwest to just under 300 millimeters in the northwest. The rainfall trend in the past several decades has shown a significant
decline (USAID Senegal 2008). The distribution and kinds of crops are
closely tied to the amount, distribution, and timing of rainfall. Crops in the
northern half of the country are particularly prone to the effects of erratic
rainfall and drought. In addition to rainfed cultivation, two other types of
traditional agriculture are practiced. One depends on the flooding of low-
lying areas due to rainwater runoff. This type is found in the humid south and
is associated with paddy rice cultivation. The second is the flood recessional
agriculture associated mainly with the Senegal River. A nontraditional form of
cultivation is irrigated agriculture. It is found mainly along the Senegal River,
where water is available year round.

The groundnut–millet rotation has dominated the cropping system, with the groundnut acreage higher now than in colonial times. Millet is now the most important crop of the country in terms of area but not production due to the low level of the millet yield. In terms of consumption, rice is by far the most important food commodity. Major imports are rice and wheat. Protected areas, including parks and reserves, are well distributed across the country and play an important role in the economy as attractive places for tourists. Some of these parks are presently in bad condition due to either lack of financial means (Niokolo) or armed conflict (Basse Casamance).

Senegalese agriculture is vulnerable to climate change. The overall impacts of climate change on agriculture are expected to be negative, threatening national food security. The regional climate model used with scenario A1B and validated for Senegal (Gaye and Sylla 2008) showed rainfall anomalies throughout the country, especially in July and August, along with large increases in temperature.

Review of the Current Situation and Trends

Population

The population of Senegal was estimated at 12.2 million in June 2009 (Senegal, ANSD 2010). Figure 11.1 shows trends in the country's total population and rural population (left axis) as well as the share of urban population (right axis). An increasing proportion of the population lives in urban areas, growing from less than 30 percent of the population in 1960 to over 40 percent in 2008. However, the overall population growth rate has been declining, from 3.0 percent in the 1960s to 2.6 percent during 2000–2008 (Table 11.1). The severe drought in the late 1960s and early 1970s contributed significantly to the migration of people from rural to urban areas, particularly youths in search of jobs. Table 11.1 provides additional information concerning rates of population growth.

Figure 11.2 shows the geographic distribution of the population in Senegal in 2000. The capital city, Dakar, and its environs host 24 percent of the total population. Dakar has 80 percent of the national wealth, 95 percent of industrial and commercial firms, 87 percent of permanent employment, 75 percent of wage-earning workers, and more than 60 percent of all health and education facilities (PNUD-Senegal 2009). Most of the population is concentrated in the former groundnut basin—along the western coast, stretching east and south.

FIGURE 11.1 Population trends in Senegal: Total population, rural population, and percent urban, 1960–2008

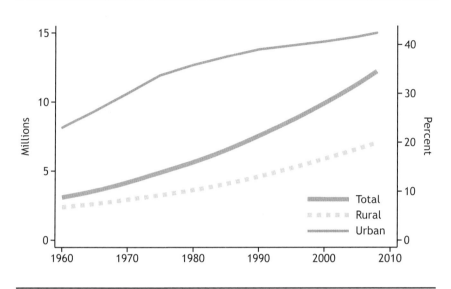

Source: World Development Indicators (World Bank 2009).

TABLE 11.1 Population growth rates in Senegal, 1960–2008 (percent)

Decade	Total growth rate	Rural growth rate	Urban growth rate
1960–69	3.0	2.0	5.7
1970–79	3.0	2.1	4.9
1980–89	2.9	2.4	3.8
1990–99	2.7	2.5	3.1
2000–2008	2.6	2.2	3.1

Source: Authors' calculations based on World Development Indicators (World Bank 2009).

Income

Figure 11.3 shows trends in GDP per capita and the proportion of Senegal's GDP from agriculture. The general decline in per capita GDP, bottoming around 1994, reflects the poor performance of the Senegalese economy since 1960. The share of GDP from agriculture has been declining since the mid-1980s despite noticeable improvement during the past decade, reflecting the emergence and growing dominance of a service sector. In general, agricultural

FIGURE 11.2   Population distribution in Senegal, 2000 (persons per square kilometer)

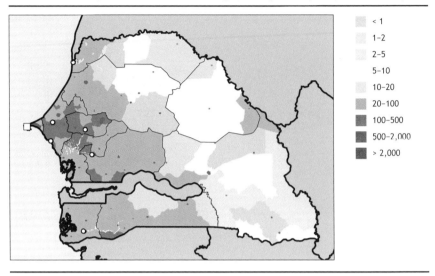

Legend:
- < 1
- 1–2
- 2–5
- 5–10
- 10–20
- 20–100
- 100–500
- 500–2,000
- > 2,000

Source: CIESIN et al. (2004).

FIGURE 11.3   Per capita GDP in Senegal (constant 2000 US$) and share of GDP from
agriculture (percent), 1960–2008

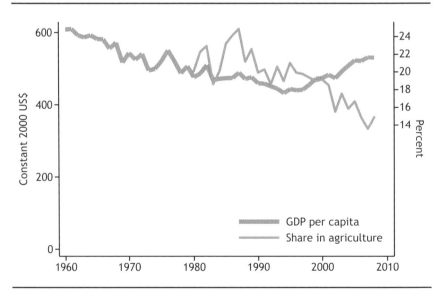

Source: World Development Indicators (World Bank 2009).

Notes: The authors graphed all data in the data set. These data did not go back to 1960 in all cases. GDP = gross domestic product; US$ = US dollars.

productivity is still low, mainly due to the low level of fertilizer use, poor seeds, and old agricultural equipment in addition to adverse climatic conditions.

Vulnerability to Climate Change

Table 11.2 provides some data on Senegal's performance on several indicators of a population's vulnerability or resiliency to economic shocks: level of education, literacy, and concentration of labor in poorer or less dynamic sectors. Primary school enrollment in Senegal is about average compared to other countries in the region but with a sharp drop-off for secondary school enrollment. Early marriage for girls, farm family labor requirements, and the need for apprenticeship in certain vocations account for the drastic school dropout rate. The agricultural sector, which employs 77 percent of the working population, is very sensitive to climate conditions and to the volatility of world prices. The percentage of under-five malnutrition (14.5 percent) is decreasing compared to previous years.

Figure 11.4 shows Senegal's performance on two noneconomic correlates of poverty: life expectancy and under-five mortality. The extension of life expectancy at birth from 40 years in 1960 to well over 50 years in 2008 was driven by improvements in healthcare, including efforts to reduce the under-five mortality rate. Health education through public media (radio and television) has played a major role in raising health awareness, especially that of poor people. Reduction of under-five mortality, from more than 300 deaths per 1,000 to fewer than 120 per 1,000 in 2008, has contributed significantly to the increase in life expectancy. A considerable effort has been made to control malaria and diarrhea. The prevalence of malaria declined by two-thirds in 2009 with the use of the new ACT (artemisinin combination therapies) medication and the distribution of mosquito nets (WHO 2010).

Figure 11.5 shows the proportion of the Senegalese population living on less than US$2 (US dollars) per day. Poverty is more prevalent in the Louga Region in upper Senegal, Tambacounda in the east, and Zinguinchor in the west. Louga

TABLE 11.2   Education and labor statistics for Senegal, 2000s

Indicator	Year	Percent
Primary school enrollment (percent gross, three-year average)	2007	83.5
Secondary school enrollment (percent gross, three-year average)	2007	26.3
Adult literacy rate	2006	41.9
Percent employed in agriculture	2006	77.0
Under-five malnutrition (weight for age)	2005	14.5

Source: Authors' calculations based on World Development Indicators (World Bank 2009).

FIGURE 11.4   Well-being indicators in Senegal, 1960–2008

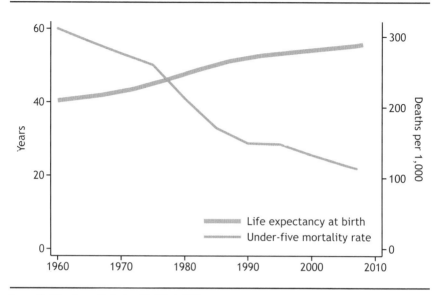

Source: World Development Indicators (World Bank 2009).

FIGURE 11.5   Poverty in Senegal, circa 2005 (percentage of population living on less than US$2 per day)

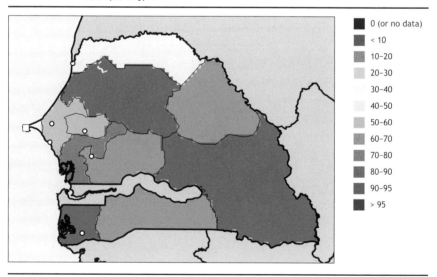

Source: Wood et al. (2010).
Note: Based on 2005 US$ (US dollars) and on purchasing power parity value.

is a very dry region populated mainly with itinerant herdsmen and offering limited crop production opportunities. Most parts of the Tambacounda Region are remote, with very few economic activities, while the Zinguinchor Region, including Casamance, continues to be embroiled in civil war. The proportion of the population living on less than US$2 a day is lower in urban areas and in areas where irrigation is developed or where important industries are located.

Review of Land Use and Agriculture

Land Use Overview

Figure 11.6 shows land cover and land use in Senegal for 2000. A shrub cover of closed-open, deciduous vegetation covers the Casamance Region in the south. The eastern part of the country is covered by a mosaic of cropland, trees, and grass, while the western part is cultivated. Crop production areas are mostly located in savanna and woodland areas.

Figure 11.7 shows the locations of protected areas of Senegal, including parks and reserves. These locations provide important protection for fragile environmental areas, which may also be important for the tourism industry. The national classified domain covers 31.7 percent of the country and includes classified forests, reforestation and restoration areas, integral natural reserves, national parks, and special reserves. It comprises 213 classified forests totaling 6.2 million hectares, including 20 sylvipastoral reserves (1.5 million hectares) and eight areas of hunting interest (2 million hectares) (Senegal, MEPN 2005).

Senegal has six national parks: Niokolo Koba National Park in the southeast (1 million hectares); Saloum Delta Park, Langue de Barbarie Park, and Lower Casamance Park in the southwest; Djoudj Park in the Senegal River delta; and Madeleine Islands Park near Dakar. These protected areas are well distributed around the country and play an important role in the economy as attractive places for tourists. The integrated ecosystem management project funded by the Global Environmental Fund has developed a new approach based on participatory management for protected areas in the major Senegalese ecosystems.

Figure 11.8 shows travel time to urban areas that serve as potential markets for agricultural products, as well as sources of agricultural inputs such as seeds and fertilizers and places for rural households to purchase consumer goods. The capital city of Dakar is connected by road to the immediate neighboring regions, including Louga, Diourbel, Fatick, and Kaolack. The major cities in the other regions are also connected by road. In general, most towns with more

FIGURE 11.6   Land cover and land use in Senegal, 2000

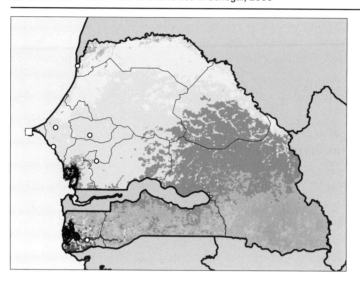

Tree cover, broadleaved, evergreen
Tree cover, broadleaved, deciduous, closed
Tree cover, broadleaved, deciduous, open
Tree cover, broadleaved, needle–leaved, evergreen
Tree cover, broadleaved, needle–leaved, deciduous
Tree cover, broadleaved, mixed leaf type
Tree cover, broadleaved, regularly flooded, fresh water
Tree cover, broadleaved, regularly flooded, saline water
Mosaic of tree cover/other natural vegetation
Tree cover, burnt
Shrub cover, closed–open, evergreen
Shrub cover, closed–open, deciduous
Herbacious cover, closed–open
Sparse herbacious or sparse shrub cover
Regularly flooded shrub or herbacious cover
Cultivated and managed areas
Mosaic of cropland/tree cover/other natural vegetation
Mosaic of cropland/shrub/grass cover
Bare areas
Water bodies
Snow and ice
Artificial surfaces and associated areas
No data

Source: GLC2000 (Global Land Cover 2000) (Bartholome and Belward 2005).

FIGURE 11.7 Protected areas in Senegal, 2009

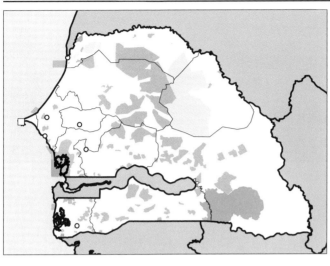

■ Ia: Strict Nature Reserve
■ Ib: Wilderness Area
▦ II: National Park
▫ III: National Monument
  IV: Habitat / Species Management Area
▦ V: Protected Landscape / Seascape
■ VI: Managed Resource Protected Area
▫ Not applicable
▦ Not known

Sources: Protected areas are from the World Database on Protected Areas (UNEP and IUCN 2009). Water bodies are from the World Wildlife Fund's Global Lakes and Wetlands Database (Lehner and Döll 2004).

than 10,000 inhabitants are accessible; the only remote area is the far eastern part of Tambacounda.

Agriculture Overview

Table 11.3 shows key agricultural commodities of Senegal in terms of area harvested, and Table 11.4 shows food for human consumption (ranked by weight). The groundnut–millet rotation has dominated the cropping system in Senegal since colonial times, with more acreage for groundnuts traditionally. Table 11.3 shows that in terms of area, millet is now the most widely grown crop in Senegal. However, rice is the main staple crop (see Table 11.4).

The next five figures show the estimated yields and growing areas of key crops grown in Senegal. The dominant cropping system is the rotation of millet

FIGURE 11.8   Travel time to urban areas of various sizes in Senegal, circa 2000

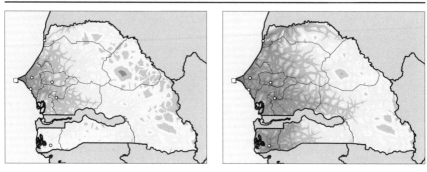

To cities of 500,000 or more people

To cities of 100,000 or more people

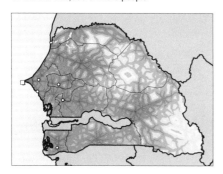

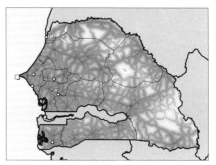

To towns and cities of 25,000 or more people

To towns and cities of 10,000 or more people

- Urban location
- < 1 hour
- 1–3 hours
- 3–5 hours
- 5–8 hours
- 8–11 hours
- 11–16 hours
- 16–26 hours
- > 26 hours

Source: Authors' calculations.

TABLE 11.3 Harvest area of leading agricultural commodities in Senegal, 2006–08
(thousands of hectares)

Rank	Crop	Percent of total	Harvest area
	Total	100.0	2,297
1	Millet	34.5	793
2	Groundnuts	27.2	624
3	Cowpeas	8.2	187
4	Sorghum	7.6	175
5	Maize	7.3	167
6	Rice	4.1	93
7	Cassava	2.9	67
8	Seed cotton	1.9	44
9	Sesame seed	1.2	27
10	Watermelons	0.7	17

Source: FAOSTAT (FAO 2010).
Note: All values are based on the three-year average for 2006–08.

TABLE 11.4 Consumption of leading food commodities in Senegal, 2003–05 (thousands of
metric tons)

Rank	Crop	Percent of total	Food consumption
	Total	100.0	3,728
1	Rice	21.1	785
2	Other vegetables	11.5	430
3	Wheat	8.7	324
4	Millet	8.0	300
5	Maize	7.0	261
6	Pelagic fish	5.8	217
7	Cassava	5.2	195
8	Sorghum	3.3	125
9	Sugar	3.0	114
10	Onions	3.0	114

Source: FAOSTAT (FAO 2010).
Note: All values are based on the three-year average for 2003–05.

FIGURE 11.9   Yield (metric tons per hectare) and harvest area density (hectares) for rainfed millet in Senegal, 2000

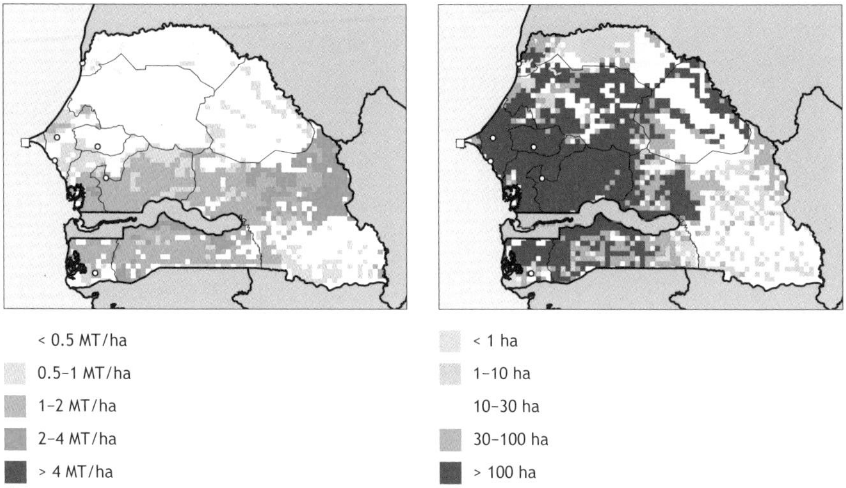

< 0.5 MT/ha	< 1 ha
0.5–1 MT/ha	1–10 ha
1–2 MT/ha	10–30 ha
2–4 MT/ha	30–100 ha
> 4 MT/ha	> 100 ha

Sources: SPAM (Spatial Production Allocation Model) (You and Wood 2006; You, Wood, and Wood-Sichra 2006, 2009).
Notes: ha = hectare; MT = metric tons.

(Figure 11.9) and groundnuts (Figure 11.10). Both crops are mainly cultivated in the groundnut basin and Casamance. Sorghum distribution is very similar to that of millet but with less extension northward (Figure 11.11). Both groundnuts and sorghum yield about 0.8 metric tons per hectare, whereas millet yields are relatively lower all over the country and seldom reach that level.[1]

Maize (Figure 11.12) is well distributed across the country, except in very dry areas (Louga and Diourbel regions). Most of the important production areas are located in the south groundnut basin and Casamance. Maize is also grown under irrigation in the Senegal River basin in the north, with higher yields (about 2 tons per hectare) than rainfed maize (about 1 metric ton per hectare). Like maize, rainfed rice is grown in most parts of the country (Figure 11.13), with the major producing area in the Casamance Region, which receives relatively higher rainfall than other parts of the country. In addition, rice is grown under irrigation in the Senegal River basin and in the Anambe irrigation scheme in the south (Kolda region). Yields are higher (up to 4 tons per hectare) for irrigated areas, where rice is intensively cultivated, than for rainfed rice (from less than 1 to 2 tons per hectare).

---

1 All tons are metric tons.

FIGURE 11.10   Yield (metric tons per hectare) and harvest area density (hectares) for rainfed groundnuts in Senegal, 2000

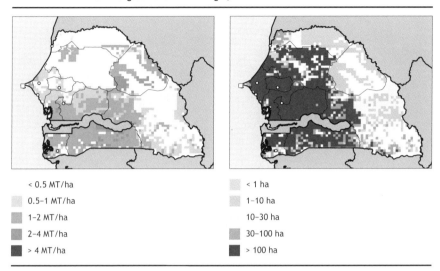

< 0.5 MT/ha		< 1 ha
0.5–1 MT/ha		1–10 ha
1–2 MT/ha		10–30 ha
2–4 MT/ha		30–100 ha
> 4 MT/ha		> 100 ha

Sources: SPAM (Spatial Production Allocation Model) (You and Wood 2006; You, Wood, and Wood-Sichra 2006, 2009).
Notes: ha = hectare; MT = metric tons.

FIGURE 11.11   Yield (metric tons per hectare) and harvest area density (hectares) for rainfed sorghum in Senegal, 2000

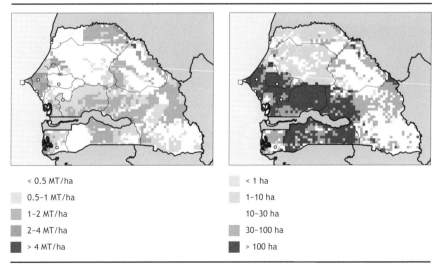

< 0.5 MT/ha		< 1 ha
0.5–1 MT/ha		1–10 ha
1–2 MT/ha		10–30 ha
2–4 MT/ha		30–100 ha
> 4 MT/ha		> 100 ha

Sources: SPAM (Spatial Production Allocation Model) (You and Wood 2006; You, Wood, and Wood-Sichra 2006, 2009).
Notes: ha = hectare; MT = metric tons.

FIGURE 11.12   Yield (metric tons per hectare) and harvest area density (hectares) for rainfed maize in Senegal, 2000

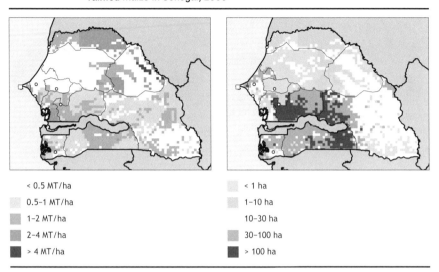

< 0.5 MT/ha		< 1 ha	
0.5–1 MT/ha		1–10 ha	
1–2 MT/ha		10–30 ha	
2–4 MT/ha		30–100 ha	
> 4 MT/ha		> 100 ha	

Sources: SPAM (Spatial Production Allocation Model) (You and Wood 2006; You, Wood, and Wood-Sichra 2006, 2009).
Notes: ha = hectare; MT = metric tons.

FIGURE 11.13   Yield (metric tons per hectare) and harvest area density (hectares) for rainfed rice in Senegal, 2000

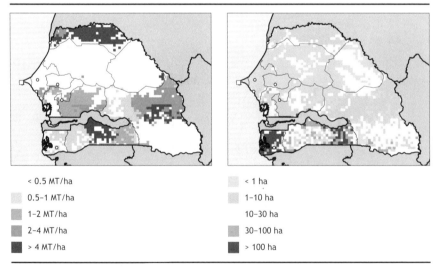

< 0.5 MT/ha		< 1 ha	
0.5–1 MT/ha		1–10 ha	
1–2 MT/ha		10–30 ha	
2–4 MT/ha		30–100 ha	
> 4 MT/ha		> 100 ha	

Sources: SPAM (Spatial Production Allocation Model) (You and Wood 2006; You, Wood, and Wood-Sichra 2006, 2009).
Notes: ha = hectare; MT = metric tons.

Economic and Demographic Scenarios

Population

Figure 11.14 shows population projections by the United Nations (UN) population office through 2050. Under the high variant, the population of Senegal would increase by 4 million every 10 years, doubling the current population by 2040. Under the low variant, the current population would not double until a decade later, in 2050.

Income

Figure 11.15 presents three overall scenarios for Senegal's GDP per capita derived by combining three GDP scenarios with the three population scenarios of Figure 11.14 (based on UN population data). The optimistic scenario combines high GDP with low population scenarios for all countries, the baseline scenario combines the medium GDP projection with the medium population scenario, and the pessimistic scenario combines the low GDP scenario with the high population scenario. The agricultural modeling in the next section uses these scenarios.

FIGURE 11.14   Population projections for Senegal, 2010–50

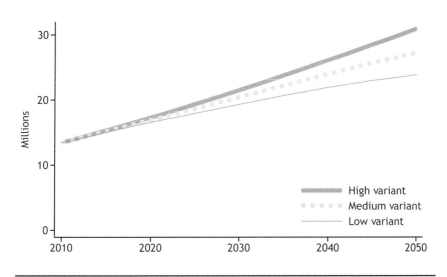

Source: UNPOP (2009).

FIGURE 11.15   Gross domestic product (GDP) per capita in Senegal, future scenarios, 2010–50

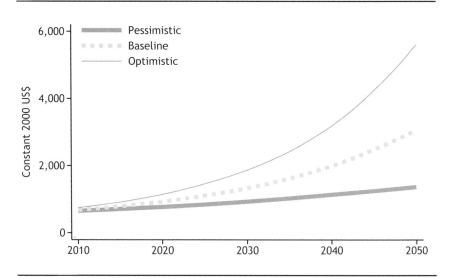

Sources: Computed from GDP data from the World Bank Economic Adaptation to Climate Change project (World Bank 2010), from the Millennium Ecosystem Assessment (2005) reports, and from population data from the United Nations (UNPOP 2009).
Note: US$ = US dollars.

The change in per capita GDP between 2010 and 2050 is very small in the pessimistic scenario compared to the other two scenarios. The optimistic scenario projects a substantial increase in per capita GDP, from almost US$750 in 2010 to US$1,866 in 2030 and more than US$5,600 in 2050. However, realizing these optimistic conditions would require sound public and private investments as part of policies targeting productive sectors that can provide employment and lead to the generation of wealth. The baseline scenario, showing moderate GDP growth, seems to be more realistic.

Biophysical Scenarios

Climate Scenarios

Figure 11.16 shows projected precipitation changes in Senegal in the four downscaled general circulation models (GCMs) we use in this chapter in the A1B scenario. All models show rainfall more or less unchanged in most

FIGURE 11.16   Changes in mean annual precipitation in Senegal, 2000–2050, A1B scenario (millimeters)

CNRM-CM3 GCM   CSIRO Mark 3 GCM

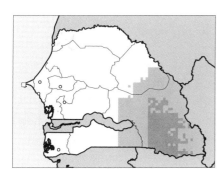   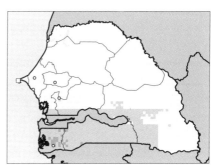

ECHAM 5 GCM   MIROC 3.2 medium-resolution GCM

■ < –400
■ –400 to –200
▨ –200 to –100
▨ –100 to –50
   –50 to 50
   50 to 100
▨ 100 to 200
■ 200 to 400
■ > 400

Source: Authors' estimates based on Jones, Thornton, and Heinke (2009).

Notes: A1B = greenhouse gas emissions scenario that assumes fast economic growth, a population that peaks midcentury, and the development of new and efficient technologies, along with a balanced use of energy sources; CNRM-CM3 = National Meteorological Research Center–Climate Model 3; CSIRO = climate model developed at the Australia Commonwealth Scientific and Industrial Research Organisation; ECHAM 5 = fifth-generation climate model developed at the Max Planck Institute for Meteorology (Hamburg); GCM = general circulation model; MIROC = Model for Interdisciplinary Research on Climate, developed at the University of Tokyo Center for Climate System Research.

of Senegal, in the range of −50 to +50 millimeters. However, both
CNRM-CM3 and MIROC 3.2 medium-resolution GCMs show increased
precipitation (in the range of 50 to 100 millimeters) in the Casamance Region,
especially MIROC 3.2. On the other hand, ECHAM 5 shows a severe reduction in rainfall (range −50 to −200) for eastern Senegal.[2]

Figure 11.17 shows the change in average daily maximum temperature in
Senegal for the warmest month based on the A1B scenario and presenting
results for various GCMs. All four models show an increase in temperature of at
least 1.0°C–1.5°C all over the country. Three of the models—CNRM-CM3,
CSIRO Mark 3, and ECHAM 5—show temperatures increasing from west
to east, with higher positive anomalies for CNRM-CM3 (1.5°C–2.0°C) and
ECHAM 5 (1.5°C–3.0°C). CSIRO Mark 3 and MIROC 3.2 indicate the lowest increase in temperature. ECHAM 5 seems to be more in accordance with the
current vertical stratification of annual maximum temperatures.

Crop Physiological Response to Climate Change

The effect of climate change on key crops in Senegal is mapped in the next
three figures. The comparison is between the crop yields for 2050 with climate change and the yields with the current (2000) climate. All models show
a general yield loss of between 5 and 25 percent for groundnuts, with varying loss in groundnut area at the northern fringes of the groundnut basin,
along with some significant areas of yield losses greater than 25 percent in
the CNRM-CM3 and ECHAM 5 GCMs (Figure 11.18). We also note a few
small areas of yield gains in the CSIRO and MIROC GCMs.

All models show maize areas with gains in yield of 5–25 percent for virtually the same areas and extent, though no significant yield change is projected for most areas (Figure 11.19). All models have some areas of yield loss
as well. CNRM-CM3 and ECHAM 5 show a greater loss in maize yields than
the other two models, and the ECHAM5 GCM shows a relatively greater loss
in base area than do the other models.

---

2   The A1B scenario is a greenhouse gas emissions scenario that assumes fast economic growth, a
    population that peaks midcentury, and the development of new and efficient technologies, along
    with a balanced use of energy sources. CNRM-CM3 is National Meteorological Research Center–
    Climate Model 3. CSIRO Mark 3 is a climate model developed at the Australia Commonwealth
    Scientific and Industrial Research Organisation. ECHAM 5 is a fifth-generation climate model
    developed at the Max Planck Institute for Meteorology in Hamburg. The MIROC is the Model
    for Interdisciplinary Research on Climate, developed at the University of Tokyo Center for
    Climate System Research.

FIGURE 11.17 Changes in the daily maximum temperature in Senegal for the warmest month, 2000–2050, A1B scenario (°C)

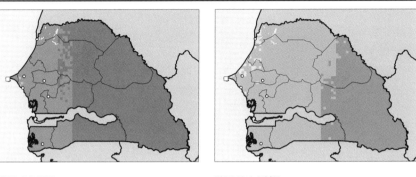

CNRM-CM3 GCM

CSIRO Mark 3 GCM

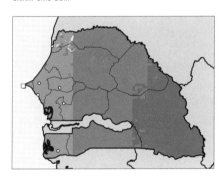

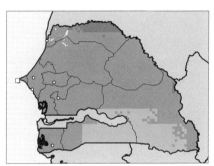

ECHAM 5 GCM

MIROC 3.2 medium-resolution GCM

 < –1

■ –1 to –0.5

  –0.5 to 0

  0 to 0.5

  0.5 to 1

  1 to 1.5

■ 1.5 to 2

■ 2 to 2.5

■ 2.5 to 3

■ 3 to 3.5

■ > 3.5

Source: Authors' calculations based on Jones, Thornton, and Heinke (2009).
Notes: A1B = greenhouse gas emissions scenario that assumes fast economic growth, a population that peaks midcentury, and the development of new and efficient technologies, along with a balanced use of energy sources; CNRM-CM3 = National Meteorological Research Center–Climate Model 3; CSIRO = climate model developed at the Australia Commonwealth Scientific and Industrial Research Organisation; ECHAM 5 = fifth-generation climate model developed at the Max Planck Institute for Meteorology (Hamburg); GCM = general circulation model; MIROC = Model for Interdisciplinary Research on Climate, developed at the University of Tokyo Center for Climate System Research.

FIGURE 11.18   Yield change under climate change: Rainfed groundnuts in Senegal, 2010–50, A1B scenario

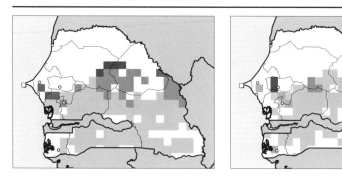

CNRM-CM3 GCM

CSIRO Mark 3 GCM

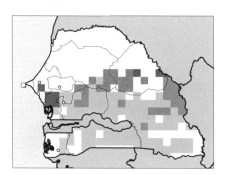
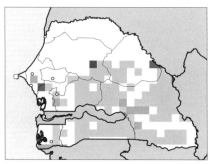

ECHAM 5 GCM

MIROC 3.2 medium-resolution GCM

- ■ 2000 old area lost
- ▨ Yield loss > 25% of 2000
- ▨ Yield loss 5–25%
- Yield change within 5%
- ▨ Yield gain 5–25%
- ■ Yield gain > 25%
- ■ 2050 new area gained

Source: Authors' estimates.

Notes: A1B = greenhouse gas emissions scenario that assumes fast economic growth, a population that peaks midcentury, and the development of new and efficient technologies, along with a balanced use of energy sources; CNRM-CM3 = National Meteorological Research Center–Climate Model 3; CSIRO = climate model developed at the Australia Commonwealth Scientific and Industrial Research Organisation; ECHAM 5 = fifth-generation climate model developed at the Max Planck Institute for Meteorology (Hamburg); GCM = general circulation model; MIROC = Model for Interdisciplinary Research on Climate, developed at the University of Tokyo Center for Climate System Research.

FIGURE 11.19   Yield change under climate change: Rainfed maize in Senegal, 2010–50, A1B scenario

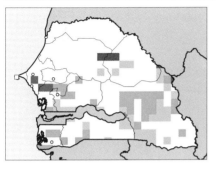

CNRM-CM3 GCM

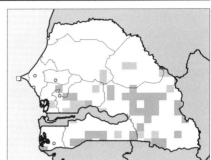

CSIRO Mark 3 GCM

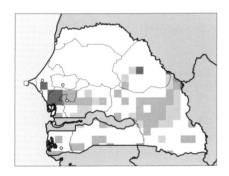

ECHAM 5 GCM

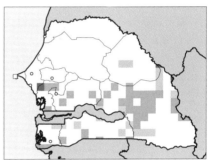

MIROC 3.2 medium-resolution GCM

- ■ 2000 old area lost
- ■ Yield loss > 25% of 2000
- ░ Yield loss 5–25%
-   Yield change within 5%
- ▨ Yield gain 5–25%
- ■ Yield gain > 25%
- ■ 2050 new area gained

Source: Authors' estimates.

Notes: A1B = greenhouse gas emissions scenario that assumes fast economic growth, a population that peaks midcentury, and the development of new and efficient technologies, along with a balanced use of energy sources; CNRM-CM3 = National Meteorological Research Center–Climate Model 3; CSIRO = climate model developed at the Australia Commonwealth Scientific and Industrial Research Organisation; ECHAM 5 = fifth-generation climate model developed at the Max Planck Institute for Meteorology (Hamburg); GCM = general circulation model; MIROC = Model for Interdisciplinary Research on Climate, developed at the University of Tokyo Center for Climate System Research.

The scenarios for rainfed rice are very similar to those for maize but with a relatively greater increase in yield (Figure 11.20). In Senegal, maize and rice seem to be less negatively affected than groundnuts by the scenarios' changing climate conditions.

Agricultural Vulnerability Scenarios (Crop-Specific)

The next four figures show simulation results from the International Model for Policy Analysis of Agricultural Commodities and Trade associated with key agricultural crops in Senegal. The box-and-whisker plots in each figure indicate the effect of climate change in a particular economic and demographic scenario. The figure for each featured crop has five graphs: production, yield, area, net exports, and world price. For millet, total production, area under cultivation, and yield per hectare are all shown to increase in all the models (Figure 11.21). All the models also show a similar trend in the world price for millet, with an optimum price between 2020 and 2035 and falling thereafter to below current prices. Net exports decline in the optimistic and baseline scenarios, whereas the pessimistic scenario has an increase in net exports from 2030 onward.

Groundnut production increases in all the scenarios (Figure 11.22). In the pessimistic and baseline scenarios, net exports decrease even while world prices increase. The decrease in exports is driven by an increase in population without a sufficiently compensating increase in groundnut production.

Similar to the production and yield of millet and groundnuts, those of sorghum increase in all the scenarios (Figure 11.23). All the models also show an increase in the world price for sorghum. However, in the optimistic and baseline scenarios net exports are shown to decrease after 2020, whereas the pessimistic scenario shows an increase in exports.

Unlike that of the other major crops, maize production increases only until 2035 and levels off thereafter (Figure 11.24). The area planted with the crop is more or less unchanged for all the scenarios after 2035 as well. All the scenarios also show an increase in the world price of maize, as well as an increase in net exports from about 120,000 tons in 2010 to around 200,000 tons in 2025, declining thereafter. The lowest range shown is for the optimistic scenario.

FIGURE 11.20   Yield change under climate change: Rainfed rice in Senegal, 2010–50, A1B
scenario

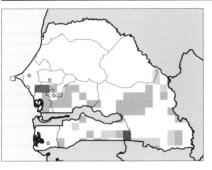

CNRM-CM3 GCM

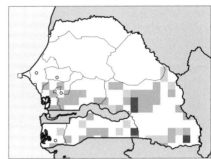

CSIRO Mark 3 GCM

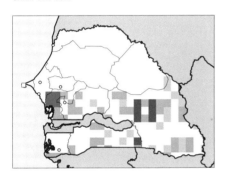

ECHAM 5 GCM

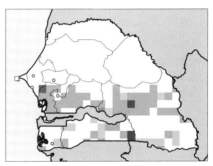

MIROC 3.2 medium-resolution GCM

■ 2000 old area lost

■ Yield loss > 25% of 2000

Yield loss 5–25%

Yield change within 5%

Yield gain 5–25%

■ Yield gain > 25%

■ 2050 new area gained

Source: Authors' estimates.

Notes: A1B = greenhouse gas emissions scenario that assumes fast economic growth, a population that peaks midcentury, and the development of new and efficient technologies, along with a balanced use of energy sources; CNRM-CM3 = National Meteorological Research Center–Climate Model 3; CSIRO = climate model developed at the Australia Commonwealth Scientific and Industrial Research Organisation; ECHAM 5 = fifth-generation climate model developed at the Max Planck Institute for Meteorology (Hamburg); GCM = general circulation model; MIROC = Model for Interdisciplinary Research on Climate, developed at the University of Tokyo Center for Climate System Research.

FIGURE 11.21   Impact of changes in GDP and population on millet in Senegal, 2010–50

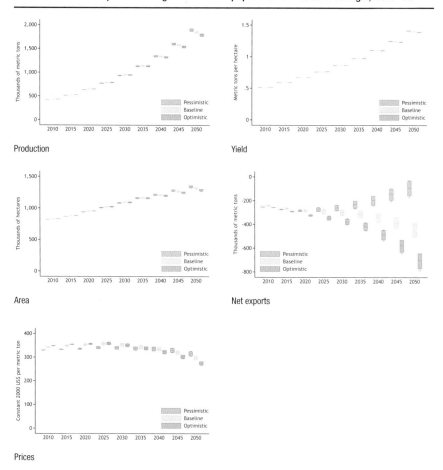

Source: Based on analysis conducted for Nelson et al. (2010).
Notes: The box and whiskers plot for each socioeconomic scenario shows the range of effects from the four future climate scenarios. GDP = gross domestic product; US$ = US dollars.

FIGURE 11.22   Impact of changes in GDP and population on groundnuts in Senegal, 2010–50

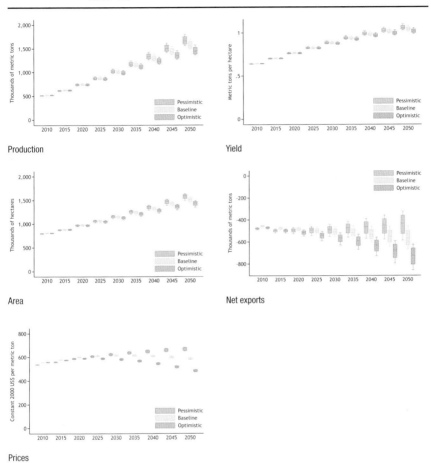

Production

Yield

Area

Net exports

Prices

Source: Based on analysis conducted for Nelson et al. (2010).

Notes: The box and whiskers plot for each socioeconomic scenario shows the range of effects from the four future climate scenarios. GDP = gross domestic product; US$ = US dollars.

FIGURE 11.23   Impact of changes in GDP and population on sorghum in Senegal, 2010–50

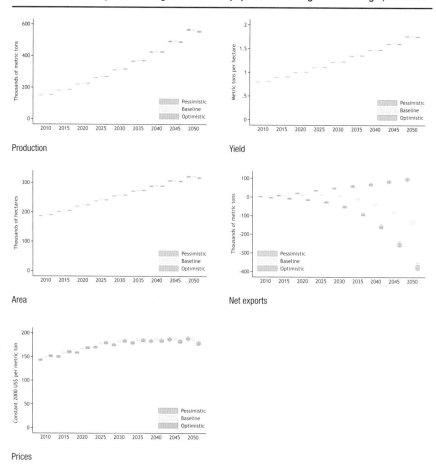

Source: Based on analysis conducted for Nelson et al. (2010).

Notes: The box and whiskers plot for each socioeconomic scenario shows the range of effects from the four future climate scenarios. GDP = gross domestic product; US$ = US dollars.

FIGURE 11.24 Impact of changes in GDP and population on maize in Senegal, 2010–50

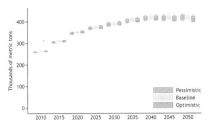

Production

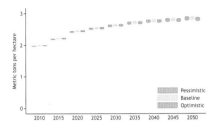

Yield

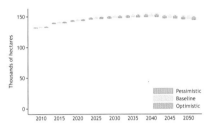

Area

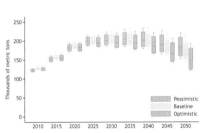

Net exports

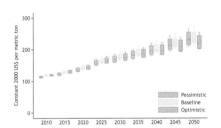

Prices

Source: Based on analysis conducted for Nelson et al. (2010).

Notes: The box and whiskers plot for each socioeconomic scenario shows the range of effects from the four future climate scenarios. GDP = gross domestic product; US$ = US dollars.

Human Vulnerability Scenarios

Figure 11.25 shows the impact of future GDP and population scenarios on under-five malnutrition rates in Senegal. The box-and-whisker plots indicate the range of climate scenario effects. A significant drop in the number of malnourished children under five years of age occurs only in the optimistic scenario (declining from 440,000 in 2010 to about 20,000 in 2050). In the pessimistic scenario, the number of malnourished children under age five drops only slightly, from 460,000 to about 400,000 in 2050. However, even though this is a small numerical decline, because the population is projected to grow, the implication is that the share of children under age five who are malnourished will decline by quite a bit.

Figure 11.26 shows the kilocalories per capita available. In the pessimistic scenario, the per capita availability of calories shows no improvement. Only the baseline and optimistic scenarios show an increase in calorie availability. Together these figures suggest that increasing the availability of calories, particularly for young children, will reduce the number of malnourished children under five years of age.

FIGURE 11.25   Number of malnourished children under five years of age in Senegal in multiple income and climate scenarios, 2010–50

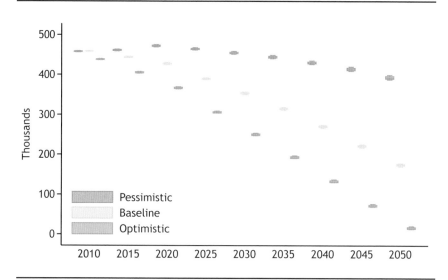

Source: Based on analysis conducted for Nelson et al. (2010).

Note: The box and whiskers plot for each socioeconomic scenario shows the range of effects from the four future climate scenarios.